ESTABLISHING
RESEARCH CORPORATION

A CASE STUDY OF PATENTS, PHILANTHROPY,
AND ORGANIZED RESEARCH IN EARLY
TWENTIETH-CENTURY AMERICA

THOMAS D. CORNELL

Edited by James E. Turner

RESEARCH CORPORATION
A foundation for the advancement of science

Research Corporation
4703 East Camp Lowell Drive, Suite 201
Tucson, Arizona 85712

ISBN 0-9633504-7-1

Design and Production
Carmen Vitello

TABLE OF CONTENTS

*I dedicate this book to
my research mentors at The Johns Hopkins University:*

ROBERT KARGON *and* LOUIS GALAMBOS

In Dr. Kargon's office one afternoon, I remarked that although my research for a particular project was well under way I had not yet started writing. "It's only four o'clock," he said, a little impatiently — implying that I had all evening to get cracking. And so I did.

Sitting next to Dr. Galambos on the "M" level of the library, I watched his stubby pencil work through an essay I had written. Like magic the sentences got better. Thus I saw for myself how to go about editing my own prose.

Research Corporation and I go back a long way. I first heard about the foundation during the 1970s, when I was an undergraduate at Southwestern at Memphis – now Rhodes College – in Memphis, Tennessee. After considering a major in chemistry and then exploring the possibility of transferring to another school for a degree in electrical engineering, I decided to stay at Rhodes and major in physics. Before graduating in 1974, however, I knew that my real interest lay in the history of science. Thus my studies were somewhat peripheral to the main emphasis of the physics department which, under Jack Taylor's leadership, aimed at preparing students for graduate work. Nevertheless, I was aware that the department received funding from Research Corporation.[1]

Since then I have learned that the ties between Rhodes and Research Corporation were quite extensive. For example, I knew that the physics department had received considerable support from Joseph C. Morris, a physicist at Tulane University. But only later did I learn that Morris had been a classmate of R. J. Van de Graaff at Princeton and had known Research Corporation founder Frederick Gardner Cottrell personally.[2] And despite the fact that Alfred Kelleher had been awarded an honorary degree during the commencement ceremonies in 1971 (which came at the end of my freshman year but which I did not attend), I had not realized anything like the full extent of his involvement with Research Corporation or his interest in Rhodes College.

I emphasize Rhodes because it illustrates quite well the role that Research Corporation has played for more than half a century. Thus the citation for Dr. Kelleher's honorary degree proclaimed:

> In early 1952 you began a significant adventure as Regional Representative and Director of Special Programs for the Research Corporation. . . . You interested yourself with the development and improvement of departmental and interdisciplinary science instruction among college faculties. . . . In the years that followed you affected profoundly academic science across the country and the evolution of the Research Corporation's own programs for the advancement of science.[3]

In his history of the physics department, Dr. Taylor added a further explanation:

5

> Dr. Alfred Kelleher... became very much interested in the Department in the early sixties. He was particularly impressed by our undergraduate research activities. By about 1964 we felt we had developed considerable expertise in infrared physics, atmospheric transmission studies and other closely related areas and that we should formalize this fact by the formation of the Laboratory of Atmospheric and Optical Physics as an integral part of the Department. [He] was of great assistance to us in urging President [Peyton Nalle] Rhodes [in whose honor the college was later renamed] to establish the laboratory....
>
> ...It is of considerable help to a department to know that an organization like Research Corporation believes in what the department is doing.[4]

More recently, a 1994 alumni publication announced that Joan T. Schmelz — a new member of the physics department — had received one of Research Corporation's Cottrell College Science Awards, to enable her and two of her students to study the sun's corona.[5] The announcement reminded me that in its quiet, unobtrusive way Research Corporation is still "out there," fostering research — not just as a career but also as a lifestyle.

Although my earliest knowledge of Research Corporation came from my experiences as an undergraduate, my interest in its history came via a different set of experiences. Only after switching from science to the history of science did research become a deep part of my own intellectual identity. Making the switch led me to the history of science doctoral program at The Johns Hopkins University in the fall of 1977. There — at the university Dr. Taylor so often described as lying at the heart of America's research culture — I too became a researcher.

The critical rite of passage for the department's first-year graduate students was a research paper. I was interested in the early history of particle accelerators and told my advisor — Robert Kargon — that a book I was reading about E. O. Lawrence's cyclotrons at the University of California referred to support from Research Corporation.[6] Dr. Kargon suggested that I take the corporation's founding as the topic of my paper — which I did.

From the outset I pursued an archival project. On a visit to the Center for History of Physics of the American Institute of Physics (then in New York City) at the end of 1977, I accompanied its director, Spencer R. Weart, and librarian, Joan N. Warnow, to Research Corporation's offices in the Chrysler Building to help inventory their early records, and later spent several days working with that material. On both occasions my main contact was W.

Stevenson Bacon, then Research Corporation's director of communications.

The bulk of my research, however, took place in Washington, D.C., in the archives of the Smithsonian Institution. Because Smithsonian Secretary Charles D. Walcott had played such an important role in establishing Research Corporation, his official papers richly reflected its early history. Over the years several members of the archival staff have ably assisted me, especially my first main contact, William A. Deiss.

After writing my paper, I presented it on two occasions in 1978. The first was to the history of science department, where it served as the required first-year paper, and the second was to a seminar in the history department where I was studying American economic history with Louis Galambos. After that, I turned to other projects, first to preparing my dissertation – about Merle A. Tuve and his use of Van de Graaff generators as particle accelerators for a program of nuclear studies in the 1930s – and then to teaching my courses at the Rochester Institute of Technology (RIT).[7]

Released time from some of my teaching duties during the spring of 1988 allowed me to return to Research Corporation's early history. But a major revision required further archival work. During the summer of 1990, Michael J. Neufeld kindly allowed me to stay in his apartment in Silver Spring, Maryland, while he was travelling in Europe. As a result I extended my research at the Smithsonian Institution Archives and broadened the scope of the project by drawing on Cottrell's diaries at the Manuscripts Division of the Library of Congress and on records of the U.S. Bureau of Mines at the National Archives – with valuable help from each staff.

In 1991 I again set the project aside in order to write about Tuve's postwar geophysical research for a conference on the history of the Carnegie Institution of Washington in June 1992. Also presenting a paper was Ellis L. Yochelson, a paleontologist at the National Museum of Natural History who has long been studying C. D. Walcott's career.[8] Between sessions he and I discussed our shared interests, and I expressed my concern that my paper on Research Corporation had become overly long for a journal article. Knowing that the foundation had started a book publishing program, Ellis suggested that I reestablish contact with Steve Bacon. I took his advice, and this book is the result.

During the summer of 1994 I made a brief trip to Pittsburgh to examine the early records of the Mellon Institute. Gabrielle Michalec helped me locate material in the archives of Carnegie-Mellon University, and Frank A. Zabrosky helped me find material in the archives of the University of Pittsburgh. I also spent several days in Tucson, working further with Research Corporation's early records. Then in the summer of 1996 I visited Wilmington,

Delaware, to work with archival material in the Hagley Museum and Library, where my main contact was Marjorie G. McNinch.

On most of these trips my expenses were defrayed by grants from the Faculty Research Fund Committee of RIT's College of Liberal Arts, and on more recent trips to Washington, D.C., my history of science colleague Patricia P. Gossel kindly offered her apartment as a base of operations.

To complement my archival work, I frequently visited the libraries at the University of Rochester, made periodic trips to the libraries at Cornell, and submitted numerous interlibrary loan requests to RIT's Wallace Memorial Library. Another way RIT assisted was through further grants of released time from my teaching duties. On many occasions my colleagues offered useful suggestions. Meanwhile, my partner, Ann Terrell Byrne, helped me keep the whole project in perspective.

In addition to facilitating my use of Research Corporation's archives, Steve Bacon also served as the book's first editor, offering feedback that consistently helped me see how to expand my original paper into a more comprehensive treatment. But Steve's retirement in 2000 necessitated new arrangements.

As the next step in turning my manuscript into an actual publication, then Research Corporation vice president, Michael P. Doyle, asked historian James E. Turner to edit it for clarity and cohesion. The first time I read one of the revised chapters, I confess I was quite disconcerted by all the suggested changes. But as I worked to put the sentences back into my own voice, I was astonished by how much better they sounded and how much more smoothly they flowed. Finally, Carmen Vitello has ably overseen the preparation of a properly formatted book — including the index and design.

I gratefully acknowledge the contributions of all those mentioned here, who have helped me keep this project moving over such an extended period of time. Without their support, I might not have finished, so I am pleased to share with them the credit for the book's strengths (though its weaknesses must be left at my door).

Research Corporation itself also belongs here. Already I have mentioned its role in helping shape the world in which I matured intellectually and its interest in publishing this book. What remains to add is the way its early history has proved — time and again — to be a research topic worthy of my best efforts.

THOMAS D. CORNELL
ROCHESTER, NEW YORK
June 2004

CHAPTER ONE

SETTING THE STAGE

Today Research Corporation defines itself as "a foundation for the advancement of science."[1] Although less visible than the more widely known foundations, it successfully pursues a well-focused mission. Specifically, it offers grants for research — in astronomy, physics, and chemistry — at colleges and universities in the United States and Canada. More generally, notes current president John P. Schaefer, it intends "to play an active, provocative, responsive role in advancing academic science."[2]

Introducing Research Corporation

Research Corporation is also distinctive because of its history. In the early years of the twentieth century, American scientist Frederick Gardner Cottrell (1877–1948) developed the electrostatic precipitator as a commercially successful pollution-control device. When he passed smoke through a chamber equipped with discharge electrodes, the smoke was subjected to electrostatic fields strong enough to impart an electrical charge (usually negative) to the suspended particles. The charged particles were then attracted to oppositely charged collectors and removed.

The character of the times made Cottrell's invention very appealing. Rapid industrial growth in the United States was producing not just new social benefits but also new social problems. Increased air pollution was especially objectionable, and among the worst offenders were smelters in the Western states whose emissions were killing livestock and harming the countryside. To limit legal proceedings against them, several quickly installed the new device. Thus a 1914 article, entitled "Enemy of the Smoke Nuisance," in the West Coast magazine *Sunset* began:

> [John] Ruskin's last years were a protest against the wanton destruction of the natural beauties of rural England. He was especially bitter against the great mining interests for having denuded the wooded hills and befouled the crystal streams of his native land. Many people of San Francisco do not know that there lives in their midst a scientist — Dr. Frederick G. Cottrell — who is doing more to preserve the natural beauties of America than Ruskin did for England with all his books.[3]

A 1906 photo by Frederick G. Cottrell shows the first experimental electrostatic precipitator on his workbench at the University of California (circle added).

The precipitator was also appealing for other reasons. It fit right into the efficiency craze, which at the time was so widespread that one historian termed it "a normal American madness."[4] By reclaiming valuable substances otherwise wasted, Cottrell's invention offered a method of "turning smoke into money."[5] One early Research Corporation director (B. B. Lawrence) pushed this view to its logical extreme. "[H]aving been impressed by the fact that an immense quantity of gold was being melted at this time and having seen the fumes from offices in the Bankers Trust Building," he suggested that a precipitator be installed at the U.S. Assay Office in New York.[6]

Full-scale precipitators could be quite dramatic in their effects, exemplifying what David E. Nye has called "the technological sublime."[7] In that spirit, English physicist Oliver Lodge wrote:

> It is amazing to me to see the ... process at work continuously, night and day throughout the year, with a potential of hundreds of thousands of volts ... and, by the aid of great electrified chambers, clearing immense quantities of blast furnace gas dust. ... [8]

Within twenty years of the first experimental installation, the precipitator became standard equipment for the mining, metallurgical, and chemical industries as well as municipal utilities. This photo from Research Corporation's 1928 annual report shows a "typical Cottrell installation for removal of ash from powdered fuel fired boilers."

Finally, the precipitator could be linked to basic scientific research. When American physicist Robert A. Millikan received an award in 1913 for his experimental studies of the electron and its electrical charge, one of Research Corporation's engineers (Linn Bradley) stated: "This work of Professor Millikan is exceedingly interesting and bears some relation to our work upon the discharge of electricity through gases, which is the means employed for precipitating suspended particles."[9]

So appealing was the precipitator that it soon became standard equipment in the mining, metallurgical, and chemical industries. Descriptions appeared in textbooks as early as McGraw-Hill's *General Metallurgy* in 1913 and its influential *Principles of Chemical Engineering* in 1923, and a 1925 exhibit at the U.S. Patent Office included Cottrell's patent as one of the fifty most important ever issued in the United States.[10] Multi-volume handbooks of chemical engineering in Germany in the 1930s and in Great Britain in the 1950s demonstrated the international scope of the process, and a 1958 study, *The Sources of Invention*, included it as one of the twentieth century's fifty most important inventions.[11] Subsequently, Harry J. White's 1963 monograph, *Industrial Electrostatic Precipitation,* described the process in detail, and a 1972 article in *Scientific American* summarized it for a broader audience.[12] In 1992, Cottrell was inducted into the National Inventors Hall of Fame for his invention of the precipitator.[13]

Despite their technological importance, precipitators were not cure-alls for industrial inefficiency or air pollution. For example, Cottrell repeatedly stressed that solving the black-smoke problem would require adopting more efficient combustion techniques.[14] Nor, at first, did those who installed precipitators fully understand how the devices worked. Yet Cottrell's invention was widely acclaimed, and it promised to generate substantial profits.

Rather than reaping those profits himself, Cottrell decided to donate his patents to an organization that would oversee their commercial development and use the profits to support a program of research grants. That aim set him apart from other inventors and made him an organizational as well as a technological pioneer.

Today's leading research universities manage their own patents, and major corporations pursue significant philanthropic programs. Both operate according to the motives of public service and private profit – though, of course, they differ in which motive they put first. But prior to World War I few organizations sought to mix such dissimilar motives – as Cottrell quickly discovered.

As the recipient of his patents, he first considered the University of California; then the American Chemical Society (ACS), the U.S. Bureau of Mines, and the Smithsonian Institution. But none was prepared to accept his gift. Accordingly, on February 26, 1912, Research Corporation was founded as a stock corporation in New York State.

From the outset, Cottrell expected Research Corporation to function as a philanthropic organization as well as a business. His intent was to see if public service could be given precedence over profit making. Circumstances at the time, however, did not allow him to dictate the exact relationship between the two motives. As a result, Cottrell's organizational experiment becomes our own, allowing us to gauge for ourselves the relative strengths of the two motives in the early twentieth century.

This book will emphasize both the engineering and philanthropic efforts of Research Corporation's formative years. At first the corporation concentrated on developing and installing precipitators, emerging as a successful engineering firm by 1915. Even in its earliest years it assessed other inventions. But not until after World War I did it pursue in a significant way its other public service mission, namely, supporting research.

Only slowly did grant making become a major focus.[15] In the 1920s Research Corporation made occasional grants, and in 1925 it established the Research Corporation Award to recognize the achievements of notable researchers (a program that continued through 1969). Although the number of grants increased in the 1930s, the corporation's grant making did not achieve its full potential until after World War II.

The expanding postwar role of the federal government in the nation's socioeconomic affairs significantly altered American private philanthropy. Nevertheless, Research Corporation maintained its distinctive niche as a source of research grants and patent services. Just after the war it addressed the problems of rapid demobilization by offering research grants in the physical sciences to faculty in American colleges and universities.[16] This developed into a long-standing policy that Research Corporation still pursues.[17]

Meanwhile, the corporation continued to attract and administer new patents. Although few brought the dramatic returns of Cottrell's original gift, the patents for the synthesis of vitamin B1 (developed by Robert R. Williams and Robert E. Waterman) and for nystatin (an antifungal agent developed by Elizabeth Hazen and Rachel Brown) allowed the foundation to support significant biomedical programs.[18]

In his memoir, *How the Laser Happened,* the American physicist Charles H. Townes has offered an especially clear and useful example of the assistance that Research Corporation was able to provide academic researchers in the complex process of applying for patents and defending patent rights. He was attracted to Research Corporation by its general aims and by the prospect of its assuming responsibility for the legal details, but he became impatient with the slow pace of the work: "... I was eager to get it done, and I told the Research Coporation's lawyers as much. That is when I got some hardnosed business instruction in patent law" — advice that he later acknowledged as being "dead right."[19]

Changing federal tax laws after World War II caused Research Corporation to spin off its electrostatic precipitation business. In response to the Revenue Act of 1950, Research Corporation in 1954 reorganized its engineering division as Research-Cottrell, a wholly owned but taxable subsidiary. By the mid-1960s further federal efforts to limit foundation control over commercial activities (resulting in the Tax Reform Act of 1969) prompted Research Corporation to lower the percentage of its ownership, by making Research-Cottrell public in 1967.[20]

The environmental movement of the 1970s brought Research-Cottrell increased business opportunities — in energy and waste management as well as pollution control. However, tragedy struck in 1977. Fifty-one men died when the scaffolding on a cooling tower that Research-Cottrell was building for a power plant in West Virginia collapsed.[21]

The decade of the 1980s was a time of dramatic change for Research Corporation. Although it retained a limited stake in what had once been its core enterprise, early in the decade it sold the few shares in Research-Cottrell it still held.[22] Another change came in 1982, when it moved its main offices from New York City to Tucson, Arizona. But the most dramatic change came when the foundation further streamlined its operations by divesting itself of its patent services.

For years Research Corporation had assisted university researchers in patenting, developing, and marketing inventions. The Bayh-Dole Act of 1980, however, allowed universities to retain the patent rights from the federally funded research they conducted, and subsequently many universities themselves assumed full responsibility for technology transfer. Also in the 1980s, the new techniques for DNA manipulation created profitable applications and helped transform university attitudes toward commercial initiatives. Finally, there were new tax laws (specifically, the Tax Reform Act of 1986).[22]

In 1987 the foundation responded to all these developments by establishing Research Corporation Technologies (RCT). As a taxable but nonprofit corporation, RCT fully assumed the mission of patent management and technology transfer.[24]

In short, during the second half of the twentieth century Research Corporation dramatically altered its organizational identity. What it held onto after World War II was neither the construction of electrostatic precipitators nor the provision of patent services. What it held onto was the mission of supporting scientific research.

The Research Revolution

While contemplating how best to frame my study of Research Corporation's early history, a particular image came to mind. In the mid-1960s I had learned to drive in my father's 1954 Ford, which differed considerably from today's cars. One distinctive feature was its manual choke. Another was its height. Even in a crowded parking lot it was easy to spot, because its white dome stood a foot taller than the surrounding cars. But the specific feature that surfaced in my thinking about Research Corporation was the view under the hood. With no effort at all I could see right through to the ground below. Unlike my current car, with its unbroken plane of components, the old Ford had wide gaps. All the essentials were there; they just were not chockablock.

Similarly, by the end of World War I, the United States had acquired its basic set of research organizations. Among them was Research Corporation, and the following chapters focus on it. But because its establishment involved so many other organizations, studying its early history also gives us an opportunity to survey the research organizations of the era.

Like automobiles, the country's research organizations have subsequently become much more complex. But at the time of Research Corporation's founding, many had just taken shape. A study of the foundation's early history thus lets us examine the essential features of the country's research organizations without the added complexity of later years. Furthermore, by taking a close look at the early twentieth century, our case study allows us to see past the component organizations to "the ground below" – to the society in which they operated.

When science is viewed as the collective effort of a society to discover how nature works, the emphasis is usually placed on conceptual achievements. Nineteenth-century examples include Darwinian evolution in biology, the periodic table of the elements in chemistry, and electromagnetic fields in physics. Far from being static, scientific concepts have long been subject to change. Indeed, one of the main contributions of the ancient Greek philosopher–scientists was devising the first generally accepted procedure for making such changes – based on verbal reasoning, mathematical proof and careful use of the senses.

Along with conceptual change, science has also undergone significant organizational change.[25] In ancient Greece, Plato and Aristotle established new centers for the pursuit of learning – the Academy and the Lyceum, respectively – and later societies continued the process. Examples are the library and museum at Alexandria during the Hellenistic Era, the universities of the European Middle Ages, the philosophical societies of the Scientific Revolution, and the experimental laboratories of the nineteenth century. Yet science remained largely an individual activity. It was not fully bureaucratized until the late nineteenth and early twentieth centuries, when the pace of the organizational change became so great as to constitute a revolution.

Historians of science and technology have long employed the concept of revolutionary change. Most agree that a scientific revolution occurred in the seventeenth century and that an industrial revolution occurred in the late eighteenth and early nineteenth centuries. In the Scientific Revolution, long-dominant ancient theories (notably Aristotle's) were replaced by new European ones (especially Newton's). Where the Scientific Revolution brought new explanations of natural phenomena, the Industrial Revolution brought new methods of manufacturing. Craftsmen using traditional hand tools in their own shops lost their primacy and were replaced by unskilled laborers operating machines in factories owned by someone else.

The lesser-known Research Revolution of the late nineteenth and early twentieth centuries involved both science and technology.[26] One of its distinctive features was the emergence of professional specialists. During the second half of the nineteenth century the middle-class professions began reorganizing along specialist lines, according to a common pattern.[27] First, subgroups of professionals would realize that they possessed distinctive expertise (e.g., physics as a scientific subgroup and electrical engineering as a technological subgroup). These pioneers had usually acquired their specialized skills on their own and not through formal education. Thus a second feature of the overall pattern was the introduction of a specialized college curriculum that allowed future generations to receive their training in the classroom. A third aspect was the establishment of a national society to set standards, sponsor periodic meetings, and publish new results in the field.

Dramatic growth in the number of specialists also characterized the Research Revolution. To see this trend within the American scientific community, let us start with George H. Daniels's count of 638 individuals who contributed articles to scientific periodicals published in the period 1815–1845.[28] For the period 1848–1860, Sally Gregory Kohlstedt has identified 2,068 members of the American Association for the Advancement of Science (AAAS).[29] Jumping to the first edition of the biographical directory *American Men of Science*, published in 1906, the count increases – to more than 4,000 names.[30] Making selective use of later editions, the fourth edition (1927) contained about 13,500 entries and the seventh edition (1944), about 34,000.[31]

So far we have focused on the practitioners themselves: they became professional specialists and their numbers rose exponentially. Still another distinctive feature of the Research Revolution was the emergence of organizations to train, employ, and otherwise support this increasingly large group. But before turning to the organizational changes of the Research Revolution, let us examine one final distinctive feature, namely, new social attitudes toward research.

Since the Renaissance there have been individuals – notably, the English philosopher–scientist Francis Bacon – who insisted that scientific knowledge has socially important applications. But as late as the 1870s, most Americans seemed indifferent to science. Thus American astronomer Simon Newcomb observed in 1874 "that the American public has no adequate appreciation of the superiority of original research to simple knowledge."[32] During the next

half century, however, popular attitudes changed – so that after World War II
the federal government was able to continue in peacetime the large-scale
funding of research it had begun during the war. Science, Vannevar Bush
proclaimed in 1945, had become an "endless frontier" of opportunity for his
countrymen.[33]

Having listed the distinctive features of the Research Revolution, let us
return to the organizational changes during the late nineteenth and early
twentieth centuries. Specifically, three types of organizations – academic,
industrial and governmental – define the main sectors of the research world
and deserve our attention.

Central to the changes taking place in academia was the emergence of
professional careers in science and technology.[34] The modern notion of a career as a structured progression through a series of stages in an all-absorbing
lifetime of activity was new in the nineteenth century. Among its pioneering
advocates were university presidents who sought to transform traditional colleges into organizations that prepared students for careers in the newly specialized professions. The result was a major shift from a uniform curriculum
based on the study of Latin and Greek classics to a series of separate curricula, each comprising a progressive sequence of courses.

University presidents sought to extend these ladders of achievement in
both directions. The result at the lower end was reformed high school curricula; at the upper, new graduate programs (often leading to Ph.D. degrees).
Individuals no longer entered careers solely through personal study or on-
the-job training. They could also enter through their formal education – beginning in high school, continuing in college, and culminating in graduate
school.

Not surprisingly, these changes provoked vigorous debate over the basic
aims of higher education. Traditionally, American colleges had sought to build
the character of upper-class gentlemen by instilling piety and discipline (especially mental discipline). As traditional colleges were transformed into
modern universities, however, three new rationales emerged. Lawrence R.
Veysey has identified these as liberal culture, utility, and research.[35]

According to the rationale of liberal culture, university curricula emphasized what students needed to know in order to become "well rounded." At
the turn of the century this meant modern languages, literature, history, and
philosophy – in general, the humanities.

According to the rationale of utility, university curricula emphasized what
students needed to know in order to succeed in American society. No longer
were students all trained the same way. Instead, an elective system allowed

them to choose from several different sequences of courses, thereby helping them enter the practical fields best suited to their individual talents, temperaments, and interests.

From our point of view, the most important rationale was research. Curricula based on this rationale emphasized what students needed to know in order to evaluate existing knowledge and to take the next step, namely, the creation of new knowledge. No longer a side interest that students and faculty pursued independently, research became an official part of campus life, encouraged as a matter of policy.

By 1900 American universities had developed a twofold role with regard to research. On the one hand, they were major sites for its pursuit; on the other, they trained the next generation of researchers. Despite the expansion of research on campuses across the country, however, not all researchers could find, or even wanted to find, academic jobs. Fortunately, other places of employment were emerging, including industrial laboratories and government research agencies.

The most important economic trend in the United States at the turn of the century was the rise of big business. By 1860 machine production and the factory system were well established in several industries. Nevertheless, the scale of manufacturing remained small. Not until after the Civil War did firms expand in size to include large amounts of capital, complex bureaucratic structures, and a variety of functions. At first, firms as large as Carnegie Steel or Standard Oil were rare. After 1890, however, the number increased, and by the time of World War I big businesses had become the rule in industry after industry.

As they arose, big businesses found themselves facing research opportunities. The new scientific and engineering specialties were producing new knowledge in ever-increasing amounts, and big businesses possessed the requisite capital to put such knowledge to use. But why would they *want* to do so? Here we need to consider a fundamental shift that was taking place in the American economy at the turn of the century.[36]

Prior to the late nineteenth century the American economy had grown primarily due to new inputs — geographical expansion across the continent, capital provided by European investors, and immigration. Gradually, however, the basic structure of the economy changed. In the late nineteenth century geographical expansion slowed. At the turn of the century the United States found itself exporting more capital than it imported. World War I cut immigration to a trickle, and federal legislation in the 1920s kept levels low. As a result, economic growth could no longer be sought on the basis of new inputs of land, capital, and labor. Instead, growth became based on increased productivity – which placed a premium on new knowledge.

One way big businesses responded involved patents. Traditionally, firms had purchased or licensed the patents they needed. During the late nineteenth century, however, Thomas A. Edison demonstrated that inventing could be organized and that organized inventing could be integrated with large-scale manufacturing. From then on, firms with sufficient resources could originate new products or processes "in house" – so that patenting itself became an important big business enterprise.

The founding of industrial research laboratories marked a logical extension of this trend. After 1900, leaders in the electrical and chemical industries – companies such as General Electric, American Telephone and Telegraph, DuPont, and Eastman Kodak – discovered the advantages of pursuing "in house" the basic research that supported their applied-science enterprises.[37]

Meanwhile, the federal government became more active in its support of research. Despite various long-standing scientific and technological endeavors (e.g., Western exploration and the patent system), the earliest systematic federal support for research came in the area of agriculture. During the mid-nineteenth century Cyrus McCormick's reaper and other new machines transformed American agriculture. Just as the increased pace of technological change in manufacturing created a need for industrial research, the increased pace of technological change in agriculture created a need for agricultural research. Unlike manufacturing, however, farming was pursued by a large number of small producers – a condition that called for federal involvement.

In 1862 President Abraham Lincoln signed legislation that created the U.S. Department of Agriculture and the land grant "agricultural and mechanical" colleges. The timing was not accidental. For years Congress had debated the constitutionality of funding these and other "internal improvements." But the secession of the Southern states after Lincoln's election opened the way for the remaining legislators to move forward. Because previous bills had deliberately avoided the constitutional issue, the legislation passed in 1862 established a precedent and started a trend. "With the Constitution no longer a stumbling block," A. Hunter Dupree has noted, "the era of bureau building had begun."[38]

This is not to say that agricultural research blossomed overnight. Just as industrial research required a generation to mature, the development of agricultural research took a similar time span. In 1887 the Hatch Act created agricultural experiment stations across the country, and in 1906 the Adams Act increased their research funds.

The Progressive Era brought other extensions of the government's research efforts. Agriculture was not the only economic enterprise that involved large numbers of small producers. Similar circumstances in the mining industry prompted Congress to establish the U.S. Bureau of Mines in 1910. Although big businesses now supported basic research, they still found some research-related activities difficult to pursue. Hence the creation of the National Bureau of Standards in 1901. Finally, national concern over resource conservation occasioned a major science and technology policy debate.

In summary, by 1915 the Research Revolution was well under way in the United States. Research was officially supported at many of the nation's universities, and researchers trained there could find employment — not only on campuses across the country but also in laboratories sponsored by private industry or government agencies. Specialized professional societies offered researchers a sense of community with fellow practitioners. Even private philanthropy turned its attention to organized research.

Until the late nineteenth century, American philanthropy was largely a matter of individual giving.[39] For example, Andrew Carnegie began his philanthropic efforts in the traditional fashion by giving away church organs and establishing municipal libraries. After 1900, however, so great was his personal fortune that he was unable to proceed organ by organ, library by library, and distribute his money faster than it came in. At that point he became an innovator, reorganizing philanthropy in much the same way as he had earlier reorganized steel production.

First Carnegie created a series of mission-oriented philanthropic trusts. He would specify the mission and provide a sizable endowment (typically five or ten million dollars) through a legal deed of trust. The trustees then made the detailed decisions regarding specific projects. Research was one of the missions that Carnegie supported. In 1902 he established the Carnegie Institution of Washington, which pursued scientific research in its own research departments. But still Carnegie failed to exhaust his wealth. Accordingly, in 1911 he created the Carnegie Corporation, a general-purpose foundation to which he gave the bulk of his remaining fortune.

Carnegie's fellow millionaire, John D. Rockefeller, followed the same pattern in almost exactly the same time frame. In 1901 he established the mission-oriented Rockefeller Institute for Medical Research, and in 1913 he established the general-purpose Rockefeller Foundation. The new foundations were subjected to close public scrutiny (notably in 1915 during the hearings of the U.S. Commission on Industrial Relations, created by Congress and known as the Walsh Commission, after its chairman, Frank P. Walsh). They were allowed to stand, however, and provided the nation with yet another set of research organizations.

But completing the Research Revolution required one more step. The individuals who led these various organizations often knew one another, forming what amounted to a "Research Establishment."[40] Yet the organizations themselves tended to act independently. Despite the presence of the American Association for the Advancement of Science (established in 1848) and the National Academy of Sciences (established in 1863), there were no real mechanisms for central planning or central control.

World War I precipitated the final step. Many American scientists and engineers wanted to make sure that their skills were used effectively if the United States entered the war. But because they also wanted to protect their professional autonomy, they preferred to work through the executive branch rather than the legislative. One result was the Naval Consulting Board. Created by the secretary of the navy in 1915, its mission was to evaluate and develop inventions for the war effort, and its work was undertaken primarily by civilian inventors and engineers. Additionally, in 1916 President Woodrow Wilson issued an executive order creating the National Research Council (NRC), which coordinated research work on many wartime projects.[41]

Unlike most other wartime agencies, the NRC was not terminated at war's end. Instead, a second executive order (in 1918) allowed it to continue, thereby completing the Research Revolution in the United States. Written into the NRC's peacetime mission were all the basic commitments of the American research community. According to the second executive order, the primary duty of the NRC was "to stimulate research." But "research" here included several possibilities. One was "increasing knowledge" — in other words, basic research. Also included were two important applications. Reflecting the NRC's wartime origins, the first was "strengthening the national defense," and — befitting its newly acquired peacetime identity — the second was "contributing in other ways to the public welfare."[42]

Organizational changes continued to occur, but these later developments did not involve the addition of major new commitments. Instead what changed was the relative mix of the commitments already in place by 1920. In mid-century, for example, researchers somewhat relaxed their demands for professional autonomy to allow for greater support from — albeit greater accountability to — the federal government.[43]

Today's researchers recognize the fundamental stability of the American research community. In an open letter to his colleagues following the demise of the Superconducting Super Collider, physicist Leon M. Lederman observed that "[o]ver the past five decades a balance has somehow been achieved among disciplines, between shared facilities and individual investigators, between targeted research and curiosity-driven research, between research and teaching."[44]

Perhaps, as Lederman suggests, we are now seeing the rise of a new balance. But future changes will not involve starting from scratch with a completely new set of organizations. Although some organizations may be new, hundreds of others have familiar names and familiar missions. Trying to understand how modern research works by examining each component organization in detail would be a dauntingly complex task. Fortunately, we have an alternative approach, namely, the use of case studies.[45] By taking a close look at a well-chosen example from the early twentieth century, we can see more clearly the basic principles that still characterize the world of organized research.

Research Corporation and the Research Revolution

The idea of the Research Revolution would have struck a resonant chord with the people who helped establish Research Corporation. Three in particular served not only as leading policymakers for their generation, but also as spokesmen for the rapid rise of research organizations. In their public writings this trio articulated the importance of research in American society. Although we shall learn more about each in subsequent chapters, brief introductions are in order: Joseph A. Holmes was the first director of the U.S. Bureau of Mines, Charles D. Walcott headed the Smithsonian Institution, and Arthur D. Little ran his own research consulting firm.

Holmes, Walcott, and Little understood that the United States had undergone — and was still undergoing — dramatic change. Thus Holmes wrote in 1912:

> In the days when our Constitution was framed, the conditions then existing were radically different from those of today.... Today ... we have factories and varied industries distributed over an area nearly ten times that of the original thirteen states....
>
> With the increasing density of population and the larger development of the country's resources, the interstate relations in agriculture, mining, manufactures, transportation, and the varied industries have grown in extent and complexity far beyond the dreams of our forefathers.[46]

In times of change, researchers had important roles to play, and in a 1907 article, Little mentioned several possibilities. During the recent war between Japan and Russia, chemists had ranged ahead of the advancing army in order to test water supplies and post warnings. Little likened their efforts to the contributions that chemists could make to American society:

> It seems to me that this little vanguard well typifies what the chemist should stand for and where he should be found in his relations to the community. He is or should be essentially a pioneer rushing forward and serving the community. . . .[47]

Little also believed that researchers established benchmarks for honest public service. "The chemist," he noted, "from the very nature of his work and training should be the unswerving enemy of graft in every form."[48] Finally, he listed specific contributions that chemists could make to industry – including "standardizing materials, controlling the course of processes, and minimizing wastes."[49]

The problem of waste greatly concerned Holmes and Walcott as well. "In our rush for present day prosperity," Holmes warned:

> let us not forget that measured in the terms of the needs of this great and rapidly growing country, our resources are *limited in quantity* and we have for the needs of all time *but this one supply*. . . .
>
> Measured in the terms of the life of the nation, at the present increasing rates of consumption and waste, we will, while the nation is yet in its infancy, exhaust the resources necessary for its future welfare.
>
> Therefore, the right of the present generation to the efficient use of these resources carries with it a sacred obligation not to waste this precious heritage.[50]

Walcott, as retiring president of the American Association for the Advancement of Science, raised the issue at the annual meeting in 1924:

> The United States' unprecedented growth and her present commanding economic position have been made possible by abundance of natural resources. . . . Minerals, forests, fur and game animals, agricultural soils, range lands, fish, and water resources were all seemingly inexhaustible in supply, and all have been appropriated and exploited recklessly and wastefully. The cream has been skimmed, and, all too often, the milk has been thrown away.[51]

For Little, Holmes, and Walcott, research was the key to solving the problem of waste. Pursuing such research was a civic duty for researchers, and supporting it was a civic duty for industrialists, government officials, and the public. Little emphasized the need for industrial research. "No one at all conversant with the facts," he wrote in 1909, "can doubt that our industrial salvation must be found in a closer alliance and co-operation between the scientific worker and the actual agencies of production."[52] Holmes emphasized not just the need for governmental research but also the constitutional justification on which it was based:

> Some of our earlier statesmen held the theory that the function of government should be restricted to the protection of life, liberty, and property. They were inclined to regard the general welfare clause in the Federal Constitution as an invention of the devil. . . . But the importance of this clause in connection with our national development is doubtless fully recognized and appreciated by all who are more or less familiar with governmental scientific researches. . . .[53]

Speaking to his fellow AAAS members, Walcott emphasized the obligation of researchers to help educate their fellow citizens.[54]

All three acknowledged the importance of researchers as individuals. In 1910 Holmes applauded the University of Alabama for naming a new building for geologist Eugene Allen Smith:

> I rejoice with you that we are here to-day, not at a funeral service, but to do honor to and enjoy with this good man himself the recognition of not only what he has done, but what he is doing, and of what he is yet to do.[55]

Research, Holmes implied, was based on the work of such individuals. Similarly, Little wrote in 1918: "The great advances in human knowledge have almost invariably been due to individual effort set in motion by the scientific imagination and sustained by a consuming desire to ascertain the truth."[56] For his part, Walcott believed that organizations should be designed to enhance, not replace, the work of talented individuals. In 1909 he wrote:

> With means to organize and conduct laboratories for research here [in Washington, D.C.], a great service could be done for young men, the men who have the initiative, ambition and force to create and develop new ideas. In association with older permanent members

of the research staff, a strong research organization would be developed. . . . It would be one of the best methods of finding and utilizing the exceptional man.[57]

As Walcott's remarks suggest, he fully understood the importance of research organizations. Individuals working alone could no longer solve society's problems. Individuals needed to have their talents developed and augmented by organizations. Little agreed, stating:

> While the superlative work in science, like the superlative work in art, must always be an expression of the genius of the individual and quite beyond the power of organization to ensure, there remains a vast deal of what may be called the secondary work of rounding out the great discoveries and especially of giving them an industrial application which may be rendered most effectively only through proper organization.[58]

All three were well-acquainted with the research organizations of their day. Writing in the journal *Science* in 1901, Walcott examined the growing need of federal research agencies for college graduates with specialized training. He listed by name more than a dozen agencies and about three dozen schools, and he proposed the creation of a new organization to "facilitate the utilization of the various scientific and other resources of the government for purposes of research."[59]

Holmes, too, had firsthand experience with a wide range of organizations. Not only did he head a new federal research agency, but he also recognized that its success required effective cooperation with state governments, mining companies, and mine workers. Researchers needed to address the concerns of groups variously motivated by conservation, states' rights, private profit, and safe working conditions.[60]

In his presidential address at the 1913 meeting of the American Chemical Society, Little surveyed the state of American industrial research. Beginning with Rochester, New York — that year's host city — he first mentioned the contributions of Kodak and Bausch and Lomb, then the electrochemical firms at Niagara Falls and General Electric's research laboratory at Schenectady. He also acknowledged the research efforts of the federal government, of leading universities, and of various other organizations, including Research Corporation. "Modern progress can no longer depend upon accidental discoveries," he concluded. "Each advance in industrial science must be studied, organized and fought like a military campaign."[61]

The three also recognized the global setting for research. "No other country is so amply provided by nature with resources that make for national greatness . . . ," Holmes told his audience at the Eighth International Congress of Applied Chemistry in 1912.[62] Although research would help turn natural resources into national greatness, Europe was the acknowledged leader in such work. Thus Little wrote in 1913: "Germany has long been recognized as preeminently the country of organized research." But, he continued, change was in the offing:

> A new competitor is even now girding up his loins and training
> for the race, and that competitor is strangely enough the United
> States — that prodigal among nations, still justly stigmatized as the
> most wasteful, careless and improvident of them all.[63]

Emerging in the same time frame as all these pronouncements, Research Corporation mirrored the concerns of policymakers such as Holmes, Walcott, and Little. To begin with, the problem of waste helped give the organization its distinctive identity. "I have had great faith in the Research Corporation," Walcott wrote Otto H. Kahn in 1914, "and [I] believe that it will be of service . . . in the conservation of our material resources."[64]

Not only was Research Corporation established on the basis of a waste-reducing device, but it was intended to reduce another kind of waste as well. Thus Cottrell observed in 1912:

> Conservation has of late become a word to conjure with, and all
> manner of economic wastes are very properly receiving a too-long
> delayed attention. The men in our universities and colleges have
> been among the first and most effective in promoting the general
> conservation movement, yet there is what we may term an intellec-
> tual by-product of immense importance, a product of their own ac-
> tivities still largely going to waste. This is the mass of scientific
> facts and principles developed in the course of investigation and
> instruction, which through lack of the necessary commercial guid-
> ance and supervision never, or only after unnecessary delay, reaches
> the public-at-large in the form of useful inventions, and then often
> through such channels that the original discoverers are quite for-
> gotten.[65]

In effect, the corporation was intended to function like an electrostatic pre-cipitator. By identifying and encouraging valuable ideas that might otherwise have gone unrecognized and undeveloped, it would ensure that the public benefited more fully from the country's intellectual talent.

Research Corporation's commitment to individual researchers and to research organizations was very much in harmony with the pronouncements of Holmes, Walcott, and Little. Its patent services and support for research demonstrated its commitment to inventors and scientists. But as an organization functioning in relation to other organizations, the corporation undertook to do more than just help individuals. It also fostered cooperation among the various research organizations spawned by the Research Revolution — particularly between academic and industrial organizations — and it did so with full awareness of the global setting for its work.

CHAPTER TWO

A PRACTICAL INVENTION

B ecause Frederick G. Cottrell played such an important role in establishing Research Corporation, our study properly begins with an overview of his life and career.[1] Descended from New England stock, Cottrell was born in Oakland, California, in 1877, not long after his parents had moved to the area. During his youth the Research Revolution was gaining momentum and helped shape his interests and education. As a result, he embarked on a career in research, and for the rest of his life he contributed to the process of new knowledge creation.

Cottrell and the Research Revolution

For centuries research had been a relatively obscure social activity, pursued by an elite few. As the Research Revolution took hold, however, the number of researchers increased and appreciation of their work became more deeply woven into the social fabric. By the late nineteenth century, even children had opportunities to learn about research. Mass circulation popular science publications, biographies of famous inventors, and readily available equipment and supplies all served to spark young imaginations.

Cottrell's experiences illustrate the grassroots character of the Research Revolution. When he was a boy his Aunt Mame read to him from *Harper's Young People*, a general-interest children's magazine that regularly discussed science and technology. For example, an 1889 article featured electricity as one of "The Six Wide-Open Professions":

> As a profession — not merely as a business for the making of money — no field offers to-day greater attractions than the study of this wonderful force and its applications. No work is calling so loudly to the young man of scientific grasp and persevering industry.[2]

Similar themes appeared in the magazine's series on "Heroes and Martyrs of Invention." An 1888 installment described Eli Whitney as "one of those bright, precocious Yankee boys who in early years reveal a great fondness for making things, and who show ingenuity in doing whatever they turn their hands to."[3] An 1889 installment underscored the appropriate response to adversity. "Never," it began, "did any man work harder, suffer more keenly, or remain more steadfast to one great purpose of life than Charles Goodyear."[4]

In 1890, probably in response to the magazine's series "The Amateur's Workshop," young Cottrell began preparing his own magazine, the *Boys' Workshop*. His Christmas issue included an article on the inventor Thomas Edison. Cottrell wrote that Edison's life should "be an incentive to every young American boy. It is one of the many instances where a poor boy has, by his own exertions, risen to a position of distinction and honor."[5]

Cottrell's reference to Edison was a sign of the times. In 1876 Edison's success with telegraphic equipment enabled him to establish an "invention factory" at Menlo Park, New Jersey, where he and his staff quickly produced a string of remarkable inventions. These included the carbon-filament incandescent lamp (and other components in a system of electric lighting), the telephone's carbon transmitter (originally just one component in the system that Edison invented to rival Alexander Graham Bell's), and the phonograph. So great was Edison's fame that his story entered American folklore, thus becoming known even to a boy in distant Oakland.[6]

Another important influence on young Cottrell was his father, Henry Cottrell, an amateur photographer who encouraged his son's interest in chemistry. He also encouraged his son to read *Scientific American*, a weekly publication that surveyed new developments in technology as well as science.[7]

Cottrell's studies at Oakland High School built on these early scientific interests. By taking courses in botany, chemistry, and physics, he benefited directly from recent reforms that made high schools an important formal step toward a research career.[8]

For the next step Cottrell had only to look as far as Berkeley. Like other universities across the country, the Research Revolution had brought new programs of instruction to the University of California, making it well suited for a student of Cottrell's interests and talents. After matriculating in 1893, he eagerly seized the available opportunities, and his restless intellect and exuberant personality quickly made their mark.

"By the end of his first year," his biographer Frank Cameron has noted, "every member of the science faculty was aware of his presence,"[9] and during his senior year they granted him special status. In particular, wrote Willard B. Rising, the College of Chemistry dean: "I wish to say to you that I consider your attainments in chemistry and your faithful devotion to the science worthy of some special recognition."[10] Along with an official title (Honorary Student Assistant) came a significant privilege. Thus an acquaintance recalled:

> [Cottrell's] student work and his aptitude were so unusual and com-

mendatory that the faculty voted him a duplicate key to every laboratory on the Campus, and authority was given him to come and go
at his pleasure, and to conduct any experiments and research he
desired.[11]

Cottrell received his baccalaureate in 1896. He then spent a year as a full-
time graduate student, followed by three years as an Oakland High School
science teacher (while still pursuing graduate studies part-time).[12] At that
point, his progress began outpacing the Research Revolution in the United
States. Impatient with the routine of secondary-school teaching, and having
taken full advantage of what Berkeley had to offer, he traveled to Europe
where he pursued graduate studies with the physical chemists J. H. van't Hoff
in Berlin and Wilhelm Ostwald in Leipzig.

At the University of Leipzig, Cottrell immersed himself in his doctoral
project, a study of the diffusion of ions in a solution. [13] His letters home to his
fiancée, Jessie M. Fulton, revealed the demands he made on himself for the
sake of research. Actually, the issue had emerged well before his departure.
Thus Cameron described a walk the couple had taken in the Berkeley Hills
toward the end of 1897:

> As the shadows lengthened in the late afternoon sun a closeness of
> spirit enveloped them and Cottrell declared his love. Before Jess
> had time to bathe in the warming tenderness of this devotion he
> dismayed her by quickly adding, "But my work comes first."[14]

Writing from Europe, Cottrell continued the discussion. He explained that
spending himself on his work was something he was willing to do:

> I look on health not only as a thing for itself but, even more, as a
> means to an end. It is a sort of capital that one must set out with on
> new enterprises and use with discretion and care, never wasting it
> if it can be helped. Yet, I believe there are times when one is justi-
> fied in taxing it to the limit. . . . [15]

Hard work (so hard that at times it amounted to self-exploitation) was something he probably saw as a characteristic of the Research Revolution:

> Since I have started this trip, I have kept my eyes open particu-
> larly to see if I could discover in the men I met just how big a part
> the rapidity and intensity factors played and I must frankly say that

Frederick G. Cottrell in a photo taken in 1920 when he was acting director of the U.S. Bureau of Mines.

I have been led to give it even more weight than before. In fact, it seems *the one* factor which you find in the top layer of men which distinguishes them from those just beneath the crust.[16]

In 1902 Cottrell received his Ph.D. degree and then returned to Berkeley as an instructor of physical chemistry. During the next quarter century he would work his way up the ranks of the American research community. At Berkeley he was promoted to assistant professor in 1906. Throughout this period he resisted Willis R. Whitney's attempts to recruit him for a position at General Electric's research laboratory.[17] But in 1911 he left academia and accepted a position with the U.S. Bureau of Mines.

At the Bureau of Mines, Cottrell became chief chemist in 1914, chief metallurgist in 1916, assistant director in 1919, and acting director in 1920. He then spent a year as chairman of the National Research Council's Division of Chemistry and Chemical Technology. Finally he became director of the U.S. Department of Agriculture's Fixed Nitrogen Research Laboratory. That position — which he held from 1922 to 1927 — marked him as one of his generation's leaders of organized research.[18]

After stepping down from his directorship, Cottrell worked primarily as a consultant. His wide-ranging interests and his genuine enthusiasm for new ideas made him a sought-after sounding board, and his regular travels and numerous contacts helped knit together the component organizations of the Research Revolution.[19] But his commitments to certain non-scientific projects – the international language, Esperanto, for example – struck many as quixotic. Thus by the time of his death in 1948 (which came while he was attending a meeting of the National Academy of Sciences at Berkeley) his reputation was that of a brilliant but somewhat eccentric figure.

Cottrell at Berkeley

Cottrell's primary scientific field was physical chemistry, a new field that despite the vital contributions of Yale's Josiah Willard Gibbs was largely European in origin. As R. G. A. Dolby and John W. Servos have each noted, Cottrell was one of several dozen Americans who studied physical chemistry in Germany and then continued similar work back in the United States.[20] At Berkeley, Cottrell taught courses in physical chemistry. He also set up an air liquefier for experimental purposes,[21] and he regularly reviewed the European literature on physical chemistry for the *Journal of the American Chemical Society*.[22]

Yet Cottrell was no slavish follower of developments abroad. In the turn-of-the-century debate over the reality of atoms and molecules he fully sided with neither extreme. On the one hand, there were times when he was critical of the mechanists. Thus his first review for the *Journal of the American Chemical Society* assessed J. J. Thomson's plum-pudding model of the atom as "a rather daring attempt to explain the structure of the elements."[23] On the other hand, he never embraced the position of Ostwald and the other energeticists, who viewed the physical existence of atoms and molecules as an unnecessary assumption.[24] Instead, in his second review he characteristically insisted on the need to *reconcile* opposing viewpoints:

> Perhaps the most significant trend of recent work is to be found in the concentration of effort toward narrowing the gap between molecular and molar phenomena. . . . The classification of natural phenomena into sharply defined subjects may in most cases be interpreted simply as an admission that we are omitting a region between, in which, as we enter it from either side, the methods of treatment gradually fail us.[25]

After his European sojourn Cottrell found Berkeley still making the transition to a modern research university. Chemistry had been represented on the faculty since the university was established in 1868. During his brief tenure as president in the early 1870s, Daniel Coit Gilman had supported the creation of a separate college of chemistry, and in 1890 the college had acquired its own building. Even so, as late as 1908 it had awarded only four Ph.D. degrees. Cottrell's efforts furthered the trend toward research, but not until 1912 – when Gilbert N. Lewis arrived from the Massachusetts Institute of Technology (MIT) to become the college's new dean – did research become a major activity.[26]

Instead, the focus at Berkeley while Cottrell was on the faculty continued to be the undergraduate program. Led by Benjamin Ide Wheeler (who served as president from 1899 to 1919), the university improved its physical plant, expanded the size of its faculty and its student body, and dealt with the financial problems caused by the 1906 earthquake. Throughout all this, research steadily acquired greater importance. But even as late as 1910 the scales had still not tipped in its favor, prompting one observer to note: "Although the California universities are ambitious to develop their graduate schools, yet it is common for the professors to advise their students to go to the Atlantic universities for their advanced work...."[27]

Despite being a positive step in the development of his career, Cottrell's faculty position was not without drawbacks. One problem was financial. After his first year he received a salary increase (from $1,000 when he arrived in 1902 to $1,200 in 1903), but further increases were slow in coming. Meanwhile, his father's death in late 1903 and his marriage in early 1904 placed considerable family responsibilities on his shoulders.[28]

In addition, Cottrell faced unmet creative needs. Although he owed his Berkeley position to his focus on physical chemistry, his intellectual interests ranged far beyond the well-defined disciplinary boundaries favored by academic departments. Even in Europe he had not been certain about pursuing a Ph.D., which was (and still is) primarily a means of specializing. But when Edmond O'Neill (one of his teachers at Berkeley, who became the College of Chemistry dean in 1901) informed him of Wheeler's plans to hire a physical chemist, he also conveyed Wheeler's reservations that "[you are] not steady enough and that you spread your efforts over too large a field."[29] Obtaining his doctorate helped Cottrell undercut those concerns. Nevertheless, Wheeler had accurately perceived the protean scope of Cottrell's creativity.

Cottrell found another outlet for his talents – and another potential source of income – by becoming what Thomas P. Hughes has called an independent inventor. According to Hughes, such inventors pursued their work largely outside the organizations that employed them. They chose their own technical problems to solve and made their own funding arrangements. Independent inventors were often professionals (as was Edison), but they could also be amateurs (as was Bell). So numerous and influential were they at the turn of the century that Hughes has labeled the period between the Civil War and World War I as "The Era of Independent Inventors."[30]

At first Cottrell worked less as an inventor and more as a consultant, which reflected established practices at the College of Chemistry. Willard Rising, for example, had long served as a consulting chemist for companies that manufactured explosives.[31] Edmund O'Neill was likewise professionally active outside the classroom.[32]

Among Cottrell's first clients were a mining engineer who wanted help with a refining process and a mining company which sought new chemical methods for extracting precious metals from ores. From the outset, however, Cottrell also posed problems for himself. "Of all fool things, what do you suppose I'm working on now?" he wrote Jess shortly before their wedding. "Well, don't tell anyone. I'm having a shot at artificially forming real diamonds."[33]

Although Cottrell's earliest projects were not huge successes, they did establish his identity as a consultant. They also placed him on the verge of becoming a highly successful independent inventor. But before we examine his work with electrostatic precipitation, let us survey the industrial context giving rise to the problem he solved.

The DuPont Connection

Existing published accounts usually link Cottrell's invention of the electrostatic precipitator to the consulting work he did for the DuPont Company. Archival sources confirm the link and offer details that permit a fuller understanding. For example, within days of Cottrell's death in 1948 his long-time friend and colleague Warren H. McBryde recalled:

> I met Fred Cottrell soon after coming to California in 1899, and
> have known him intimately ever since. . . .
> [From] 1900 to 1903 I was assistant to Wm. C. Peyton in the
> designing, constructing and operating at Martinez, [of] one of the
> first contact-sulphuric acid plants on the West Coast, and from our
> earliest operating troubles Fred Cottrell got his idea of particle pre-
> cipitation.[34]

Although not explicitly stated, the purpose of the acid plants was to supply a critical material for the manufacture of dynamite.

Dynamite — a stabilized form of nitroglycerin — was invented by Alfred Nobel in 1866, and its first American demonstration came in San Francisco the following year. Also in 1867 the Giant Powder Company was formed to manufacture it, so that the American dynamite industry virtually began on the West Coast. Local black-powder manufacturers quickly followed suit. In 1869, for example, the California Powder Works (established in 1861 when the Civil War disrupted shipments from the East Coast) developed a product doped with nitroglycerin which they marketed under the name "Hercules." Although Giant sued the California Powder Works (and other companies making similar products), the U.S. Supreme Court in 1878 sustained a lower-court ruling that Giant's patent rights did not cover such mixtures.[35]

Black powder manufacturers in the East responded more slowly, but soon they too were producing the new explosive. Especially important for our purposes were steps taken by the DuPont Company — steps that included purchasing an interest in the California Powder Works. As the California Powder Works expanded, so did the percentage of DuPont's ownership. But expanding the scale of production also increased the danger of explosions. After a serious plant explosion in 1877, company president Bernard Peyton advised du Pont family stockholders that "city authorities will probably forbid the reconstruction of the Hercules plant in San Francisco."[36] The upshot was a move to a rural site on San Pablo Bay, near the town of Pinole.[37] It was here that Cottrell would later undertake his earliest commercial-scale work on the electrostatic precipitator.

By the time that Bernard Peyton's son, William C. Peyton, began experimenting with smokeless powder in the 1890s, the DuPont Company owned 44 percent of the company's stock, and together DuPont and the California Powder Works met most of the federal government's need for smokeless powder. As a result, the two companies cooperated extensively. For example, after DuPont provided the California Powder Works with details regarding a new smokeless shotgun powder, Peyton dropped his own efforts in favor of DuPont's. Similarly, after Francis I. du Pont informed Peyton of the work he was doing on a particular production technique, Peyton extended those results.[38]

Alongside Peyton's business and technical ties to DuPont we can add family ties, for Peyton's wife was Anne du Pont, the daughter of Francis's Uncle Eugene. When the Peyton Chemical Company was formed in 1900, Eugene was president of DuPont and DuPont invested in the new firm.[39] Following Eugene's death in early 1902, however, a momentous change in leadership occurred. Faced with possible sale of the company out of the family, three du Pont cousins — Alfred I. du Pont, T. Coleman du Pont, and Pierre S. du Pont — arranged to purchase it from their elders. They then reorganized the company so effectively that it became a model that other big businesses copied.[40]

Acting quickly, Coleman du Pont traveled to California in 1903 to bring order to the chaotic West Coast industry. Not only were several manufacturing companies competing with each other, but each was integrating vertically by undertaking the production of raw materials. The California Powder Works, for example, purchased the acids it needed until 1881, when it built a sulfuric acid production facility (based on the chamber method) at its Hercules plant. Later the Peyton Chemical Company became its acid-making subsidiary.

Once in California, however, du Pont reorganized the West Coast industry along horizontal rather than vertical lines. The California Powder Works became a wholly owned DuPont operation, to which were added the other local producers of explosives (Giant being the sole exception). Producers of raw materials — including the Peyton Chemical Company — were deliberately excluded.[41]

In the wake of all these changes, Warren McBryde left Peyton Chemical and joined DuPont. He was then assigned to DuPont's Repauno Works in Gibbstown, New Jersey, where he served as "its first resident engineer in charge of construction . . . building large sulfuric and nitric acid plants and an experimental nitroglycerine plant."[42]

The Repauno Chemical Company was established in 1880 by Lammot du Pont specifically for manufacturing dynamite. Like other early dynamite companies, it initially purchased the acids it needed. Later it continued to follow the industry trend by making its own acids. For sulfuric acid, the chamber method was preferred until a new method was introduced from Europe at the turn of the century. Commonly called the contact method, it yielded sulfur trioxide by combining oxygen and sulfur dioxide in the presence of a catalyst. For the American rights to one version of this process, DuPont turned to the New Jersey Zinc Company and hired the services of its chief chemist, Charles L. Reese.[43]

In 1900 Reese had given up academic work to help New Jersey Zinc develop the contact method. He quickly identified one of the main problems, namely, contamination by arsenic (which combined with the catalyst, thereby undermining the catalyst's effectiveness). Later that year he began working for DuPont as a consultant, and in 1902 he was made director of DuPont's newly formed Eastern Laboratory at the Repauno Works. Eventually he presided over the full range of the company's research efforts, thus helping to pioneer industrial research in the chemical industry.[44]

Inventing the Electrostatic Precipitator

Having built a contact-method plant for Peyton Chemical and having worked on a similar process for the Repauno Works (a major research center for the contact method), Warren McBryde was well aware of the problems the contact method involved. More to the point, he was most likely the person who brought these problems to Cottrell's attention.

In 1905 Cottrell responded to requests from DuPont's Hercules Works at Pinole by addressing the problem of arsenic poisoning, and his earliest efforts employed a centrifugal separator. He then realized that a similar method could be used to solve a second problem — namely, how to eliminate the sulfuric acid mists that formed in the process and limited its efficiency. All the while, his financial needs remained pressing. As Cottrell recalled in 1937:

> The work started purely as a private venture, a summer vacation's excursion into the technical commercial field when it was drastically necessary to supplement a university instructor's salary by outside work of some sort.[45]

At that point Harry East Miller, a consulting chemist, offered his assistance. Cottrell had begun the project at Berkeley. Now he was able to pursue it further in a laboratory located in the San Francisco Stock Exchange building, where Miller had his office.

Miller's ties to the West Coast dynamite industry were extensive. In addition to serving various companies as a consultant, in 1898 he supervised the manufacture of gelatin dynamite at the Judson Dynamite Works — one of the companies that DuPont would absorb in 1903. Miller also had strong ties to Berkeley. He was an 1885 graduate, and when Edmund O'Neill founded a local American Chemical Society chapter in 1901, Miller joined it. O'Neill was also the person who informed Miller of Cottrell's work.[46]

The centrifugal separator was successful enough to justify a pair of patent applications, and because of his support Miller was assigned half the rights.[47] The process was also successful enough to justify preliminary testing at the Hercules Works. In the end, however, it was not sufficiently promising to warrant full commercial development. "Mechanically," McBryde reported, "[Cottrell] found that he could precipitate the smelter smoke or fume particles by revolving, at high speed, a long vertical tube, but this was impractical on a large industrial scale."[48] Similarly, Walter A. Schmidt — a 1906 Berkeley graduate — recalled:

> [Cottrell] first tried a high speed centrifuge, consisting of a long

cylindrical glass tube. At that time I was a student of his; in fact, in that year I was the only student in his laboratory physical chemistry class, and consequently, was more or less his assistant, and I was quite familiar with the work that he was doing. His centrifugal device operated on a small scale and he subsequently obtained a patent thereon. However, it failed to function properly on a large scale, and he looked about for a more effective method.[49]

Soon after the centrifugal separator work, Cottrell turned to electrostatic precipitation. But here our sources do not allow us to reconstruct his precise train of thought.[50] The most complete account is the one offered by Harry J. White:

> In a personal interview with Dr. Cottrell in 1945, he told me that his interest in collecting fumes and dusts came about through a problem in the amalgamation of black sands by centrifuge. An experimental centrifuge for collecting fumes and mists was built and tried out in an office over the old stock exchange in San Francisco. The centrifuge performed moderately well, but he soon discovered that this was not the answer, because of its relatively poor performance on fine particles. He stated that about this time he became interested in the competitive aspects of the process and decided to put in some time investigating this. Then he made the significant statement: "I had heard of Lodge's work on gas cleaning but couldn't find anything in the literature on it so I tried to visualize it and built an experimental setup using a spark coil and a couple of discharge points and it worked very well."[51]

The main point is that after Cottrell began the project, he altered his approach. Originally the problem was defined by the technical needs of the dynamite industry. As a physical chemist, however, Cottrell was conversant not only with existing chemical practices but also with those of the physics community. Our sources do not supply the details of just how he shifted his perspective. Nevertheless, in later years he consistently cited the work of English physicist Oliver J. Lodge (1851–1940).[52]

In the early 1880s Lodge and his associate, J. W. Clark, sought to determine experimentally what caused a dust-free space to appear above hot bodies — a phenomenon previously observed by John Tyndall and studied by Lord Rayleigh (J. W. Strutt). Lodge and Clark concluded that the cause was molecular bombardment from the hot surfaces. Meanwhile, Lodge wondered if an electric field would produce a similar effect. He and Clark determined that it did, and Lodge successfully demonstrated the effect before the British Association for the Advancement of Science in Montreal in 1884.[53]

Since 1881 Lodge had been professor of physics at University College in Liverpool, and his main areas of research were electromagnetic waves and the electromagnetic ether (the supposed medium of electromagnetic waves). In 1876 he read James Clerk Maxwell's 1873 *Treatise on Electricity and Magnetism*, and thereafter he was a vigorous proponent of the new theory. The result was his *Modern Views of Electricity*, serialized in *Nature* in 1887–1889 and published separately in 1889. "Lodge's book," Bruce J. Hunt has noted, "was the first and one of the most successful popularizations of Maxwellian ideas. . . ."[54]

Lodge knew full well that the topic of dust and smoke had practical implications. Speaking to the Canadians in his Montreal audience, he observed:

> The old country has in many things made experiments for you. . . .
> [One] experiment we have tried only too successfully . . . [is] that of
> fouling the atmosphere, wherever a large number of human beings
> have to live in it, to such an extent that it is not fit to breathe.[55]

In the main, however, he followed Tyndall's lead and discussed "the floating matter of the air"[56] — which is to say "dust" as a general phenomenon of nature. When he did mention applications, he emphasized how clouds form, not how cities generate smoke. Thus in Lodge's work we see an emphasis on "natural philosophy" (a term for which "physics" has now been largely substituted) and a preference for basic science.[57]

As his source of electric charge at Montreal, Lodge used a Voss machine — a new type of electrical apparatus. Electrical studies have long been apparatus-dependent. Among the earliest pieces of equipment were frictional machines for generating electric charge. The 1740s saw the advent of the Leyden jar, which allowed electric charge to be stored for the first time. So much charge could be stored in a Leyden jar that its sudden release produced large sparks or shocks that could knock a person flat. Only then did it make sense to liken electric discharges to lightning bolts (which is just what Benjamin Franklin proceeded to do). In 1800 Alessandro Volta announced the invention of yet another important device. By alternating pairs of dissimilar metallic disks with moistened cardboard in a stack, he was able to produce a steady flow of electric charge — a laboratory phenomenon quite different from the lightning-like discharge of a Leyden jar.[58]

In contrast to the traditional electrostatic generator, the Voss machine was an influence machine. It utilized rotating disks to induce electric charge, relying on field effects rather than frictional effects for its operation. Originating circa 1860, Robert Voss's 1880 design was an improvement.[59]

One of the main problems with the early influence machines was their sensitivity to atmospheric humidity — which we can see in Lodge's account:

> [Prior to giving the evening lecture] I went to the lecture-room in the afternoon to see how [the assistant] was getting on. I found him in a state of despair and ready to wash his hands of the whole business. . . . I worked away, erecting my own apparatus . . . till the people began to come in. I remember going to the top of the stairs as Sir William Thomson came up, and saying, "I'm afraid it is going to be a failure." The atmosphere was very damp, and the Voss machine declined to work, so that the chief experiment seemed bound to fail.[60]

Then Lodge got a lucky break:

> . . . the Canadian climate took a sudden turn for the better, and after I had done successfully the early part of the lecture, I turned with some trepidation to my chief experiment of the bell-jar. To my surprise the atmosphere was now dry, the Voss machine insulated perfectly and was in excellent order.[61]

Subsequently, the experiment proceeded just as it had in his laboratory at Liverpool:

> On gently turning the handle of the Voss machine, the first effect was a great agitation of dust [in the bell jar], then the formation of snow flakes or streamers, and then total disappearance, and clearness of the air, though the walls were all dusted over.[62]

So pleased was Lodge with the response of his audience that years later he fondly recalled how ". . . Sir William, dear old man, showed his enthusiasm by getting out of his seat and going to the bell-jar, clapping his hands as he went, to inspect the artificial snowstorm more narrowly. [And afterward] Lord Rayleigh proposed a vote of thanks. . . ."[63]

Despite Lodge's preference for basic science, published accounts of his smoke studies soon led to inquiries regarding practical applications. In Lodge's own words:

> Mr. Alfred [O.] Walker, of Walker, Parker & Co., first informed me of the difficulty which lead smelters labour under in condensing the fume which escapes along with the smoke from red-lead smelting furnaces, and he wished to put an electrical process of condensation to the test on a large scale.[64]

In consultation with Lodge, Walker experimented with electrostatic precipitators at his company's lead-smelting works at Bagillt in North Wales. Success with the earliest phases of the project led to optimistic published accounts, as well as applications for patents in various countries. But constructing and operating a full-scale device failed, due to problems with insulating the electrical equipment and handling the lead fumes.[65]

Both the initial optimism and the ultimate disappointment were based on a development better described as technological than scientific. In early 1883 James Wimshurst proposed a more robust design for an influence machine. "These machines," noted one account, ". . . displaced all other generators of static electricity on account of their possessing the property of being self-exciting under any atmospheric conditions."[66]

Wimshurst refused to patent his design, thus making it immediately available to all — including Walker at the Dee Bank Lead Works. Although Walker first used a Voss machine with an eighteen-inch disk, he soon shifted to a Wimshurst machine with five-foot disks. Nevertheless, the effort failed. "We gave it up in Wales," one of Walker's co-workers later reported:

> after very long trials and every effort to make it "go." I carried out all these experiments, and was in the beginning very hopeful that we were going to have a great success. It *was* a success as long as we worked on small volumes of fume either enclosed in small holders (such as a large cask or box) or even when fume passed slowly through such holders. But we never succeeded in any way as soon as we got to work on the actual flues, in which great masses of gas were in rapid motion.[67]

Just how Cottrell first learned about Lodge's work is uncertain. One possibility was a letter to the editor that Lodge wrote for an April 1905 issue of *Nature* magazine. The letter added an "historical note" to his accounts from the 1880s by mentioning the 1824 work of Hohlfeld, which had just come to his attention.[68] However, Cottrell probably knew of Lodge's work before then — if only indirectly. For example, his Christmas 1890 issue of *Boys' Workshop* mentioned "the deposition of smoke and dust by electrical aid" as a new application of electricity.[69]

Cottrell's colleague and former student, Walter Schmidt, offered another possibility:

> About 1900, Exum P. Lewis, professor of physics at the University of California, whose discovery of the so-called "after-glow" in nitrogen and other electrical effects in gases attest his interest in this field, inaugurated a course in electrical discharge through gases, where one of his lecture demonstrations was a repetition of the Hohlfeld experiment. Among his . . . students [was] J. G. Davidson, later professor of physics at the University of British Columbia. One of Doctor Davidson's research problems under Professor Lewis was the motion and precipitation of ions and charged particles in an electric field, where the primary charging action took place in a stage separate from the precipitating action.[70]

On a later occasion, Schmidt added the punch line: "After discussions with Dr. James G. Davidson . . . [Cottrell and Davidson] looked up the early work of Sir Oliver Lodge on electrical precipitation. . . ."[71]

Although the record is fragmentary, I believe we can reassemble the various pieces in the following way. The problem first came to Cottrell through Warren McBryde, with regard to acid production at the Hercules Works. But Cottrell had a knack for "thinking outside the box." After testing the centrifugal separator, he somehow thought of Lodge's work on smoke. As he told White in 1945, he was unable to locate a published account of the setup, so he tried building a similar device of his own. That response was fully in keeping with his personal laboratory style. For example, when he was a graduate student at Berkeley one of his instructors had suggested buying an oscillograph for a project they were working on. "Let's make one," Cottrell had countered, ". . . you make the magnet and I'll make the mirror."[72]

Fortunately, the sequence of events after the moment of inspiration is easier to document. Working at Berkeley in mid-1906, Cottrell quickly confirmed Lodge's earlier results. Because of DuPont's production needs, he used sulfuric acid fumes — which proved much easier to handle than lead fumes. To enhance the effect, he added two novel features: fine filaments as "pubescent electrodes" (initially in the form of the wire's cotton wrapping) and higher voltages, which he obtained by replacing the spark coil with a mechanical rectifier that changed alternating current (AC) to direct current (DC).[73]

Pubescent electrodes enabled Cottrell to produce corona discharge at lower voltages than would have been possible otherwise, and later he described the serendipitous moment of discovery:

> Working one evening in the twilight when the efficiency of the different points could be roughly judged by the pale luminous discharge from them, it was noticed that . . . a piece of cotton-covered magnet wire which carried the current from the transformer and commutator to the discharge electrodes, although widely separated from any conductor of opposite polarity, showed a beautiful uniform purple glow along its whole length.[74]

Although not as fundamental as the Principle of Archimedes, Cottrell's invention of pubescent electrodes echoes the classic "Eureka" story. Both Cottrell and Archimedes initially met with failure, and when success finally did come it came unexpectedly for both of them.[75]

The other novel feature of Cottrell's approach — the use of rectified AC — owed more to the changing technological landscape than to the psychology of individual creativity. Edison's original electric system had been DC, and his first installations were central stations for urban business districts. During the 1890s, however, the need for long-distance power transmission prompted a wholesale shift to AC — with Nicola Tesla and the Westinghouse Electric and Manufacturing Company being the pioneers. In 1892 the Edison General Electric Company responded by merging with the Thomson-Houston Company, thus acquiring that firm's AC capabilities. In the process, the expanded company was renamed General Electric.[76]

The need for long-distance power transmission arose because the main markets for electrical power (cities) were not always the best places to produce it. This was especially true for San Francisco, which lacked local coal deposits for use in coal-fired generators. Waterpower offered an alternative. But terrain suitable for generating hydroelectricity lay many miles to the east. The moisture-laden ocean air that regularly blanketed San Francisco in fog was largely unaffected by the Berkeley Hills. Not until reaching the western slopes of the Sierra Nevada Mountains was the moisture precipitated as rain or snow.[77]

Mountain streams had first been harnessed after the Gold Rush of 1849.

By diverting the water into gently inclined flumes, engineers created heads that measured in the hundreds of feet, for use in the hydraulic mining of gold. Toward the end of the century, however, such flumes were put to a new use. Although the earliest hydroelectric plants served only their local communities, by 1901 a 140-mile line stretched from the recently completed Colgate power plant on the Yuba River all the way to Oakland. Hailed by the *Journal of Electricity, Power and Gas* as having achieved "the world's longest electric power transmission," the new line powered Oakland's streetcar company but served other customers as well — including DuPont's Hercules Works.[78] By 1903 a writer for *Scientific American* noted that California's electric transmission lines "fairly cobweb the central portion of the State from east to west," thereby turning "remotely separated electrical systems into a single unit of vast proportions."[79]

It was no accident that the electrostatic precipitator was first developed successfully in a region that possessed a high-voltage transmission network. The basic idea of electrostatic precipitation was not new with Cottrell. His work in the first decade of the twentieth century was predated by Lodge's in the 1880s — which, in turn, was predated by C. F. Guitard's work in the 1840s and Hohlfeld's in the 1820s.[80] Until Cottrell's day, however, the wherewithal to develop the idea on a commercial scale did not exist. Thus the basic idea was destined to be discovered and then lost from view, time after time, until the physical conditions changed. Cottrell finally succeeded because the place where he worked was one of the first in the world with access to high-voltage electrical power.

Taking Out a Patent

After his success at Berkeley, Cottrell began the hard work of transforming the laboratory process to a full-scale industrial device. Here Warren McBryde again played a role. He had returned to the West Coast in 1905 to supervise the construction of a sulfuric acid plant at DuPont's Hercules Works.[81] Later that year, when DuPont executive Hamilton M. Barksdale visited California, McBryde introduced him to Cottrell. So interested was Barksdale in Cottrell's work that when the idea of electrostatic precipitation came along McBryde believed "he would wish for me to do whatever I could to help my friend Fred Cottrell."[82]

Despite the brevity of Barksdale's contact with Cottrell, it demonstrated the proximity of Cottrell's work to the ongoing Research Revolution in American industry. Not only did Barksdale represent a critical level of management at DuPont — the level at which technical expertise combined with access to

A demonstration of the experimental electrostatic precipitator installed in 1906 at DuPont's Hercules Works contact–sulfuric acid plant in California.

high-level policymaking — but he also played a central role in establishing the company's research facilities (notably, Eastern Laboratory at Repauno).[83]

Bolstered by Barksdale's interest, McBryde actively facilitated Cottrell's efforts to develop the electrostatic precipitator. Thus with regard to "the duPont Company's Contact–Sulphuric Acid plant at Hercules," he recalled:

> ... in its early operation in 1906 I offered Fred Cottrell the facilities and helped him in constructing his commercial demonstration plant in this plant with "step-up" transformers for his electrical precipitation and all the other necessary apparatus he needed. It's a wonder he and I were not killed in this work many times. I also gave him all the sulphuric acid gas he needed for his demonstration and furnished the labor and material gratis.[84]

As McBryde's remarks indicate, their first efforts to build a commercial version of Cottrell's invention came during the summer of 1906, when they installed an experimental precipitator for one of the sulfuric acid units.[85] Before they completed this project, however, Cottrell shifted his attention elsewhere.

Further up the bay, at Vallejo Junction near the Carquinez Straits, the Selby Smelting and Lead Company faced opposition from the farmers of Solano County and residents of the town of Benicia. In 1905 they began legal proceedings to prevent smelter smoke from blowing across the straits and damaging local property, and in 1906 the case went to trial.[86]

During the summer of 1907, Cottrell began to install electrostatic precipitators at Selby. He succeeded in reducing the sulfuric acid fumes, the primary visible emissions in the refining of gold and silver. But he failed to reduce the visible emissions from the roasting process — a problem the company later solved by installing a new type of furnace. Finally, in order to minimize lead and arsenic emissions the company installed a bag house. Thus electrostatic precipitation became one of several quite different techniques whereby the company responded to the legal proceedings against it.[87]

The importance of the Selby case warrants a look at its outcome. After an unfavorable ruling by the state superior court of Solano County in July 1908, the company appealed, only to have the state supreme court affirm the original judgment in 1912. Meanwhile, the company continued operating — despite the injunction against doing so — yet it also worked vigorously to reduce the objectionable emissions (as we have just seen). When the case was referred to Ligon Johnson, the special assistant to the U.S. attorney general, he declined to enforce the injunction and instead proposed the formation of the Selby Smelter Commission, whose members were to be agreed upon jointly by both parties in the suit. "The examination of the Selby Commission," Johnson later reported:

> extended over a period of about a year and a half [from mid-1913 to late 1914] and in the end clearly demonstrated that the smelter was doing none of the things found against it in the original decree; and the injunction was vacated.[88]

Far from dying out, issues such as those raised in the Selby case became even more important after World War II. As a result, the Selby Smelter Commission report became "one of the classics of the smelter smoke controversy."[89] It set a precedent as "probably the first attempt in the U.S. to analyze the smelter smoke problem scientifically and under controlled field conditions,"[90] and it established an "industry standard" against which later studies were measured.[91]

Returning to Cottrell's story, his work at Selby resulted in new technical developments. The corrosiveness of the fumes led him to construct the electrodes out of mica strips. Trial and error also revealed that the discharge electrodes were more effective when they were charged negatively, rather than positively. Based on these new developments, electrostatic precipitation at Selby became a routine practice, with the device collecting about 3,000 gallons of sulfuric acid daily. Thus the installation was the first to demonstrate fully the invention's commercial feasibility.[92]

At about the same time that he began working at Selby, Cottrell applied for a patent. Despite the earlier work of Lodge, Walker, and others, his application was broadly worded. He argued that the distinctive features of his method — including the use of pubescent electrodes and rectified AC — enabled him to do what no one before him had done, namely, to build successful commercial devices.

The patent examiner initially rejected the broad wording of Cottrell's claims — especially with regard to rectified AC. One reason was Walker's American patent, which stated that "the electricity may be supplied at high potential by *any other known means.*"[93] Cottrell replied that Walker's patent had specifically originated in connection with the Wimshurst electrostatic generator, which proved unsatisfactory for commercial work. As a result, the patent had long been inoperative, leading Cottrell to point out:

> Were it a question of safeguarding the Walker patent, during its life, to allow its natural development under its inventor's progressive improvements, there might be more justice in the contention, but in view of the fact that during its whole life, this patent apparently had no appreciable effect on the progress of the art, and has long since expired, it hardly seems consistent with the purpose and spirit of our patent laws to interpret such a sweeping and indefinite expression. . . .[94]

Cottrell also replied to the patent examiner's objection that other inventors had already patented AC rectifiers:

> Neher and Müller were both aiming primarily at the charging of commercial storage batteries. . . .
> The requirement of the two cases [theirs and mine] are so widely different that the one would not necessarily suggest the other, even to the technical expert, as my conversations with practical men in this line . . . have proven to me.[95]

Such arguments proved persuasive. The Patent Office finally accepted

Cottrell's broad wording and on August 11, 1908, issued him a patent on the "Art of Separating Suspended Particles from Gaseous Bodies."[96] In his patent Cottrell noted that the basic effect was already known and understood:

> Modern theories explain this action [of precipitating suspended particles] on the ground that the gas in the neighborhood of the points becomes ionized, chiefly by brush or glow discharge, and the ions combine with or condense upon the suspended particles, dragging these with them toward bodies of opposite polarity.[97]

But he insisted that previous knowledge had not been sufficient to overcome the difficulties posed by practical applications. Hence the novelty of his claims lay in the specific methods he employed. "For the production of an electric current," he offered rectified AC as possessing "the great advantage of extreme simplicity, coupled with ease of installation and maintenance of the apparatus required."[98] Equally important were the problems he had solved using pubescent electrodes:

> These difficulties are all avoided and the efficiency and ease of adjustment of the apparatus greatly increased, if the electrodes are simply covered in whole or in part, with some soft, fibrous material, such as cotton or asbestos, presenting a pubescent surface.[99]

Despite the breadth of his claims, Cottrell's original patent was insufficient by itself. Like many other industrial processes, commercial success required building up an appropriate set of patents. A year later, for example, Cottrell applied for a patent that strengthened the pubescent electrode claims.[100] Later still, he patented the idea of negative polarity for the discharge electrodes.[101] Nor did the list stop there. As we shall see, the process of taking out patents would become an ongoing feature of Research Corporation's efforts.

Nonetheless, Cottrell's first patent possesses special importance. It conferred on Cottrell the mantle of the independent inventor, allowing his story to be cast in the popular tradition of Edison, Bell, and others. By endowing Research Corporation with his patent rights, Cottrell was thus able to provide it not just a legal mandate to undertake the business of building electrostatic precipitators but also a distinctive social mission. His gift empowered Research Corporation to help future inventors achieve similar success.

Before considering how Research Corporation itself was established, however, let us examine one more point about Cottrell's early work on electrostatic precipitation. To summarize the ground we have covered so far, he began by applying his professional expertise to the problem of unwanted emissions at DuPont's Hercules Works. What he sought was a technical solution to a particular industrial problem. He then shifted his attention to the Selby smelter and applied for a patent. In formulating his solution he drew on the earlier work of Oliver Lodge. But where Lodge explicitly acknowledged the social problem of air pollution, not until Selby did Cottrell's work demonstrate a similar concern.

To appreciate the significance of the shift from Hercules to Selby, we should review the main facets of the environmental movement in Cottrell's day.[102] One facet was urban reform. The rapid rise of American cities after the Civil War created unprecedented needs for safe drinking water, effective sewerage systems, sanitary disposal of solid wastes, and reduction of urban smoke. Although many people felt overwhelmed by the magnitude of such problems, others responded with calls to action. For these civic reformers, urban pollution was "a tangible . . . by-product of industrialization and urbanization which had to be confronted."[103]

Occurring in the same time frame as urbanization were industrialization and the end of the frontier, and together these trends produced an unprecedented sense of resource depletion. Thus conservation — the efficient use of increasingly scarce resources — was a second facet of the environmental movement. Here engineers claimed for themselves a special role. For example, after attending President Theodore Roosevelt's 1908 White House conference on natural resources conservation, Charles S. Howe, president of Case School of Applied Science, sounded a warning: "Unless we can prevent the absolute destruction of the natural resources the ruin of the nation is assured."[104] While admitting the need for specialists in many fields, Howe emphasized: "this work of conservation is the work of the engineer."[105]

Representing a third facet of the environmental movement were those who loved nature for its own sake. Notable here was John Muir, a nature writer who helped found the Sierra Club and who believed that some tracts of land should be set aside and preserved from development.[106] This aspect of the environmental movement was firmly rooted in the American literary tradition (including, for example, Henry David Thoreau), and it took on special importance in California. As citizens of a distinctive region, many Californians believed it their duty to forge "a special relationship to nature" based on "respect for the non-human world on its non-human terms."[107]

Cottrell's earliest work with electrostatic precipitation seems not to have been directly motivated by the environmental movement in any of its facets. Likely he was inclined toward the movement's engineering component.[108] But initially this was implicit rather than explicit. For example, in discussing "[t]he utility and economic importance" of electrostatic precipitation, his patent referred to sulfuric acid plants, lead and copper smelters, and iron blast furnaces — not to conservation (or air pollution or the beauties of nature).[109]

As the work progressed, however, it became strongly linked to the environmental movement. From the outset the Selby smelter required not just a technical solution to an industrial problem, but also a cost-effective solution to a legal problem. At the same time, the project acquired an urgency it had not possessed earlier. Thus Cottrell commented in 1914:

> Looking backward on the history of the work, it appears doubtful whether it would ever have lived through the difficulties encountered in its early stages had it not appeared as a possible solution of the life and death struggle some of the plants were then making in the courts on fume-damage suits.[110]

In a chronological sense, therefore, electrostatic precipitation was first a technological process, and as such its effectiveness could be measured in narrowly technical terms. But to survive the harsh climate brought on by legal proceedings against the Selby smelter, Cottrell's invention had to be given additional meaning. Specifically, it became an important part of the company's legal position, allowing it to claim that it was taking appropriate steps to meet the plaintiffs' objections. But the added meanings did not stop there. For the process to achieve maximum effectiveness in American society, the technical invention had to be given more than just a legal identity. It also had to be given an appropriate organizational structure.

CHAPTER THREE

AN ELEEMOSYNARY IDEA

R EVOLUTIONS IN SCIENCE and technology are never complete. When they occur, not all aspects of the past disappear. Thus our claims for the Research Revolution would be far too sweeping were we to say that organizations replaced individuals wholesale as the basis for new knowledge creation. Talented individuals remained the heart of the enterprise. Yet the context for their work changed dramatically as they became supported and guided by organizational structures and policies.

Giving the Project an Organizational Structure

Cottrell's work on electrostatic precipitation typified this shifting context.[1] Although his early efforts were facilitated by a variety of organizations (notably, the University of California at Berkeley, the Hercules Works of the DuPont Company, and the U.S. Patent Office), he pursued the project largely on an individual basis. Its scale was limited to what he was able to do alone.

Financial need was the most pressing motive for adopting an organized approach. Even at the laboratory stage, expenses outstripped Cottrell's personal resources, thus necessitating the recruitment of financial backers. The earliest was Harry East Miller, who provided $500 to Cottrell (for Cottrell's half interest in the process) and $2,000 to continue the work. When more funds were required, Miller approached Edmond S. Heller, another Berkeley alumnus. The two had been classmates at Berkeley (Class of 1885). While Miller subsequently received a doctorate from the University of Strassburg and became a consulting chemist, Heller received a law degree from Berkeley and established a successful legal practice – so that in addition to financial support, he provided important legal advice. Also included in the group of backers was Edmond O'Neill, who had recommended Cottrell to Miller. O'Neill was an older Berkeley alumnus (Class of 1879) who subsequently joined the faculty and served as teacher and mentor for the others.[2]

At Heller's suggestion the group formed a pair of business companies. Cottrell assigned his patent rights to the International Precipitation Company, whose purpose was to administer those rights worldwide (by taking out foreign patents and licensing other companies to do business on the basis of the patents it controlled). By contrast, the Western Precipitation Company was an engineering firm, authorized to build and operate electrostatic pre-

The founders of the International and Western Precipitation Companies: Edmond O'Neill and Frederick Gardner Cottrell (left to right, standing), Edmond S. Heller and Harry East Miller.

cipitators in the West. Each was chartered in the state of California in September 1907, and each had the same slate of officers: Heller as president, Cottrell as vice-president, and Miller as secretary–treasurer. Although each was authorized to issue stock amounting to $20,000, the actual starting capital was much smaller: $3,000 from Heller and a $1,500 bank loan.[3]

Beyond providing the patents, Cottrell supervised the ongoing technical work. His diaries from the period mention numerous trips to San Francisco offices and rural plant sites. In addition to Hercules and Selby, he oversaw a major installation at the Balaklala Smelter of the First National Copper Company at Coram, California, on the upper Sacramento River — another facility where legal steps had been taken to limit environmental damage.[4]

To help him with the installations at Selby and Balaklala, Cottrell recruited Herbert A. Burns, one of his former students at Berkeley. Nevertheless,

Cottrell's own participation remained so extensive that he took a leave of absence from his teaching duties in early 1908 to devote more time to the project.[5] After Cottrell underwent a medical operation in May, O'Neill recommended that he extend his leave into the new academic year. At first Cottrell resisted. "I don't want to drift out of academic work into business life as so many have," he told a professional acquaintance, ". . . the more time I take off from college just now, the harder it will be to settle down in the old traces once more."[6] Nervous stress, however, forced him to resume his leave during the second half of the 1908–1909 academic year.[7] Meanwhile, Walter A. Schmidt (another of Cottrell's former students) successfully developed electrostatic precipitators for the Portland cement industry, and Cottrell himself — working at Berkeley with former student Buckner Speed — invented a related process for removing water suspended in crude oil.[8]

In summary, as the technical work matured and became more complex Cottrell augmented his individual efforts with an organized approach. This approach had two main features: formally creating International Precipitation and Western Precipitation, while at the same time mobilizing an informal network of Berkeley alumni (thereby gaining financial assistance and legal advice from his partners and technical assistance from his former students).

Although some sort of organized approach was required, we can imagine alternatives to the one that Cottrell actually took. The most obvious would have been a big business approach. Instead of pursuing electrostatic precipitation through newly formed small businesses and the support of his Berkeley colleagues, he could have turned to an existing big business. The DuPont Company might have taken over the project as a separate division within its corporate structure, or Cottrell could have accepted General Electric's offer of employment and taken the project with him.

Archival sources suggest that Cottrell did consider alternatives along these lines. Specifically, his diaries refer to the possibility of a formal arrangement with DuPont. Several individuals participated in the discussions. One was R. S. Penniman, a former superintendent of DuPont's Atlantic Dynamite Company who became vice president of the California Powder Works in 1903.[9] Another participant was one of the Haskell brothers — probably Harry Garner Haskell, who had become director of high explosives at DuPont after the company's reorganization in 1902 (rather than Jonathan Amory Haskell, president of Repauno Chemical Company and of Laflin and Rand Powder Company).[10]

A final figure in Cottrell's diary entries was "Reese" — presumably the DuPont chemist Charles L. Reese. In 1907 Reese still headed DuPont's Eastern Laboratory. Not until 1911, after Francis I. du Pont's leadership at the

Experiment Station (DuPont's other research arm) proved unsatisfactory, was Reese was given full authority over both facilities.[11]

In his diary entry for July 26, 1907, Cottrell noted that he and Miller met "McB[ryde], Haskell, and Reese" at the Hercules Works. "Went through acid plant with them," Cottrell continued, "showing them the apparatus[,] which worked well."[12]

Back at the Hercules Works ten days later, Cottrell met with Penniman, Reese, and Haskell. In a lengthy diary entry he described their negotiations:

> Penn[i]man opened by advising me to promote my interests by treating the matter "in a broad Western way don't you know" and give the Powder Co. the rights free for the Hercules plant. This I indicated was out of the question and after some discussion in which I proposed putting it on a cash per ton of installed capacity (Reese quoting the Man[n]h[eim] units at 4 tons) and if necessary giving them rights to first unit free ("1/10 broad W[estern] w[ay]" as Penn[iman] called it) Reese finally proposed our giving them the right to five units free and charging full price for anything beyond. He also urged me to take up the application of the app[aratus] to their Schröder plants & offered to send a man out to get the details with me.
>
> I told them I would consider both propositions but wished to move very conservatively and could not at the time commit myself to any positive course.[13]

That evening Cottrell discussed the day's events with Miller and then reported in his diary: "We decided in no case to give [the] Powder Co. more than two units free and preferably to hold the whole matter up until [the] process was developed elsewhere."[14]

As Cottrell also noted in his diary, he and his partners considered asking McBryde to join them:

> In evening went in to Millers and talked over form of proposition to put up to Penn[i]man in letter. Also discussed possibility of making a place in the new undertaking for McB[ryde]. Possibility of his taking our construction department discussed at length.[15]

Although McBryde was told about the idea,[16] nothing came of it.

A different round of negotiations involved W. C. Peyton and the use of electrostatic precipitators at Martinez. After a conference with Peyton on March 24, 1909, Cottrell carefully listed the "Chief Questions Raised":

Guarantee against damage for infringement

Refund of royalty in case of infringement

Guarantee on Part of Peyton not to interfere with our
subsequent applications

Prohibition against use of similar process during
continuance of License

Question of exclusive rights for radius of 100 miles around
S[an] F[rancisco][17]

That last question proved the most critical. "He didn't object to our dealing with the works already equipped," Cottrell reported, "but [he] did not want to develop [the] process at his expense which might make it possible for a competitor to come in & build a works for half the cost of his own."[18] When Cottrell and his associates refused to grant him an exclusive license, the negotiations ended.[19]

An Endowment of Patent Rights

Although his efforts to develop the precipitator were time-consuming, Cottrell did not want to leave Berkeley for a full-time position with the companies he and his partners had founded. Instead, he had a more philanthropic goal in mind. He wanted to organize a way of helping academic researchers develop promising new ideas while retaining their faculty positions. Instead of individuals making ad hoc arrangements for their inventions, the process would be handled systematically by an organization. That way socially important inventions arising from academic settings could be developed commercially without disrupting either traditional campus activities or traditional business practices.

As the technical work matured and the commercial installations became more successful financially, Cottrell turned his attention to this eleemosynary idea. Later documents suggest that he had always planned to give away his patent rights, but the idea surfaced relatively late in his diaries, which provide the earliest existing record of his intentions. Specifically, he noted in the entry for April 19, 1909, that during a "[l]ong talk with O'Neill" about business and academic matters, he "[d]iscussed the possibility of eventually turning the I[nternational] P[recipitation] Co. into an endowment for scientific work &c."[20] Later he conferred with Miller, who expressed a "growing interest" in the idea.[21] Apparently, however, Miller's interest waned over the following year, leading Cottrell to note that Miller "wished to see what Selby was going to do before he made any proposition as to what he would sell out for."[22]

Later sources shed further light on Cottrell's intentions. For example, the opening paragraph of his 1912 article on Research Corporation referred to "the old dilemma of adjustment between academic and commercial activities."[23] Traditionally, the public viewed college teachers as altruistic figures — similar to ministers in that regard, and often as penurious.[24] With the Research Revolution gaining momentum in the late nineteenth century, university professors increasingly found themselves possessing knowledge or skills of great practical value, yet they often lacked sufficient means to make sure that society benefited from their ideas. Having himself experienced these difficulties, Cottrell wanted to help others overcome them — not just through personal effort but also through some sort of organized assistance.

He probably had other motives as well. Thus his associate, Percy H. Royster, recalled:

> Doctor Cottrell was of the firm conviction that at least 95% of every invention was not due to the work of the inventor himself but belonged to the past. . . . He, therefore, held that an inventor would be presumptuous if he should lay claim to credit or profit arising from his invention.[25]

Because it was often impossible to compensate past inventors, Cottrell reasoned that the debt could be acknowledged and repaid by assisting present and future inventors.

Initially, Cottrell planned to offer his patent rights to the University of California. Years later he noted that in 1904 he and others at Berkeley had discussed how the university might administer patents in order to generate research funds. Donating the precipitator patent rights to the university's board of regents would have provided an opportunity to test this idea.[26] Also pointing to Berkeley as the natural recipient were the ties of those most closely involved in the project (Cottrell, his financial partners, and his technical assistants).[27]

As commercial development of the precipitator matured, however, Cottrell realized that managing his patents on a global scale far exceeded the capabilities of his alma mater. "By the time the work had thus reached a self-supporting basis," he explained in 1912, "its significance was felt to have broadened to a degree which made its control by a local institution such as a single University inexpedient. . . ."[28] Moreover, by 1915 he began to fear that success at Berkeley might lead to similar practices on other campuses and that the ensuing intercollegiate competition to obtain and develop valuable patents would result in "the commercialization of educational laboratories."[29]

Cottrell next considered giving his patent rights to a suitable national professional society, and the occasion he chose for exploring this possibility was a meeting of the American Chemical Society (ACS) in San Francisco in mid-July 1910. During the twenty years since its founding, the ACS had never before met on the West Coast. But despite the long railroad journey required of many who attended (and a train wreck en route), the registration was better than half what it had been at the Boston meeting the previous December.[30]

The ACS, itself a product of the Research Revolution, had recently addressed one of the characteristic issues of that revolution: how to handle the increasing specialization of its members. Already a separate American Electrochemical Society (1902) and a separate American Institute of Chemical Engineers (1908) had emerged. To minimize further defections, the ACS started creating separate divisions for various professional subgroups, thereby allowing each a degree of autonomy. Formed in 1908, the Division of Industrial Chemists and Chemical Engineers was one of the earliest. It published its own journal, the *Journal of Industrial and Engineering Chemistry* (distributed to all ACS members), and it held its own meetings (as part of the general ACS meetings).[31]

At the San Francisco meeting Cottrell contributed an illustrated paper to the "Symposium on Smelter Smoke" sponsored by the Division of Industrial Chemists and Chemical Engineers. "By the use of numerous lantern slides," read one account, "the author indicated the development, from the crude laboratory stage to the successful commercial installation, of his process. . . ."[32] The next day Cottrell supplemented his talk with a laboratory demonstration at Berkeley.[33] An even more vivid presentation came a few hours later:

> The party then took a special steamer as the guests of the Selby Smelting and Lead Company, being entertained at luncheon by the Company and afterwards conducted through their plant, where the various processes of lead smelting and the recovery of gold and silver therefrom were explained. One of the chief attractions of this plant was the opportunity given to view the new Cottrell precipitating apparatus installed for the purpose of removing sulphur trioxide and any other solids or liquids present in smelter smoke.[34]

Finally, Cottrell's paper was published in the *Journal of Industrial and Engineering Chemistry*.[35] All these events taken together — the symposium paper, the laboratory demonstration, the plant tour, and the journal article — meant that Cottrell had presented the electrostatic precipitator to excellent advantage. Thereafter his invention would receive worldwide attention.

In all probability Cottrell used the ACS meeting to discuss with other members whether or not the society would be willing to administer his patents. As a result, in mid-January 1911 he specifically noted in his diary that he and his partners had agreed "to make endowment of Smelter rights to Am Ch Soc or similar body. . . ."[36] Several days later he outlined the plan in more detail:

> I have been going over the matter of disposal of our smelter rights with my associates here and they have agreed to the general proposition of turning these over as far as all new business, not covered by our present contracts, is concerned to some organization such as the Am. Ch. Soc. or a board of trustees or corporation representing this society jointly with such other societies as the Am[erican] Met[allurgical] Soc[iety] or the Institute of M[ining] & M[etallurgy] to administer on a business & technical basis as a research endowment.[37]

Yet this route quickly proved as unsatisfactory as that of assigning the patent rights to the University of California. "Consultation with the officers of several of our national scientific societies," Cottrell explained, "made it clear that none of these societies was organized to administer adequately such a business. . . ."[38]

Joseph A. Holmes and the U.S. Bureau of Mines

As 1910 gave way to 1911, a third possibility emerged for institutionalizing Cottrell's gift. The key figure was Joseph A. Holmes (1859–1915), the first director of the newly formed U.S. Bureau of Mines. A Southerner by birth, Holmes graduated from Cornell in 1881 and joined the faculty of the University of North Carolina. Ten years later he became state geologist, and in 1904 he oversaw the fuels testing program at the Louisiana Purchase Exposition in Saint Louis. He then joined the U.S. Geological Survey (USGS), and to his work on fuels testing he added the improvement of coal mine safety. The result was the creation of the Technology Branch of the USGS (in Pittsburgh) in 1907, followed by a separate Bureau of Mines in the spring of 1910. Although Holmes expected to be appointed director of the new agency, he was not President William Howard Taft's first choice. This was perhaps due to Holmes's friendship with Gifford Pinchot, who had recently displeased Taft and his secretary of the interior, Richard Ballinger. In September 1910, however, Holmes was finally offered the position.[39]

Rather than functioning as a regulatory agency, the Bureau of Mines sought "to increase health, safety, economy, and efficiency in the mining, quarrying, metallurgical, and miscellaneous mineral industries of the country" by under-taking investigations and setting examples.[40] The bureau's interest in smelter fumes was probably what sparked Holmes's interest in Cottrell, and when the two first met in San Francisco in October 1910, Holmes offered Cottrell the job of establishing the bureau's laboratory there.[41]

Reluctant to give up his Berkeley position, Cottrell's first response was to propose a cooperative arrangement with Holmes's agency:

> I am sure that the University through both its chemistry & min-ing departments (as well as any other departments necessary) would be only too willing to place its general equipment at the service of the Bureau and we could probably get all the room necessary in these departments. . . .[42]

Such arrangements, he added, were not without precedent at Berkeley:

> A somewhat similar relation of course already exists between the U.S. Experiment Stations & our Agricultural Department. Last year we gave the Reclaimation [sic] Service 2 rooms in the Chem Build-ing and the year before Dr. [G. K.] Gilbert of the Govt. Survey had the basement of the Mining building for his stream erosion & trans-portation experiments.[43]

Working gratis with two assistants, he believed that he could start on a small scale right away.

Cottrell's proposal to Holmes was made through H. Foster Bain, a mining engineer who edited the journal *Mining and Scientific Press* in San Francisco. Familiar with the careers of both Holmes and Cottrell, Bain strongly sup-ported Holmes's appointment as bureau director and the development of Cottrell's precipitator. Moreover, he brought Holmes and Cottrell together and continued to serve as their go-between. After taking Holmes's job offer to Cottrell, for example, he forwarded Cottrell's reply, adding that even though Cottrell did not fully appreciate "the strategic advantage" of keeping the bureau's laboratory in San Francisco, "he approaches the matter in exactly the right spirit, which confirms my judgment that he is the man you want."[44]

During the next several months Holmes successfully weaned Cottrell from his university position. At first Cottrell resisted the transition to full-time gov-ernment service. In January 1911, after Holmes expressed his preference for locating the bureau's laboratory in San Francisco, Cottrell insisted: "Even though I went entirely over into the U.S. employ I should still plan for the present to do much of the experimental work in the Berkeley laboratories. . . ."[45]

Another sticking point involved the precipitator. Cottrell recognized that the bureau's effectiveness required strict impartiality in all its activities. Thus his ties to International Precipitation and Western Precipitation stood in the way of accepting Holmes's offer. "As I think I may have mentioned to you when [you were] here," he reminded Holmes, "I have hoped before long to be able to cut myself entirely free from the commercial end of this work."[46]

As a solution, Cottrell briefly considered giving his patent rights to the Bureau of Mines. Specifically, he wrote Holmes at the end of January 1911:

> In regard to turning over our patent rights to the Am. Chem. Soc. or other of the National Engineering or Scientific organizations, I have been talking with some of the people I feel are best able to judge of the probable efficiency and expediency of such a management of the work and they all seem to raise the question whether these organizations are on a definite enough basis and stable enough to properly undertake the guidance of the work at present.
>
> They all seem to look to the government itself as the more natural and fitting custodian of such matters. I had not personally thought so directly of the government in this connection before, chiefly for the reason that I had doubted any of the existing departments caring to undertake the business administration of this work which I had in mind.
>
> . . . At all events would you care to consider the Bureau of Mines taking over our U.S. Patents along the same general lines as described in my former letter when I was thinking of the Am. Chem. Society.[47]

Although Cottrell recognized the benefits of such an arrangement, he also acknowledged its "socialistic tendency" — which, he explained, was what had compelled him to seek Holmes's "opinion and advice."[48]

After carefully considering Cottrell's offer, Holmes chose not to accept it. To begin with, he knew that assigning patent rights to the public could actually hinder a new product's commercial development. Thus he explained:

> . . . in view of the fact that any person had the right to manufacture it, this seems to have created the impression that its manufacture could not be accompanied by profit to the parties making it, and therefore no one undertook its manufacture.[49]

He also believed that government agencies faced legal barriers in accepting patents with an intent to derive income therefrom:

> The Chief Clerk in the Patent Office informs me that there appear to be no records of any case in which the Government itself had accepted a patent, other than to make it free and open to all parties ... and that probably special legislation would be necessary before this could be done.[50]

Finally, Holmes believed that accepting Cottrell's patents would compromise the kind of work he expected the new bureau to undertake. In his opinion, the best way for the bureau to settle a wide range of disputes was to provide an independent and impartial point of view. For example, he noted in his preface to the report of the Selby Smelter Commission that:

> ... much controversy and much needless and expensive litigation ... can be avoided by the appointment of commissions composed of unbiased experts who, from their knowledge of the principles involved, will determine with precision the essential facts and their relation to matters in controversy and will lay down findings that, because of the manner in which they had been formulated, will be accepted as final by the parties at interest. Absolute freedom of judgment is necessary for the success of such a commission. Expert testimony produced by either litigant is under suspicion by the other, but scientific and technical investigations by the Federal Government or by an unbiased commission inspire confidence, and findings based on such investigations command respect.[51]

In short, he believed that accepting Cottrell's patents would violate the bureau's credo of disinterested expertise.

Fortunately, Holmes came up with an alternative. At the end of February 1911 he suggested that Cottrell make his gift to the Smithsonian Institution.[52] Cottrell moved quickly along these new lines and was able to report by mid-March:

> I find my associates well pleased with the idea of the Smithsonian Institution as the recipient of the rights in question. Personally I also think it a most excellent solution.... In fact I had thought of the Smithsonian a good while ago in this general connection but had not expected it would be possible to interest them so directly in the matter....[53]

Others, he admitted, were less sanguine:

> I have talked with a number of people of late who have had expe-
> rience in handling new processes and other large technical ventures
> in a business way and nearly without exception they look upon the
> successful handling of such developments by any public institution
> as out of the question and merely the dream of an enthusiast.[54]

Such reservations affected Cottrell by increasing his determination to proceed. But they also suggest that his desire to give away his patent rights was
challenging the capacity of the nation's research organizations: it was not
clear that *any* existing organization combined the ideals of public service and
private profit in quite the way he required.

Charles D. Walcott and the Smithsonian Institution

The Smithsonian Institution arose from James Smithson's bequest and an
1846 act of Congress. It took as its mission "the increase and diffusion of
knowledge among men," and under the leadership of its first Secretary, Joseph Henry, it quickly became one of the nation's premier research organizations. As the pace of the Research Revolution increased, the Smithsonian lost
ground relative to universities, government agencies, industrial research laboratories, and research organizations funded by private philanthropy. Nevertheless, as late as the eve of World War I, the Secretary's position could still
be described as "the greatest honor that can come to an American man of
science."[55]

Charles Doolittle Walcott (1850–1927) had been Secretary since 1907,
rising to that position through the governmental sector of the American research community. In 1876 he went to work for New York's state geologist,
James Hall, and on Hall's recommendation he joined the USGS when it was
founded 1879. Walcott first demonstrated his administrative talents in the
1890s when he succeeded John Wesley Powell as USGS director. Despite his
predecessor's controversial leadership and the effects of an economic depression, he managed to preserve – and even increase – the agency's annual
appropriations. As Secretary of the Smithsonian he revamped its organizational structure and extended its reach. He similarly left his stamp on a variety of other organizations, including the Carnegie Institution of Washington.
Thus Theodore Roosevelt's judgment was not too wide of the mark when he
noted in 1911 that Walcott was "by far the greatest scientific administrator of
the day."[56]

Despite the burden of his administrative duties and his lack of a formal

Charles Doolittle Walcott served as Secretary of the Smithsonian from 1907 to 1927 and on Research Corporation's board of directors from 1912 to 1927.

college education, Walcott was deeply committed to research. His field of specialization was paleontology, and throughout his career he concentrated on the oldest fossils he could find. In his book *Wonderful Life*, Stephen Jay Gould has argued that if only Walcott had spent more time with the fossils he collected, the scientific rewards would have come more quickly.[57] Well aware of the constraints he faced, Walcott himself noted in a typical diary entry: "Am getting behind with my scientific work owing to trivial incidents taking so much time."[58] Nevertheless, Walcott deserves continued recognition for his extraordinary ability to combine important field work with equally important service as an administrator.

Walcott's central position within the American research community enabled him to propose a workable solution to Cottrell's problem of giving away his patent rights. He first learned of Cottrell's eleemosynary idea through Holmes, who had been one of his protégés at the USGS. On February 7, 1911, Holmes telephoned him and immediately followed up with a letter. Based on Walcott's response, Holmes then advised Cottrell that an offer to the Smithsonian would meet with "friendly consideration."[59]

As Holmes explained to Cottrell, giving the patent rights to the Smithsonian had several advantages: "... there is no question as to its permanency, its continuity of policy when once adopted, or the high standard of the investigations that it would conduct with funds derived from those or any other sources."[60] But Cottrell recognized that success depended on other factors as well:

> ... I hardly suppose the Smithsonian has facilities or funds which
> it could devote to such work without criticism. It may very likely be
> necessary therefore to interest others ... to get this business side
> of the administration under way.[61]

Meanwhile, Walcott brought Cottrell's proposal to the attention of the Smithsonian's board of regents. Noting that "this form of gift was entirely different from the usual estate of money or bonds or real estate," he suggested that the board's permanent committee study the matter.[62]

In April 1911 Walcott reported informally to Holmes, who then told Cottrell, that the Smithsonian could accept patents as donations but that "each individual case would be considered on its own merits."[63] There the matter rested until June, when Cottrell left California for the East Coast. On April 15 he met Holmes in Pittsburgh and the two traveled to Washington by overnight train. On the evening of their arrival, they stopped by Walcott's house, and their conversation (followed by a second conversation later in the month) left Walcott favorably inclined toward Cottrell and his idea. "... I became convinced," he later wrote, "that Dr. Cottrell meant just what he said, and that something could be brought out to the advantage of research, if a scheme for handling the patents could be devised."[64]

At that point Cottrell began preparing the necessary legal documents. His association with the Bureau of Mines called for prompt action. Earlier in the year, as he worked to set up the bureau's San Francisco laboratory, he realized he would be willing to leave Berkeley after all. Thus he explained to Holmes in March:

> As a practical result of having the project constantly before me I
> find myself rapidly shaping my whole plans toward and in confor-
> mity with the new work and my university interests as such
> receeding [sic] in proportion to such an extent that I have come to
> feel that the fairest thing to all concerned would be for me to make
> the change as promptly as possible. ...[65]

In May Cottrell resigned his academic position, and in August he received his commission from the bureau. But he was reluctant to accept it officially until the patent arrangements were completed.[66]

Finally, in mid-October Cottrell and his partners made their formal offer to the Smithsonian's board of regents. Basically it included full rights to Cottrell's patents, with some exceptions. Reflecting a previous agreement, Western Precipitation retained the rights to construct precipitators in six Western states (California, Oregon, Washington, Arizona, Nevada, and Idaho). Also reflecting a previous agreement, private parties retained the rights to use precipitators in the manufacture of Portland cement. In both cases, however, the agreed upon royalty payments (10 percent of net profits) would now be paid to the Smithsonian.[67]

Toward the end of October Walcott replied that he would contact the Smithsonian's executive committee concerning Cottrell's offer.[68] Included on that committee were Augustus Octavius Bacon, a three-term U.S. senator from Georgia; John Dalzell, a U.S. representative from Pittsburgh (and a former corporate attorney); and Alexander Graham Bell, a "citizen of Washington, D.C."[69]

Bacon was traveling, which gave him little time to consider the matter, and Dalzell had already talked briefly with Cottrell in Washington. But Bell responded with a lengthy evaluation that could not be ignored. Writing from his home in Nova Scotia, he told Walcott:

> The proposition is a generous one and well worthy of consideration by the Regents although I am a little doubtful how far it would be proper for us to accept an endowment in the form of patent rights. The intent of the proposition is to establish under the charge of the Smithsonian an endowment fund to be devoted to a particular line of research. It would be a very proper thing, I think, for us to allow such a fund to be established and to accept from these gentlemen such donations of cash as they may desire, from time to time, to add to the fund. But how we can accept patent rights or run an industry ourselves, it is a little difficult to see. I am favorably impressed with the spirit of the donors and shall be very glad if I can have any part in helping them to put their proposition into a form that would be satisfactory to the Regents.[70]

As thoroughly versed as Bell was in the difficulties that often accompanied the development of commercially valuable patents, his concerns were ones that Walcott would have to consider seriously.

In addition to the members of the executive committee, Walcott contacted

two other members of the Smithsonian's board of regents: George Gray and
Charles F. Choate, Jr. Formerly a U.S. senator from Delaware, Gray was then
serving as judge of the U.S. Third Circuit Court. Although busy with court
matters, Gray found time to reply:

> The proposition of Mr. Cottrell seems to me so unusual and so
> out of the line of our past conduct of the affairs of the Institution,
> that I hardly feel that I could make any suggestion that would be
> helpful until the whole matter had been laid before the Board and
> there discussed. . . . The difficult question is, what are we to do with
> these patent rights after we obtain them? Can we conduct business
> ourselves under them, or merely treat them as property from which
> an income could be obtained, by giving licenses on a royalty basis? Or,
> do you think that this method of metallurgical precipitation is, as a
> scientific invention, germane to the purposes for which the Institu-
> tion was founded, and that its further development can be promoted
> as belonging to the field of scientific activities?[71]

Here was another response that Walcott could not take lightly.

Choate, a notable Boston lawyer, came out even more strongly against
direct acceptance:

> I should not think it would be wise to accept the letters patent as
> such, and attempt to conduct the business of giving licenses and
> collecting royalties under them. It seems to me that it is quite
> foreign to the general purposes of the Institution. It might also be
> misunderstood, and it would be exceedingly likely to involve the
> Institution in litigation from patent infringement, or otherwise,
> which I believe would be undesirable.
>
> Your suggestion that the patents be given to a corporation, of
> which the Smithsonian should hold the stock, seems to me to obvi-
> ate most of these objections. If anyone should offer us the stock or
> securities of an established corporation, I do not see why we should
> hesitate to accept them, provided they did not involve the Institu-
> tion in the probability of loss or obligation. I think the position of
> the Regents is rather analogous to that of trustees for the public,
> and that they ought not to enter into an undertaking which will, to
> carry it out, require the use of the Institution's other funds.[72]

To this Walcott responded: "I think you have expressed the right view. . . . I will try and work out with [Cottrell] a plan for having the patents handled entirely outside the Institution. . . ."[73]

According to Research Corporation oral tradition, Walcott also consulted President Taft. Given Taft's judicial experience, his opinion would have been valuable, and Walcott had ready access to him. Yet the only hint of Taft's involvement that I have found in the archival sources is an entry in Cottrell's diary: "Evening with Holmes at Dr. Walcott's [and] discussed patent matters. Walcott spoke of intention of taking up Gov't Pat. matter with [the] Pres[ident]."[74]

Whatever the extent of Taft's involvement, by the end of 1911 Walcott had obtained sufficient advice from others. The result was a formal decision at the annual board of regents' meeting not to accept direct ownership of Cottrell's patent rights. But the board left the door open for an indirect arrangement, whereby a separate organization would manage Cottrell's patent rights and donate the net profits to the Smithsonian.[75] In reporting this decision to Cottrell, Walcott expressed the board's appreciation of Cottrell's offer. He also expressed his personal commitment to helping Cottrell follow the route the board had recommended.[76]

Assembling a Board of Directors

Now that the Smithsonian had given him a mandate to establish a separate organization, Cottrell lost no time in taking the necessary steps, the most important of which was assembling a board of directors. The choice of directors was important because he believed that organizations were best run on a personal basis. In his view, managers who merely implemented policy were far less effective than those who also exercised their own judgment. Later he would write:

> The more I see of the really big men of all nationalities and of really big business, both in this country and abroad, the more I am impressed with what a very large and important part of it has of necessity to rest solely upon mutual confidence and reliance upon men in positions of trust to do what to the best of their ability they believe to be just and right as the various situations develop.[77]

Due to his position at the Bureau of Mines Cottrell himself chose not to become a director, but he asked Walcott to serve, explaining that his presence "would have a very beneficial steadying influence."[78] In the end Walcott would acquiesce. Meanwhile, he promised to help recruit other directors, often traveling to Boston or New York to assist Cottrell with the interviews.

Even back in Washington, Walcott offered Cottrell his support. "You are doing great missionary work for research," he wrote encouragingly, "and I think large results will ultimately come from it."[79] On another occasion he reported: "I saw Dr. Holmes at church on Sunday. He thinks you are acting wisely in sticking to the organization of the Research Corporation and thus rounding it up in good shape."[80] Cottrell, in turn, recognized the important role that Walcott was playing: "I find my work securing the men goes much more smoothly and effectively with your aid."[81]

Walcott was not Cottrell's only ally in assembling the new board. Assistance also came from Arthur D. Little (1863–1935), a Boston-born chemist whose career bridged industry and academia. In 1886 Little established a private consulting laboratory in Boston, which was known after 1909 as Arthur D. Little, Inc. A former student at MIT (from 1881 to 1884), in 1908 he helped the university establish its Research Laboratory of Applied Chemistry. By the time Research Corporation began its work, Little was a leading figure in chemistry and chemical engineering circles, serving as president of the American Chemical Society from 1912 to 1914 and as president of the American Institute of Chemical Engineers in 1919. He was also well known as a vigorous and articulate spokesman for the importance of research to the country's economic well-being.[82]

Little probably heard of Cottrell's eleemosynary idea at the ACS meeting in San Francisco in 1910. The two crossed paths again in the months that followed — for example, at the Indianapolis ACS meeting in June 1911. After the Smithsonian's board of regents made its decision, Little agreed to serve as a director of the new corporation. Furthermore, he offered to contact others who might be willing to help.[83]

As a result, Cottrell traveled to Boston in January 1912. There he spoke with Elihu Thomson, the inventor and electrical engineer who had co-founded the Thomson-Houston Company. In addition, Little helped Cottrell recruit James J. Storrow and Charles A. Stone. Storrow was a banker for Lee, Higginson, and Co. (and his father was the leading counsel for patent litigation at American Telephone and Telegraph). As for Stone, he was a founding partner of the Stone and Webster construction firm.[84]

Little also approached T. Coleman du Pont, one of the three du Pont cousins who had transformed the DuPont Company from a family firm into a modern big business. At first du Pont hesitated, writing to Little:

> I am in receipt of your letter... and of course feel very much
> honored at Dr. Walcott's wanting me to serve as a director of the
> Research Foundation [sic]. My time is so entirely taken up at present
> that I hesitate to accept because I am afraid it would not be fair.

> However, after this year goes by, I hope to have more leisure time
> to do some good for the country in which I live. Of course I shall be
> glad to talk with Dr. Walcott and if he thinks I can be of any use to
> my fellow men, it will be a pleasure for me to serve.[85]

In the end, du Pont agreed to serve. He also subscribed to five shares of stock, though the $500 he invested in Research Corporation was a trifling sum compared to the $500,000 he had just given MIT to help his alma mater acquire a new site for its campus (namely, its current site, in Cambridge along the Charles River).[86]

Despite Little's base in Boston and Walcott's in Washington, D.C., the headquarters of Research Corporation when it emerged in 1912 was New York City. At the time, not everyone found New York an hospitable place for applied-science organizations. To cite one example, the city's political environment was so complex that it frustrated the efforts of the chemist L. P. Brown to implement public health reforms like those he had successfully established in Tennessee.[87] In Research Corporation's case, however, the rich array of urban organizations was precisely what made the city so attractive.

To begin with, New York offered opportunities to recruit additional directors, including Charles W. H. Kirchhoff, Lloyd N. Scott, and Elon H. Hooker (1869–1938). Trained as a mining engineer, Kirchhoff pursued a career in technical journalism. He had just retired from a twenty-one-year career as editor-in-chief of the journal *Iron Age*, but he was still serving as president of the American Institute of Mining Engineers.[88]

Scott too began his career in mining engineering, but after graduating from Berkeley in 1899 he attended New York Law School and became a lawyer for Columbia University. As Research Corporation's secretary (as well as a director), he quickly emerged as a company mainstay and was formally commended by his fellow directors for his many activities – "such as assisting in the preparation of contracts, keeping the office accounts, supervising the office during the engineer's absence and rendering valuable services in promoting the welfare of the Corporation."[89]

Of the three, however, Hooker played the most important role in Research Corporation's early history. After receiving his Ph.D. in civil engineering from Cornell in 1896, he served as deputy superintendent of public works for New York State during Theodore Roosevelt's gubernatorial administration. In 1901 he joined a firm whose aim was to identify, fund, and manage promising new technological enterprises. Two years later he founded a similar firm of his own and built a plant at Niagara Falls that produced caustic soda (sodium hydroxide), chlorine, and hydrogen using the electrolytic process invented by

Clinton P. Townsend and Elmer A. Sperry. In 1909 Hooker consolidated his holdings and founded the Hooker Electrochemical Company.[90]

Cottrell first met Hooker in New York. Toward the end of January 1912 he informed Walcott that he planned to consult the secretary of the local Cornell alumni society, to "see if he can put me in touch with some of their stronger & more representative men."[91] The secretary did have someone to suggest, and Cottrell acted promptly. "Called on Hooker," he noted in his diary entry for the following day, "& found him quite interested in the Smithsonian project. . . ."[92] Thereafter Hooker would be a regular participant in the efforts to establish Research Corporation.

In addition to providing a pool of prospective directors, New York served as a convenient meeting place. Walcott could easily take a train from Washington; Little, likewise, from Boston. Other directors either had offices in the city or visited there frequently. Cottrell too found New York a convenient base. Not only was it was a center for his various professional societies, but it was also the location of the Chemists' Club, where he had the option of staying (as well as holding meetings) when he was in town.[93]

Founded in 1898, the Chemists' Club moved to its new building at 52 East 41st Street in the spring of 1911. By 1912 it had become a more important local center of scientific activities than the Section on Astronomy, Physics, and Chemistry of the New York Academy of Sciences. At the time of the Eighth International Congress of Applied Chemistry in September 1912, for example, it facilitated interactions among the participants. "Throughout the Congress," the *Journal of Industrial and Engineering Chemistry* reported, "the Chemists' Club was the center of social activities; here many informal meetings and social gatherings took place."[94]

Another important New York organization was Columbia University, and two alumni of the university's School of Mines agreed to become Research Corporation directors: Frederick A. Goetze (1870–1950; the dean of Columbia's Faculty of Applied Science) and Benjamin B. Lawrence (a consulting mining engineer and a member of Columbia's board of trustees). "They are both very enthusiastic over the plan," Cottrell told Walcott, "and ready to [give] a good deal of their own time in seeing it through. This will also assure the facilities of the College laboratories &c being at [our] disposal for the work."[95]

Cottrell's last comment suggests that he expected Research Corporation to pursue much of its work through the voluntary efforts of academic personnel. Writing to Walcott in November 1911, he made this hope explicit:

> There should be little or no expense for actual laboratory studies,

as whatever is necessary in this direction can readily be carried on at the plants undergoing installation, on the one hand, and in the University laboratories, who would be glad to cooperate with the work.[96]

So important to Cottrell was the idea of voluntary collaboration that he later elaborated:

> One of the chief motives which led me to work for the establishment of the Research Corporation was to open a practical channel through which members of the faculties could feel . . . that they were directly contributing to the material success of the scientific institutions representing their profession, and not feel that they were of necessity merely employees, and must leave all such matters as support or endowment of their chosen work to the wealthy and successful business man. The injustice of this is all the more apparent when we realize that often the business man's success and ability to make such contribution is largely dependent on the accumulated work of many of those scientific workers whose connection with the eventual endowment, though important, is so indirect as to carry with it no recognition or satisfaction.
>
> I do not mean to say that all academic men . . . will be anxious or even willing to lend their aid gratuitously to the cause. . . . All I want to emphasize is that there are such men in sufficient numbers if searched out to take care of nearly everything that the Research Corporation is apt to need outside of what its own regular employees can do, and that . . . one of the primary motives of the organization was to give those men a chance. The whole operation is in a sense peculiarly theirs. . . .[97]

As Research Corporation took shape, Cottrell found himself pleased with the extent that it seemed to embody his ideals. "Every day," he wrote Walcott, "I am coming on friends & coöperation in one line or another for the new movement and all looks very encouraging."[98]

A Corporation That Pays No Dividends

Much of the planning for the new firm took place in early 1912, in the thirteen-story office building at 63 Wall Street that became Research Corporation's headquarters once it was formally established.[99] What brought Cottrell and the others to that particular location was the law office of John B. Pine. A

Columbia alumnus and trustee, Pine also served the university as its attorney. Similarly, he served Research Corporation as director and legal counsel, and he led the efforts to draft the new firm's certificate of incorporation.[100]

Serious organizational work began on February 2, 1912, at a meeting in Columbia's trustees room, which was part of the university's downtown office, also at 63 Wall Street. At Walcott's request Little agreed to serve as chair and Cottrell, as secretary. Others present were Pine, Hooker, Stone, Storrow, J. Hennen Jennings, and William L. Dudley.[101]

One question the group considered was how many directors the new firm should have. Cottrell's earlier consultations with Lawrence had left the specific number open, and to Little he had explained: "We have not decided whether there shall be seven, nine or more directors as the number depends largely upon who are available...."[102] Based on their successful recruiting efforts, however, the decision was now made to increase the total to thirteen. Cottrell and Walcott were not on the list, but all the others present were — along with du Pont, Goetze, Kirchhoff, Lawrence, Scott, and Thomson.

Soon after the meeting the number was expanded to fifteen, the two additional directors being Walcott and Mark S. Reardon, III. The larger number allowed the board to be divided into three "classes" of five directors each. For a given class, the three-year terms all expired at the same time, but because the expiration year for each class was different, not all the directors would come up for reelection or replacement at the same time. (See Tables 1 and 2 [Appendix, page 191] for listings of the original board, alphabetically and by class years.[103])

Also considered at the meeting was the name of the new organization. Until then, Cottrell had referred to it as the "Technical Research Company," a choice that Pine had already cleared with state officials in Albany.[104] As a new possibility, however, Little had recently suggested "The Research Corporation," and the list discussed at the meeting was even more extensive:

> Institute for Technical Research
> Institute for Technical and Scientific Research
> Bureau of Technical Research
> Research Corporation
> Public Research Corporation
> Technical Research Corporation
> Technical Research Institute[105]

The result, as Cottrell's handwritten minutes show, was a clear-cut decision: "It was finally moved by Mr. Jennings[,] seconded by Mr. Stone[,] and carried

unanimously that the name of the new organization be the 'Research Corporation.' "[106]

The thorniest issue raised at the meeting — and the one that most affected Research Corporation's organizational structure — was the possible
liability of individual directors in the event of a patent infringement suit. Everyone involved with the founding of Research Corporation knew that patent
litigation was a characteristic feature of American technology at the turn of
the century. If nothing else, one of the era's most prominent cases had only
recently been settled. After receiving his automobile patent in 1895, George
B. Seldon attempted to collect royalties from all automobile manufacturers.
When Henry Ford refused, Seldon sued. That was in 1903. In 1909 Seldon
won a favorable ruling. But Ford appealed, and the new ruling in his favor was
announced on January 9, 1911.[107]

Another famous case hit closer to home. In 1909 the Wright brothers
sued Glenn Curtiss for infringing on their airplane patent, and in 1910 they
won a favorable ruling. On appeal, however, the injunction that prohibited
Curtiss from manufacturing aircraft was lifted — though the litigation continued until the onset of World War I. Meanwhile, in an effort to vindicate Samuel
P. Langley (Walcott's predecessor as Smithsonian Secretary), during the spring
of 1914 Walcott and Bell agreed to allow Curtiss to reconstruct the aircraft
that Langley had built and crashed in 1903 — just days before the Wrights'
successful first flight.[108]

The cases of Seldon vs. Ford and Wright vs. Curtiss actually represented
just the tip of the iceberg. Although American patent law had been modestly
reformed after the Civil War, the rise of big business often made it harder for
individual inventors to protect their patent rights. The heart of the problem
was that patents tended to lack validity until tested in the courts, where the
outcome depended as much upon the resources of the participants as on the
merits of their cases. As one inventor noted in 1909:

> My relations with the United States patent examiners have shown
> me that with very few exceptions these officials are able, earnest
> and fair. . . .
> On the other hand . . . I must lift my voice of protest when it
> comes to testing the rights of the inventor before the courts. Here
> the poor inventor is entirely at the mercy of a legalized system of
> piracy. . . .[109]

Such views were widespread at the time. In September 1912 President
Taft would comment unfavorably on "the amount of money that has been un-

necessarily wasted, and the inequality that has been produced between the rich litigant and the poor litigant...."[110] Similarly in 1912 Thomas Edison would inform a congressional investigation: "The long delays and enormous costs incident to the procedure of the courts have been seized upon by capitalists to enable them to acquire inventions for nominal sums."[111]

Thus the group that gathered at 63 Wall Street on February 2, 1912, realized that any organization they formed was likely to become involved in patent litigation. With that in mind, what type of organization would be best? Originally Pine had not aimed at a stock corporation. "It was first proposed," Scott later recalled, "to organize a membership corporation."[112] But some of the directors (notably Storrow and Stone) worried about their liability. "In order to meet this difficulty," Scott continued, "Mr. Pine evolved the idea of incorporating under the Stock Corporation Law of the State of New York...."[113] The decision to shift from a membership corporation to a stock corporation was probably made at the February meeting. Specifically, Cottrell reported "that in a non stock company or organization under the New York [Membership Corporation] law the liability of individual members of the Board would not be as definitely defined as in a Stock Corporation having a specified capital."[114]

Even so, the issue was not yet fully settled. As Little later reported, Storrow and Stone remained worried:

> Under these circumstances, it is their belief that if an infringement suit were successfully prosecuted against the company, the directors would be liable for damages, and unless some satisfactory way of avoiding this danger can be devised, they doubt if it would be advisable for them to serve as directors.[115]

In conveying this message to Pine, Cottrell confided: "The matter doesn't particularly disconcert me but we must be careful & considerate of the point of view here presented" — and in that spirit he asked Pine to determine "the exact status of the law on this point" in time for the next meeting.[116]

At the meeting on February 16, Pine presented his results. Individual directors, he believed, could not be held liable "for acts done by them in their official capacity and in good faith except possibly for acts done when the corporation is insolvent," and he cited specific cases as precedent.[117] "The tendency of these decisions...," he emphasized, "has been to restrict rather than to extend the personal liability of directors for the acts of a corporation which they represent...."[118]

Pine's assessment convinced the members to proceed with the firm's incorporation. Although Stone, Storrow, and Little were not present, Little telegraphed from Boston several days later to say that "Mr. Stone . . . finds your letter regarding personal liability satisfactory."[119]

Thus the nature of Cottrell's distinctive gift — assets in the form of patent rights — continued to steer the new organization toward becoming a business. Nevertheless, Cottrell's eleemosynary idea had not been abandoned. On the contrary, it was written directly into the certificate of incorporation. As stated in the preamble, the general aim of the new company was "aiding and encouraging technical and scientific research," with no reference to the usual business aim of profit making. Furthermore, the body of the certificate explicitly stated: "No dividends shall be declared or paid thereon, and the entire net profits . . . shall be applied to or expended for the aforesaid purposes."[120]

As planned, the certificate named the Smithsonian as a potential recipient of Research Corporation's net profits, but the certificate also included the phrase "and such other scientific institutions and educational institutions and societies as the Board of Directors may from time to time select . . . ."[121] That qualifying phrase — which became the basis for Research Corporation's subsequent identity as a grant-making organization — originated with Pine. Thus Cottrell informed Walcott in mid-January 1912:

> . . . Mr. Pine wanted me to explain that he introduced the provision for "such other scientific & educational Institutions" in the 2nd Article in order to cover the cooperation with universities &c which may be necessary in developing patents &c. We worked over this quite a little to see if we could more closely limit it but in the end it seemed best to leave it in this form.[122]

As a stock corporation, Research Corporation had to find investors. (See Table 3, page 192, for a list of the original stockholders and the number of shares each owned.[123]) But the stockholders never actually received their stock certificates. Instead, the company retained them, and the stockholders were merely given receipts.[124]

Taken together, these departures from standard business practice made Research Corporation a peculiar organization from the outset. Thus Cottrell recalled in 1937:

> I well remember one of [the stockholders who was not also a director] remarking at the time: "Your project of a non-profit but business corporation strikes me as too bizarre and self-contradictory to succeed, but if these busy and successful business men you have secured as directors are willing to give their time and effort

to the experiment, they can count on me for a thousand dollars toward trying it out.[125]

Recognizing that New York's secretary of state might be reluctant to approve the certificate of incorporation, Pine wrote to defend the new company's business aims:

> As the title "Research" may suggest the idea that the corporation is formed for educational [rather than business] objects, permit me to add a word of explanation to the statement of purposes contained in the Certificate.
>
> A number of gentlemen who are interested in industrial development have reached the conclusion that important discoveries and inventions often fail to be utilized through inability on the part of the inventor to carry his invention to the point of commercial success, and it is the purpose of the corporation to take up promising inventions and have them thoroughly tested. To provide for the expense which this will involve they propose to turn over to the corporation certain valuable patents which they now control and to operate the same and apply the profits to technical and scientific research and experimentation, without personal profit to themselves. The corporation is therefore a strictly business corporation and does not propose to engage in educational work.[126]

Despite the uniqueness of Research Corporation's aims, its official formation proceeded quickly. Acting as the founding stockholders, Kirchhoff, Hooker, and Goetze signed the certificate of incorporation on February 26, 1912. The next day at their first official meeting, the board of directors elected Goetze, Hooker, Lawrence, Little, and Walcott as members of the executive committee (with Goetze as chair). For a variety of reasons, however, no one was willing to accept the presidency (with Storrow, Jennings, and Walcott each declining to serve). By mid-March, Walcott and Cottrell had finished raising the start-up capital. The sum was the decidedly small amount of $10,100 (of the authorized $20,000), mainly because Cottrell expected additional capital to be generated by new precipitator installations.[127]

Having secured the necessary funding, Walcott informed the Smithsonian's board of regents that Cottrell's eleemosynary idea had now been given corporate form, and in the Smithsonian's annual report he summarized the organization's philanthropic goals:

> First, to acquire inventions and patents and to make them more available in the arts and industries, while using them as a source of income; and, second, to apply all profits derived from such use to the advancement of technical and scientific investigation and experimentation . . . .[128]

What remained was to see how effectively the new organization would function. Pine spoke for all those associated with Research Corporation when he wrote Walcott: "Now that the machinery has been constructed and set up, I hope that it may be found to work well and successfully."[129]

CHAPTER FOUR

A SUCCESSFUL ENGINEERING FIRM

We have just seen how Research Corporation originated with strong links to the academic and governmental sectors of the research world. The precipitator patents and the idea of giving them away came from Cottrell while he was still at Berkeley, and the idea for how to institutionalize his gift came from Walcott at the Smithsonian. Yet the main setting for the company's early work was industrial, and the most pressing task it faced was using Cottrell's invention as the basis for new commercial installations. Before any funds would be available for patent services or research grants, Research Corporation had first to succeed as an engineering firm.

Research Corporation's Early Technical Work

Here the central figure was Linn Bradley (1880–1956). Although he did not take a degree, Bradley had studied at the University of Minnesota, and he was working for Schmidt in California when Research Corporation was founded. In early March 1912, after the executive committee approved Bradley's appointment as the firm's engineer, Cottrell reported to Walcott: "The next few days I shall be pretty busy . . . taking him to the different plants and introducing him to the men & discussing the situation with them."[1]

From the outset there was plenty of technical work to engage Bradley's attention. For example, the day after the Smithsonian's board of regents rejected Cottrell's original offer, Walcott wrote Cottrell about someone who might be interested in the proposed company's services:

> Mr. J. W. Lieb, Jr., Third Vice-President of the New York Edison Company, was just in to see me, and after he had transacted the business that he came for, I asked him if he was interested in the suppression of the smoke nuisance connected with the plants of the Edison Company. He replied: "Very much so, as I am in charge of the active operation of the plants and am looking for some method to abate the nuisance." I suggested to him that he communicate with you at the Chemist's Club, and told him that I was very much interested in the success of the patents, as it was probable that certain income derived from them would be used for research under the direction of the Smithsonian.[2]

Walcott had sized up Lieb's position all too accurately. Coal smoke was a matter of widespread concern at the time, and in New York the vigorous enforcement of new smoke laws had led *The New York Times* to claim: "When black smoke goes up somebody is on the way to arrest and a penalty."[3] In early 1911 the New York Edison Company was fined $500 — the largest amount at the court's discretion — because of smoke emitted by its Waterside Power Station No. 2. Lieb assured the city's health department that the company was trying every technical means at its disposal to reduce the smoke. In the absence of a satisfactory solution, however, it resorted to placing lookouts on the plant roof. Whenever these men spotted health department photographers, they could order the coal feeding stopped before the company got caught breaking the law.[4]

Research Corporation offered New York Edison another option, and by March 1912 the two companies had begun negotiating. Lieb and Frederick A. Goetze, the Research Corporation director most closely associated with the firm's technical work, formally agreed that Research Corporation would install an experimental precipitator at the plant. But even though the project was soon under way and even though it was actively pursued for a year, Bradley was forced to report to the executive committee in June 1913:

> Owing to the tremendous pressure brought against the Edison Company by the Health Department of New York City, and the tremendous difficulties in connection with installing the Cottrell Processes at their plant, due principally to the character of the material to be collected, the lack of available space, and the short length of time at their disposal within which to equip their plant with smoke preventing devices, it was agreed between the Edison Company and ourselves to discontinue the experimental work in connection with the Cottrell Processes at their plant.[5]

By then, Research Corporation had turned to other projects. Cottrell's process was successfully applied to silver refining at the Raritan Copper Works at Perth Amboy, New Jersey. Installations were also arranged for the American Smelting and Refining Company at Garfield, Utah, and the Ohio and Colorado Smelting and Refining Company at Salida, Colorado. These projects gave Bradley material for technical papers at professional meetings, such as the Eighth International Congress of Applied Chemistry held in New York in September 1912. As a result, Bradley replaced Cottrell as the leading figure in Research Corporation's engineering efforts. For example, even though Cottrell attended the 1912 congress and contributed a paper on Research Corporation as a new type of organization, during the discussion that followed Bradley's paper Cottrell commented: "My own activities in the technical details of the work came practically to an end over a year ago."[6]

Under Bradley's leadership, most of Research Corporation's technical work was pursued at the installation sites. In addition, primary financial responsibility was born by the client companies; Research Corporation was paid only for its engineering services. In part, these distinctive arrangements were dictated by the process itself. Precipitators were difficult to standardize, so that new tests were necessary at each new location. Another factor, however, was Research Corporation's low level of capitalization.[7]

A full-scale precipitator typically cost $100,000 and required nearly a year to bring into operation. With an initial stock issue of only $10,100 Research Corporation had nothing like the capital resources required to finance projects of such magnitude, and until it had constructed many precipitators, royalties would not provide much income — making the engineering service fees its only significant source of operating funds. This situation made the engineers uncomfortable, especially in light of the domestic and international competition the company faced. Thus Walcott reported to Cottrell: "In both Bradley's and Lawrence's letters the question is raised as to increasing the capital of the R[esearch] C[orporation]. Both feel that it must be done if suitable development is to go on."[8]

The company's finances reached a low point in mid-1914, at which time Walcott and others feared that Research Corporation would be forced to issue more shares of stock. Fortunately, a major contract with the Anaconda Copper Mining Company later in the year put its affairs on a much sounder footing. As a result, the board of directors exercised its option to buy back the original stock issue. The board also decided to invest some of the company's capital and to award no grants until the invested capital exceeded $100,000. With a tone of relief, Lawrence wrote Walcott: "I believe now that the Research Corporation is on its feet, and firmly established."[9] Walcott, in turn, wrote Hooker: "I congratulate you upon having passed the danger point in the business, and on the fine outlook for the future."[10]

The need to expand its technical operations led Research Corporation to hire more engineers. Thus along with reorganizing its financial affairs it also reorganized its technical staff. Toward the end of 1915 Bradley was formally designated chief engineer, and early the following year his assistant, H. D. Egbert, was named head of the Commercial Department with responsibility for the business side of the technical work. That spring Bradley proposed an even more comprehensive division of responsibility: H. F. Fischer, P. E. Landolt, and A. A. Heimrod would serve as his advisors; J. C. Hale, C. I. Weir, and C. K.

Wirth would serve as field engineers; and several other men would serve as field assistants.[11]

In expanding its technical staff, Research Corporation drew heavily from Columbia University. So strong were these ties — which involved not just the engineering staff (Egbert, Landolt, Heimrod, and Hale) but also the directors (Goetze, Lawrence, Pine, and Scott) — that Walcott commented to Hooker: "Dr. Cottrell said long ago that it would not be wise to have the men of any one university dominate the Corporation, as this would arouse the antagonism of men connected with other universities. We already have a very strong contingent from Columbia University. . . ."[12]

Generally speaking, the ties between Research Corporation and Columbia illustrated one of the university's most characteristic features. "It is distinctly a city university . . . ," Edwin E. Slosson had commented in 1910:

> As the University of Wisconsin has blurred its outlines by dissolving itself in the State, so Columbia University is willing to lose somewhat of its identity . . . through merging itself in the city. . . . Its influence permeates the city through thousands of unofficial channels, too numerous and too delicate to follow.[13]

The ties between Columbia and Research Corporation also reflected the general views of Nicholas Murray Butler, the university's president from 1902 to 1945. Butler hoped that the Carnegie Institution of Washington, the Rockefeller Institute for Medical Research (in New York), and other newly emerging, separately endowed research organizations would cooperate closely with major universities.[14] Likewise he advocated close cooperation with industrial firms. Thus at a meeting of the American Chemical Society's New York Section he noted: "Many of our professors . . . are, as individuals, in close contact with industrial leaders and with industrial needs. We have always thought it wise at Columbia University, to encourage such a relationship."[15]

Given its character as a university, the relevance of its technical training program, and its proximity, Columbia's influence on Research Corporation is not surprising. But regardless of where the firm's engineers received their training, the difficulties of the precipitator work necessitated an expanded technical staff. To express why such tasks are hard, historians of technology have employed various terms. "Development" is the act of transforming an invention from conceptual breakthrough to commercial reality. "Scaling up" is the act of moving a process from laboratory setup to pilot plant to full-scale facility. Finally, there is engineering research. Although engineering research, like scientific research, involves both theory and experiment, the two are not identical. They are similar but distinct; they are "mirror-image twins."[16]

Whatever the concept used, the tasks Research Corporation faced were complex and demanding. Thus Bradley addressed a meeting of the American Institute of Electrical Engineers in 1915:

> A well-known chemical engineer . . . has stated that after one has completely solved all of the problems which it is apparently possible to solve in a laboratory, and has obtained comprehensive patents and has thoroughly studied the conceivable theories, and is therefore likely to consider his work almost finished, he is rudely awakened when confronted with the cold, hard fact that fully 90 per cent of *the real work* remains to be done.[17]

Bradley then described some of the technical challenges — "the real work" — that he and his engineering staff were pursuing. Corrosive fumes were one problem. Another was how to use electrostatic precipitators not just to eliminate "nuisances" or collect "values" but also as an intermediate step in the production process itself, to isolate difficult-to-separate components. Further problems were posed by the need for suitably designed electrical equipment (notably, the rectifiers) and the need to measure temperature, gas flow, voltage, etc., under the conditions found at each plant.

Complicating all this was the sheer variety of installations, as Research Corporation's engineers applied electrostatic precipitation not just to smelter smoke, cement dust, and silver refinery fumes, but also to boiler plant gases, foundry gases, blast furnace gases, various evaporation processes, etc. Finally, where the strictly technical problems left off, commercial ones began: for every individual plant and each specific gas stream, the engineers had to consider what type of installation would best justify the expense.[18]

Another force shaping Research Corporation during its formative years was competition in the field of electrostatic precipitation. From the outset, the company held a strong and enviable position. Successful installations prior to its founding clearly demonstrated the commercial value of Cottrell's patents. Also valuable were its Smithsonian ties. As Cottrell later acknowledged, "the patronage and prestige of the Smithsonian" were critical in getting the company started.[19]

Yet Research Corporation's range was not unfettered. To begin with, it had to define itself with respect to larger, more well-established firms in the electrical industry, especially the General Electric Company (GE). In May 1912 Bradley recommended that Research Corporation obtain an exclusive license for GE's mechanical rectifier, the device used to transform alternating current to direct current. Arthur D. Little discussed the matter with his fellow Research Corporation director (and neighbor) Elihu Thomson, but he soon reported that obtaining an exclusive license would not be easy.[20] Meanwhile, Bradley acquired other intelligence regarding GE's interest in electrostatic precipitation:

> I have been advised that Dr. Whitney has been granted Patent No. 1,022,012 and Patent No. 1,022,523. These have undoubtedly been assigned to the General Electric Company. I understand that these two patents are modifications of the Cottrell Process, which we control.[21]

Not until 1917 did Research Corporation and the electrical giant reach a formal agreement. General Electric promised that it "would refer to the Research Corporation all inquiries which it received for electrical precipitation apparatus and would sell electrical precipitation apparatus only to clients of the Research Corporation," while Research Corporation agreed to order "a considerable portion" of its electrical equipment from GE.[22]

Later the two companies also reached an agreement regarding Hermann Lemp's patents for high-voltage mechanical rectification. Cottrell's original rectifier had been an independent reinvention of Lemp's basic idea, and Cottrell's work on electrostatic precipitation had proceeded on the basis of an informal understanding with GE. An agreement in 1918 released Research Corporation from any legal claims or damages based on its prior installations and licensed it to make further installations — though only for electrostatic precipitators (thus excluding it from GE's primary rectifier market, namely, for x-ray tubes).[23]

Although General Electric continued developing a type of vacuum tube, the kenotron, for use as an electronic rectifier in electrostatic precipitators, this work posed little commercial threat to Research Corporation, because (in the words of a Western Precipitation engineer) "such rectifiers have the disadvantage of being fragile and consequently require much care in handling."[24] Even GE admitted the problem — for example, in a 1921 article on "The Cottrell Process of Electrical Precipitation" in *General Electric Review*. More to the point, however, the appearance of the article in the company's house journal demonstrated that the patent issues with Research Corporation had been settled to GE's full satisfaction.[25]

Another set of negotiations involved inventor–manufacturer Charles Girvin and his direct-current generator. Begun during the latter part of 1916, these negotiations were part of Research Corporation's effort to acquire "other inventions which will strengthen its position and prolong the life of the process."[26] Subsequently, Research Corporation lent funds to the Girvin Electrical Development Company, and in early 1918 (responding in part to GE's bid to buy the company) Research Corporation obtained an exclusive license. In the end, however, the advantages of Girvin's generator proved insufficient to warrant replacing the mechanical rectifiers.[27]

Although Westinghouse also took an early interest in electrostatic precipitation, the evidence regarding its ties to Research Corporation remains piecemeal. Several of the early installations used Westinghouse equipment, and Westinghouse soon developed standard electrical equipment for the growing electrostatic precipitator market.[28] The company also demonstrated its interest with a pair of 1919 technical articles by two of its engineers, H. D. Braley and O. H. Eschholz.[29]

Another Westinghouse connection involved Charles Girvin. Just after World War I, Research Corporation began further negotiations with Girvin, this time regarding his patent for a new type of electrostatic precipitator. But "an interference developed with L. W. Chubb . . . of the Westinghouse Electric & Manufacturing Company," and when Chubb won, Research Corporation suspended its negotiations with Girvin.[30] Schmidt commented in 1945 that Westinghouse was still manufacturing the "Precipitron," a device "only applicable to the cleaning of air or gases carrying [a] very small quantity of suspended material."[31] Such a device, he explained, posed no competitive threat:

> This is a field which Western [Precipitation] has left alone because it has too many headaches in it. Western has felt that its field of usefulness is in the heavy industries and that it should stay out of air cleaning, but it has certainly never blocked anybody else from going into this business. . . .[32]

In summary, the role played by GE and Westinghouse in the commercial development of electrostatic precipitation was rather marginal, relative to their overall standing in the electrical industry. Both GE and Westinghouse supplied electrical equipment used in precipitator installations. In addition, General Electric provided Research Corporation with certain patent rights, while Westinghouse provided them with certain engineering staff members (notably, A. F. Meston and E. P. Dillon). But having said all that, the direct participation of GE and Westinghouse in the field of electrostatic precipitation remained strictly limited.[33]

Walter A. Schmidt and Western Precipitation

Far more important to the early history of Research Corporation than either General Electric or Westinghouse was the Western Precipitation Company, led by Walter A. Schmidt (1883–1962).[34] Schmidt was one of Cottrell's students at the University of California. Born in Los Angeles, he received his bachelor of science degree from Berkeley in 1906, and in 1908 he joined Western Precipitation to help develop the method that Cottrell and J. Buckner Speed had invented for removing water from crude oil.[35]

In 1910 Allen C. Wright bought the rights to the Cottrell-Speed process and formed the Petroleum Rectifying Company to continue the work.[36] But Schmidt remained at Western Precipitation and began applying electrostatic precipitation to the production of Portland cement. The Portland cement industry was relatively new, especially on the West Coast. During the late nineteenth century California had imported most of its cement. Not until the first decade of the twentieth century were local plants of significant size constructed. One of these was the Riverside Portland Cement Company, which emerged in 1906. Located near Los Angeles, the plant emitted dust that settled onto orange groves downwind. An injunction against the company led it to contact Cottrell in 1910, and Cottrell proposed that Schmidt — through Western Precipitation and a license from International Precipitation — use electrostatic precipitation to solve the problem.[37]

Although the gas streams at the Riverside plant were hotter and drier than the other places where Cottrell's process was first put into practice, Schmidt succeeded by using higher voltages and a new fine-wire electrode design.[38] At the Balaklala Smelter in Coram, California, Cottrell and H. A. Burns were still relying on Cottrell's original electrode design. But at the Garfield Smelter in Utah, Ross B. Rathbun (formerly the electrical engineer at Balaklala) confirmed the effectiveness of Schmidt's fine-wire technique.[39]

At about the same time that Cottrell began his efforts to give away his patent rights, Schmidt purchased the rights to build precipitators for Portland cement plants throughout the United States. Later Schmidt acquired an option to purchase Western Precipitation, and he exercised it when Cottrell and his partners made their formal offer to the Smithsonian in the fall of 1911. As Schmidt later explained: "Cottrell and his associates thought it would be wise to maintain an active Western concern to keep the process from dying while Research Corporation was getting on its feet."[40] Furthermore, within weeks after the Smithsonian decided against accepting the original offer, Schmidt purchased International Precipitation — again with the full support of Cottrell and his partners.[41]

Walter A. Schmidt (left), then president of Western Precipitation, and Frederick G. Cottrell in a photo taken in 1916.

Because of these developments, Schmidt became an important player in the transfer of Cottrell's patent rights from International Precipitation to Research Corporation. Initially Cottrell believed that a telegram to his former student would be sufficient to start the process, but Schmidt replied that International Precipitation had not yet been officially notified of the action taken by the Smithsonian's board of regents regarding the original offer. As Cottrell explained to Walcott: "This point which he raises is evidently [raised] in order to carry out the exact form prescribed in the contracts between the International & Western precipitation companies and the various individuals concerned. . . ."[42]

Schmidt also believed that the Smithsonian's rejection of Cottrell's gift significantly altered the legal situation, prompting him to write Bradley that the new arrangement "does away with the protection which we thought we had in the Governmental Backing."[43] Bradley, in turn, reassured Goetze that Schmidt had no contrary purposes in mind. "You understand, of course," he wrote the Research Corporation director, "that there is no disposition on the part of Walter, to hinder in any way, or to defer the making of these assignments. . . ."[44]

Given the complexities of the patent situation, Schmidt wanted to talk with Cottrell in person before transferring the legal rights. [45] Cottrell was planning to travel to California anyway, and after his visit the transfer proceeded smoothly. On May 13, 1912, the directors of International Precipitation formally withdrew their offer of patent rights to the Smithsonian and offered them instead to Research Corporation.[46]

Meanwhile, Schmidt reorganized Western Precipitation. The relative ranking of International Precipitation and Western Precipitation was reversed, so that the former became subordinate to the latter. The firm also moved its main offices from San Francisco to Los Angeles and created a research lab to pursue "constant work upon the fundamentals of the electrical processes."[47]

In 1916 Schmidt wrote Walcott that Western Precipitation was rebuilding its lab as "a permanent precipitation research laboratory, in which we expect to be able to follow down some of the more intricate physical problems which we have to deal with in the field and which did not lend themselves to field investigations."[48] One of the lab's most notable results came from Edson R. Wolcott. Before his arrival at Western Precipitation in 1914, Wolcott had received his bachelor of science degree from the University of Wisconsin and pursued graduate studies at the University of Berlin and the University of Chicago. He had then worked several years as a college physics teacher and a consulting engineer. In a 1918 *Physical Review* article on his work at Western Precipitation, Wolcott described more precisely than anyone else previously the conditions under which sparking took place between two electrodes (one a point, the other a plate) covered with dust. Another notable result from the lab was an empirical formula for the rate of precipitation, determined by Evald Anderson and George H. Horne.[49]

German and British Competitors

Schmidt's cautious approach to the transfer of Cottrell's patent rights from International Precipitation to Research Corporation was based on his realization that Cottrell's patents were not the only ones involved in the newly emerging field of electrostatic precipitation. Specifically, Schmidt's patent application for the fine-wire technique was being challenged by Erwin Möller, an engineer in Germany.

At the same time that Cottrell began arranging the gift of his own patents, he also began negotiating with Möller regarding a patent taken out by Möller's father, the German inventor Karl Möller. On a visit to the United States during the summer of 1911, Möller conferred with Cottrell and others about the possibility of a cooperative effort. At first the Americans were hopeful, but then Möller surprised them by filing for several American patents. One of these involved the same fine-wire technique that Schmidt had invented, and the result was a Patent Office declaration that the two applications were in interference. Although the eventual ruling favored Schmidt, he considered Möller's applications "a nuisance . . . and a source of expense."[50]

During his 1911 visit, however, Möller was sufficiently impressed by Cottrell's eleemosynary efforts that he agreed to a cooperative arrangement. When Cottrell and his partners offered to give their patent rights to the Smithsonian, Möller offered to do the same, "so that both his and our patents would be handled exactly similarly throughout. . . ."[51] But Möller insisted on two restrictions. One was that the Smithsonian would accept the offer of Cottrell's patents by August 1912. The other was that if the Smithsonian extended its commercial work to Europe, "it would not enter into destructive competition with him in these particular fields."[52]

A separate document delineated the agreement's international aspects. North and South America, Japan, New Zealand, and Australia would comprise International Precipitation's "operating territory," while Europe and Africa (except for the Cape Colony of South Africa) would comprise Möller's. Each of these larger territories would include a smaller "'free operating territory' in which operations by one party are exempt from all charges by the other party."[53] For Möller, the "free operating territory" would be Germany and Austria; for International Precipitation, it would be California, Oregon, Washington, Arizona, Nevada, and Idaho. With the exception of its free operating territory, each party was to give the other party 10 percent of "the gross profits arising from all business in the 'operating territory.' "[54]

Schmidt worried that the Smithsonian's rejection of Cottrell's original offer would unravel the agreement with Möller. If so, then the international development of electrostatic precipitation was likely to become highly competitive — for Möller was not the only European player. Also figuring into these early negotiations was Oliver Lodge.

Lodge's institutional standing had advanced considerably since his earliest smoke studies. When the University of Birmingham received its charter in 1900, he was appointed its first principal, and in 1902 he was knighted.[55] Meanwhile, he retained a strong interest in reducing air pollution. For example, he served as president of the 1905 London "Conference on Smoke Abatement" (sponsored jointly by the Royal Sanitary Institute and the Coal Smoke Abatement Society), and in his presidential address he castigated "the barbarous combustion of crude coal" and commented that he still had a personal interest in combating "the evil" through "the electrification of the air on a large scale. . . ."[56]

Drawing on the newly emerging technology of vacuum tubes (or "valves," in British parlance), Lodge had recently patented an electronic rectifier for use in electrostatic precipitation, and on that basis he had revived his commercial efforts. When Cottrell contacted him toward the end of 1911, the British physicist replied:

> With the help of my son [Lionel] we have been developing electrification of the air a good deal . . . and there has now started an Agricultural Electric Discharge Co. at Gloucester, for the use of my high-tension Valves for the purpose of electrifying crops. . . .
>
> . . . We have also got a method of depositing fume, which seems quite efficient, but we have not yet applied it on a large scale.[57]

Cottrell wrote again in February 1912, this time specifically referring to his negotiations with Möller. Delaying his reply until he had heard from Möller directly, Lodge finally wrote Cottrell in June:

> It does not seem an easy matter to arrange for commercial cooperation and yet I feel sure that something of that kind is highly desirable and that we should be able to give some important assistance. . . .
>
> I recognise the friendly tone of your letter, and realise from what you have sent that your devices as regards precipitation are very similar to those that we have arrived at. . . .
>
> I am afraid however that you have let the interests get out of your hands into those of others, though I only hope that you are in a position to make some proposal with regard to cooperation. You have gone much further than we have into actual commercial applications, and accordingly have gained more experience in that field.[58]

Enclosed in Lodge's letter was a copy of the message that his son had sent to Möller, emphasizing the importance of cooperation and the need to avoid "unnecessary competition."[59] Also enclosed was a copy of Möller's brief reply, and in his own reply Cottrell cast Möller's note in a favorable light, assuring the British physicist that "its brevity and conventional tone represent in no sense a lack of interest in the broader and deeper aspects of cooperation, but rather a certain diffidence in assuming the initiative in this correspondence, a feeling which I am sure your son's cordial response should completely dispel."[60]

Cottrell went on to inform Lodge that he was bringing Schmidt into the picture. Given the vast distances that separated the various parties, Cottrell believed that their negotiations would succeed only if they were personally acquainted. Accordingly, he sent Schmidt copies of his recent correspondence with Lodge and encouraged him to write Lodge directly.

Meanwhile, Lodge continued his commercial efforts by establishing the Lodge Fume Deposit Company on May 2, 1913. The company's initial capitalization was £9,000, and its directors included two of Lodge's sons, Noel and Lionel. Its purpose was to use electrostatic precipitation "for the deposition of dust, fume, smoke, fog and mist, and for other purposes, with the exception of such purposes as those for which the Agricultural Electric Discharge Co. is licensed."[61]

In Möller's case, the German engineer responded to Research Corporation's formation by writing Walcott that he was still willing to cooperate:

> For it seemed to me, not only from the financial point of view in the case of commercial success, but also from the experience that the cooperation of science and industry fertilizes both, to serve to the advancement of science in the spirit of the original bequeather of the [Smithsonian] Institution.[62]

But Möller remained worried about the possibility of legal contests. To forestall what he termed "noxious interferences," he wanted an ongoing exchange of patent rights.[63]

Because he expected that Research Corporation would eventually undertake foreign installations, Möller also worried about the possibility of direct competition. The new company would be constructing precipitators across a vast protected territory — all the American states except those in which Western Precipitation operated. The result would be considerable engineering know-how, thus making Research Corporation a formidable player in any other territory it chose to enter.

As indicated by a draft letter to Möller, Research Corporation knew full well the advantages it held. Field installations would give rise to "a large amount of valuable data" that company engineers could use "to develop some patentable features which should prove of considerable technical value."[64] Along with field experience, laboratory research would also strengthen its competitive position. Thus Cottrell wrote Walcott that Möller:

> wanted to protect himself from . . . the possibility that the Research Corporation might, in time, with the resources at its command,

develop a far more powerful *research department* along these lines than he or his associates could in any sense keep pace with; and if no formal cognizance of these relations were taken at the outset, it might well happen that the Research Corporation, without intentionally going into destructive competition with him, . . . would inadvertently draw such a contract, for instance with one of his European competitors, as would put the whole of their developing resources behind this competitor, to be used against him, even though he had, himself, contributed to its foundation.[65]

In Cottrell's eyes, it was a narrow line that Research Corporation was attempting to walk. As a business, it would have to succeed on the basis of the accepted business practices of the day. But in order to benefit society through the support of inventors and scientific researchers, it would have to be allowed greater freedom of action than businesses of the usual sort — an arrangement that was likely to gain acceptance only if its conduct was beyond reproach. Accordingly, he continued his letter to Walcott:

The Research Corporation must, of necessity, so much more carefully consider the doing of even justice to everyone with whom it has to deal, not merely in a legally technical, but in a higher sense, that it must be given a somewhat wider range of discretion in these matters than is perhaps usually granted even the best type of our purely commercial concerns.[66]

To settle the international patent rights issue, Cottrell hoped that all the interested parties would be able to meet at the Eighth International Congress of Applied Chemistry in September 1912.[67] Neither Möller nor Lodge could attend, however, and correspondence alone proved inadequate.[68] Thus the matter remained unsettled until Schmidt traveled to Europe in 1913.[69]

In an assessment prepared many years later, Schmidt described his views at the time. He believed that installing electrostatic precipitators would never become routine. Due to the different conditions at each plant, the equipment could not be standardized. Instead, "temperature, gas composition, characteristics of the suspended material, gas volume flue connections, and available space dictate the design."[70]

Because each installation required so much custom engineering work, each geographical region would have to have its own construction firm.[71] Even so, commercial success was likely to require cooperation on the part of the various regional firms. Only then would electrostatic precipitation emerge as

a viable alternative to other smoke-reducing techniques. These other techniques included "Settling Chambers, Howard Dust Catchers, Coke Boxes,
Cyclonic Devices, Baffle Chambers, Scrubbers and Filters," and Schmidt noted
that they "offered extremely difficult competition to meet."[72] Although electrostatic precipitators were far more efficient, they were also more expensive —
so that if costs became too high, companies would adopt some other technique.

In order to lower costs and increase their competitive advantage, precipitator companies could accept what Schmidt called "ridiculously small" profits. "This small profit," he added, "explains why others have not entered the
field. It is very alluring technically but most discouraging commercially."[73]
Low profits also meant low salaries for company employees.[74]

There was an alternative to small dividends and low salaries, however.
Schmidt recognized that precipitator companies could keep their costs low by
sharing their technical knowledge. This was the approach he emphasized in
1913. He went to Europe planning to guarantee each major group an exclusive geographical territory but insisting "that it would be essential that these
groups be tied together in a broad technical program. . . ."[75] In addition to the
American group, he envisioned "an enterprise on the Continent of Europe
around the nucleus that had been established by the Metallgesellschaft and
another in Great Britain around the nucleus that had been started by Sir
Oliver Lodge."[76]

Möller quickly agreed to transfer his American patent rights to Research
Corporation.[77] World War I disrupted further efforts at international cooperation, but the process resumed after the Armistice.[78] In 1919 the Lodge Fume
Deposit Company was replaced by the Lodge Fume Company Limited. An
agreement with International Precipitation led to a full exchange of patent
rights in 1921–1922, at which time the British company changed its name to
Lodge-Cottrell Limited.[79] The corresponding German firm after World War I
was the Lurgi Apparatebau Gesellschaft, a subsidiary of Metallgesellschaft.[80]

These firms continued their cooperation for years, constituting what
Schmidt called "a fraternity in the art."[81] He insisted that at no time were
their practices unfair:

> They do not maintain their position in the art by virtue of pressure
> or manipulation or false publicity. They maintain their position by
> giving high class engineering service and by having organization
> available to do this highly specialized work. . . . It is true that they
> have exchanged technical information and patent rights for the
> benefit of the group and for the benefit of the public, but this is

something quite different from setting up a procedure for raising prices or for defrauding the public.[82]

After the basic patents expired, however, continued cooperation ran afoul of American antitrust laws. The upshot was a federal complaint against Western Precipitation and Research Corporation in 1945 and a consent decree in 1946, which ended the international electrostatic precipitation cartel.[83]

Returning now to the pre-World War I era, in the wake of his European trip Schmidt took the lead in redefining the relationship between Research Corporation and Western Precipitation. The new agreement, dated February 4, 1914, was intended to remain in effect for ten years. Its main purpose was to spell out the extent to which the two companies would exchange technical knowledge. Anticipating the advent of other electrical methods, each agreed to share only those improvements directly related to Cottrell's. If Western Precipitation developed an alternative electrical process, it would retain exclusive rights. On the other hand, if someone else developed such a process and wanted to give those rights to Research Corporation, Research Corporation would not be required to share them with Western Precipitation.[84]

According to the new agreement, this sharing was likely to favor Research Corporation. Already Schmidt had invented the pipe-electrode technique, and also by then Western Precipitation's lab was fully established. Thus the 1914 agreement ensured that Research Corporation would have continued access to the latest technical developments.[85]

The 1914 agreement represented the capstone in the early efforts to establish not just a new engineering firm but also an entire industrial field. More than merely an additional firm in that field, Research Corporation was intended to possess special status. With this, Western Precipitation concurred fully: "We feel that the agreement as it stands avoids all features opposed to the principles upon which the Research Corporation is founded."[86]

Robert Kennedy Duncan and the Mellon Institute

On the basis of their international agreement, Research Corporation played a central role in the development of electrostatic precipitation as a capitalistic enterprise. But Research Corporation also had philanthropic aims that set it apart from other engineering firms. It intended to distribute a significant portion of its profits in the form of patent services and research grants. One of the main reasons for the international agreement was to maximize the funds available for such purposes.

Because it combined business practices and private philanthropy, Research Corporation could be dubbed an experiment in "eleemosynary capitalism."

Its use of capitalism for philanthropic purposes was not unique, however, and it found its strongest competitor not in a business organization but in another instance of eleemosynary capitalism: the industrial research program that Robert Kennedy Duncan (1868–1914) established at the University of Pittsburgh.

Duncan was a Canadian-born chemist who – like Arthur D. Little – was a successful popular-science writer and a vigorous proponent of industrial research. Before coming to Pittsburgh, he pioneered the use of industrial fellowships at the University of Kansas. Beginning in 1907, private firms were invited to propose topics for academic research. According to Duncan's contracts, the firms provided the necessary funds and received privileged access to any discoveries that resulted, along with the option of hiring the fellows engaged in the work. Impressed with what Duncan had accomplished, the Pittsburgh capitalists Andrew W. and Richard B. Mellon offered to support an expanded program at Pittsburgh as a memorial to their father (making the program, in their eyes, an example of philanthropic public service). Duncan joined the University of Pittsburgh faculty in 1910; he started the first industrial fellowships there in 1911; and he became director of the newly established Mellon Institute for Industrial Research in 1913.[87]

The Mellon Institute and its program of industrial fellowships were successful from the outset. By 1913 more than a dozen fellowships had been established. One led to a method that halved the amount of sugar and yeast required to make bread, and other examples were the studies of crude oil and natural gas sponsored by the Mellons' own Gulf Oil Company. More to the point for our purposes, however, among the earliest of the fellowships were three "On the Abatement of the Smoke Nuisance."[88]

Although "the smoke nuisance" actually included a variety of problems, the particular form that dominated Pittsburgh was black smoke from the incomplete combustion of coal. Not all cities suffered equally in this regard. The bituminous coal used extensively in Pittsburgh and Midwestern cities caused more black smoke than the anthracite coal used in Boston, New York, and other Eastern cities or the natural gas used extensively in San Francisco. By the turn of the century, most American cities were addressing the problem in one way or another, but it was particularly pressing in Pittsburgh. For example, the chief fellow of Duncan's smoke program, Raymond C. Benner (a chemical engineer with a Ph.D. in chemistry from the University of Wisconsin), informed the city's board of trade in May 1912 that "[m]ore than $500,000 worth of laundry articles are destroyed every year by smoke in Pittsburgh. . . . The life of lace curtains in other cities is one-third longer than in Pittsburgh; house cleaning here is necessary twice a year, and from 20 to 40 per cent. of the fog in the city is soot."[89]

Initially, Duncan hoped to include Cottrell in the Pittsburgh smoke program. He wrote Cottrell in the spring of 1911, outlining his plans and inviting Cottrell to serve as one of the fellows. In contrast to Cottrell, who focused on chemical plants and smelters in rural locations, Duncan emphasized urban smoke. In describing his approach, Duncan said: "We want to clean up Pittsburgh and afterwards to use Pittsburgh as an object lesson to other manufacturing cities. . . . My present idea is to surround myself for this particular problem with several strong men as a nucleus and then, after the work develops, to add as many other men as will seem desirable and advantageous."[90] Duncan also described the role that the program's sponsor, R. B. Mellon, would play:

> He is not entering into the matter from the standpoint of speculation or with personal pecuniary returns in view. If, as will be the case, I request him to control the results, it will simply be in order that with the immense power and with all the machinery of establishing new processes that are in the possession of the Mellon family it would make the successful introduction of such apparatus a foregone conclusion.[91]

What Duncan did not know was that Cottrell had already decided to join the Bureau of Mines and make separate arrangements for his patents. Nevertheless, Cottrell was impressed with his Pittsburgh colleague. "He seems to be a man of a good deal of energy," he wrote Holmes in May 1911, "and if not too prone to sensationalism may be a very useful agent in cooperative work for the common good."[92] Although "sensationalism" was too strong a charge, Duncan's writing did have dramatic flair. For example, he noted in his account of the Eighth International Congress of Applied Chemistry: "Industrial research has to-day all the glamour that ever obtained in any age of romantic interest. . . ."[93]

Despite Duncan's literary proclivities, Cottrell (whose writing style was far more prosaic) continued to respond favorably. For example, he wrote Walcott in February 1912: "I am better impressed with the work he is doing each time I go to Pittsburgh, and feel he should get a little more friendly recognition and encouragement than he has received in the past from a good many of the Academic people."[94]

As promised, Duncan launched his smoke studies on a grand scale. The program drew on professional experts to examine all facets of the problem. By 1913 the twenty-eight-member staff (most of whom served in advisory capacities) included physicians, architects, engineers, chemists, biologists, a meteorologist, an economist, and a physicist. The program also encouraged public education and participation. Notable here was the assistance the Mellon Institute gave to the Smoke and Dust Abatement League, which the Chamber of Commerce established in 1912.[95]

Having said all that, however, the main emphasis of the three smoke fellows was technical. Even more to the point, their work included research on electrostatic precipitation. The physicist, W. W. Strong (Ph.D., Johns Hopkins), and one of the program's engineers, A. F. Nesbit (B.S., MIT), concentrated on applying the process to coal smoke. Soon they were publishing articles on their work and submitting patent applications.[96]

An Awkward Situation for Research Corporation

Cottrell and Duncan had much in common. Both had received college training in chemistry, both were interested in making academic science more relevant to industrial problems, and both believed that the smoke problem could be solved through research. Furthermore, both accepted the capitalistic system of profits, markets, and patents, and both wanted researchers — rather than capitalists alone — to benefit from the work. Despite these similarities, however, they had difficulty understanding each other's intentions.

In his letter asking Cottrell to consider a fellowship at Pittsburgh, Duncan noted: "In addition to this stipend there will be a reasonable, and I should say, considerable additional remuneration."[97] Taking Duncan's phrase "considerable additional remuneration" to mean "a purely commercial interest," Cottrell explained that he was seeking an alternative, "and now that we seem to be just reaching that point you can readily understand why an opportunity to re-inlist [sic] in pure commercialism for myself does not strongly appeal to me."[98]

Duncan lost little time in providing a more detailed explanation:

> You must understand . . . that any successful solution of the smoke problem through the principle of smoke condensation means a certain auxiliary plant or apparatus. This must be manufactured and must be sold, and must naturally be sold at a profit. Consequently, if the workers concerned do not take a share of this profit . . . the makers of this plant or apparatus will take it themselves.[99]

He also indicated that he would be able to meet Cottrell's material and organizational needs.[100]

But Cottrell was not seeking a guaranteed position for himself and his work — at least, not with regard to electrostatic precipitation. Instead, he sought a "method for our cooperation" that would "better subserve the best interests of the cause."[101] In contrast to Duncan's reliance on the Mellons' patronage, Cottrell turned to Holmes, Walcott, and others to make capitalism benefit researchers via voluntary cooperation among peers. He therefore refused Duncan's offer but expressed his hope that the two of them, acting as equals, could discuss "possible ways of cooperation."[102]

Two months later, after the negotiations in Washington regarding his patents were securely under way, Cottrell met with the Pittsburgh chemist and reported to Holmes: "I had quite a chat with Prof. Duncan this AM and formed even a better impression of him than I anticipated. I believe . . . he will heartily cooperate."[103] Out of their meeting came a specific cooperative act. One of the Mellon smoke fellows, W. W. Strong, was invited to visit the precipitation facilities at Balaklala and at Riverside.[104]

Cottrell knew that Duncan's approach to the smoke problem differed from his own. For example, when Walcott asked him to estimate the expected income from the precipitation patents during the upcoming year, Cottrell listed the possibilities. He then admitted: "I myself am entirely at a loss to estimate what the chances are in the immediate future for income from the fuel smoke side. Perhaps Prof. Duncan can tell you better of this, as he has undoubtedly been looking into it in detail."[105]

Through personal visits Cottrell kept in touch with the Pittsburgh group.[106] As he shifted to his duties at the Bureau of Mines, however, the problem of responding to Duncan's expanding smoke program fell to Research Corporation's engineers and directors. Bradley, for one, lost little time in speaking out. At a meeting of the executive committee in May 1912 he reported that various people — including the Pittsburgh group — were conducting research on electrostatic precipitation. The executive committee responded by giving Bradley greater freedom of action. Specifically, they authorized Bradley and the chair of the executive committee "to exercise supervision over persons or corporations experimenting with the Cottrell Process, to the end that any improvement made thereon . . . shall become the property of the Research Corporation."[107]

During the next several months Cottrell kept tabs on the situation. After attending the Eighth International Congress of Applied Chemistry in New York in September 1912, he traveled to Pittsburgh with some of the delegates. Bradley and Schmidt came too, and the three of them met with Duncan, Benner, and Raymond F. Bacon. After their "second and last conference," Cottrell noted in his diary, the two groups "[d]ecided to work ahead independently."[108] In December, Cottrell attended Pittsburgh's Smoke Exposition and also visited Duncan's lab. Although Duncan was absent, he did talk with Bacon.[109]

Meanwhile, during the academic year 1912–1913 the pace of the Pittsburgh smoke program picked up. Engineer A. F. Nesbit joined the team in mid-July 1912, and together he and Strong submitted patent applications for an entire system of coal-smoke prevention, a system that they believed would increase the efficiency and reduce the size and cost of the installations.[110] In the face of increasingly stringent smoke-reduction laws, their system looked commercially promising. "Several exhibitions of the process in actual operation have been given," they noted in a report they prepared during the summer of 1913:

> and the witnesses have invariably expressed themselves of the opinion that it is now possible for cities to pass very stringent and sweeping smoke ordinances[,] since the electrical method of precipitation can be applied at a very reasonable cost to all nuisances of this kind.[111]

What prompted further action by Research Corporation were efforts by the Pittsburgh group to move their work out of the laboratory and into a specific commercial setting. When Scott wrote Walcott regarding a meeting of the executive committee in mid-January 1913, he said he hoped the committee would consider "the problem which has confronted the [Research] Corporation by reason of the action of Prof. Duncan . . . in entering into an arrangement with the Pennsylvania Railroad, for installing the electrical precipitation processes in their round-house."[112]

At the meeting Bradley reported on the Pittsburgh situation, and Pine described his recent meeting with Duncan.[113] Meanwhile, Lawrence "opened negotiations with Mr. Gibbs, the Consulting Engineer of the Pennsylvania Railroad," a step that Goetze, for one, wholeheartedly endorsed because it meant approaching "the Pittsburgh situation along friendly lines instead of running the risk of increasing any friction. . . ."[114]

For Walcott's benefit, Bradley summarized the larger sequence of events. During the fall of 1912 Research Corporation had arranged for D. A. Lyon at the Pittsburgh laboratory of the Bureau of Mines to serve as the firm's consultant, and working for him was a former Westinghouse employee, A. F. Meston. It was through Meston and his Westinghouse contacts that Lyon learned about the commercial efforts of Duncan's group. Lyon, in turn, reported to Bradley, who passed the news along to Walcott:

> The University of Pittsburgh people had sent their attorney to Washington to investigate the patents and subsequently reported that they could get around the patents and not become infringers

in a legal sense. Personally, I do not believe that it will be possible for them to do this in a practical way.[115]

Throughout all this, Cottrell continued to work informally on Research Corporation's behalf. During a visit to Pittsburgh in early January 1913 Lyon told him about Duncan's arrangements with the Pennsylvania Railroad. The next morning he, Lyon, and Bradley discussed the situation with Holmes, who agreed to authorize $1,000 to have the Pittsburgh laboratory of the Bureau of Mines undertake experimental work on roundhouse smoke. That afternoon Cottrell, Lyon, and Bradley met with J. M. Searle, the city's smoke inspector, to discuss the matter. Then the trio called on an official of the Pennsylvania Railroad. After offering him a "history of the case," Cottrell "left it up to Bradley & Lyon to work [things] out."[116]

Soon, however, Bradley sounded a new alarm. He telegraphed Schmidt, who passed the message along to Cottrell: "Gossip says Mellon formed one hundred thousand dollar corporation to exploit Duncan and associates patents in Pittsburgh. This apparently means competition in the field of electrical precipitation."[117]

Other sources confirmed that a new company was indeed taking shape. For example, *Electrical World* carried the following notice in its "New Industrial Companies" section:

> The Electrical Precipitation Company, of Pittsburgh, Pa., has been incorporated under the laws of the State of Delaware with a capital stock of $100,000 by H. E. Latter, W. J. Maloney and O. J. Reichard, of Wilmington, Del. The company will acquire and deal in patent rights of every kind for the prevention of the emission of smoke or dust of any deleterious gases.[118]

Archival sources suggest that Duncan and his colleagues envisioned a far less ambitious enterprise than Bradley feared. For example, a letter from Bacon to Duncan demonstrates that the new company planned to pursue its efforts on the same scale as the existing project. The smoke fellows would "be loaned to the company," and the company would install the experimental precipitator for studying roundhouse smoke for the Pennsylvania Railroad.[119]

Bacon added that strict limits would be placed on how much money the new company would be allowed to spend. He recommended to Duncan:

> That until the experimental installation in the Pennsylvania Railroad Roundhouse shall have thoroughly demonstrated the validity

of the work developed under this Fellowship no more money be
put into this company than is necessary for purchasing such apparatus as will be needed in making this demonstration and that until
such time as experiments are completed in the Pennsylvania Railroad Roundhouse this company should not have any salaried employees but should be operated as indicated above by means of
Fellows.[120]

Despite the modest scale of its work, however, Bacon did recommend that the
company be formed immediately.[121]

Several undated drafts of a "Plan for Company to Put Upon Market Smoke
and Dust Prevention Apparatus" provide additional details.[122] As mentioned in
Electrical World, the proposed company was to be incorporated in Delaware,
with an initial capitalization of $100,000. The draft plan went on to specify
that 51 percent of the stock "would be retained by the Donor" (i.e., by R. B.
Mellon) "and the remaining 49% . . . distributed by the University [of Pitts-
burgh]. . . ."[123] Salaries for the following positions were to begin July 1, 1913:
"General Manager" (R. C. Benner), "Physicist in charge of experiments" (W. W.
Strong), and "Mechanical Engineer in charge of installation" (A. F. Nesbit).[124]
The basic idea was for the new company to extend the technological beach-
head that Strong and Nesbit had already established, by continuing the re-
search as aggressively as possible.[125]

In response to what little he knew about these developments, Cottrell
downplayed the prospects of a serious commercial rival actually emerging.
"This may, after all, not mean much with regard to the Research Corporation's
interests," he wrote Walcott.[126] Yet Cottrell was unwilling to ignore what was
going on. He expressed his concern "that no possible misunderstanding of
intent should be permitted to exist between [R. B. Mellon] and the Board of
Directors of the Research Corporation."[127] He also encouraged Walcott to contact the Pittsburgh banker personally, so as to put him "directly in communication with ultimate headquarters."[128]

Always the optimist, Cottrell hoped that the affair could be settled to
Research Corporation's benefit. In his view the key was adopting "the broadest and most disinterested standpoint," thereby avoiding "endless, unnecessary and destructive misunderstanding."[129] Later he elaborated:

> In the matter of Prof. Duncan's work, I do not think it is so much a
> matter of working up the exact legal status of the different patents
> in question as it is to sound out the fundamental spirit of the move-

ment particularly from Mr. Mellon's standpoint and my idea was not so much to ask of you any detailed treatment of the subject, but more to get into direct communication as informally as possible with Mr. Mellon and his associates in frank and friendly discussion of the significance of the Research Corporation as well as their own organization, and the possible relations of one to the other in the broadest possible sense and without attempting to dip too deeply into details which later, once the general plans and aims are mutually understood and accepted on both sides, could, I think, be advantageously handled by Dean Goetze and Mr. Bradley. . . . [130]

Cottrell's behind-the-scenes efforts on behalf of Research Corporation never flagged. What was more, Research Corporation had other allies, including not just its directors, but also Bradley, Schmidt, and Holmes. Even so, the firm's first two years were uncertain ones. Although Western Precipitation was well established in its geographical market, opening up Research Corporation's market in the East was slowed by the company's low level of capitalization and by its efforts at international cooperation. [131]

One can easily imagine how shaky Research Corporation's prospects might have appeared to Duncan. First, his own alliance with R. B. Mellon gave him access to levels of capitalization more in keeping with actual commercial needs (an authorized capitalization of $100,000, as opposed to Research Corporation's $20,000). Second, Strong and Nesbit's technical work suggested that Cottrell's patents were not all-encompassing. Third, although electrostatic precipitation was undeniably useful for the metallurgical industry, neither Western Precipitation nor Research Corporation was giving much attention to the equally urgent problem of urban smoke. Finally, the attempts at international cooperation may have appeared amateurish and prone to failure.

There is little direct evidence documenting Duncan's viewpoint, but a letter to Raymond F. Bacon offers us a glimpse. Although his remarks involved a specific set of circumstances, they also reflected his larger doubts about Research Corporation's viability:

> The Chancellor's office [at the University of Pittsburgh] informed us that Dean Goetze was not available by telegraph or any other means. Yesterday Dr. Benner informed me that Dr. Cottrell was expected in town last night and that he expected to meet him this morning. However, it appears that he did not turn up. Meanwhile, some Dr. Ross of the Bureau of Soils [at the U.S. Department of

Agriculture] has informed Dr. Benner that this Research Corporation is bankrupt. Whether this is actually true or not, of course I
have no idea and I give it to you simply for what it is worth.[132]

Resolving the Pittsburgh Situation

Despite Duncan's tone, Research Corporation was no gimcrack operation, and the efforts of those associated with it no Keystone Cops comedy. In
short order, it succeeded in placing limits on the commercial efforts of the
Pittsburgh group — though tying down the loose ends took several years.

To begin with, Research Corporation used every opportunity to make its
presence felt in Pittsburgh. For example, on March 18, 1913, Bradley presented a paper describing the Cottrell process at the regular monthly meeting of the Engineers' Society of Western Pennsylvania. "The Bureau of Mines,"
he noted — thereby reminding his audience that Research Corporation had an
important organizational ally — "has made arrangements for installing a demonstration plant upon the stack gases from one of their boilers at the Testing
Station in Pittsburgh."[133] On that same trip he met separately with both Strong
and Nesbit, and after returning to New York he reported to Walcott:

> I understand Mr. Mellon has stated that he will not engage in the
> commercial exploitation of electrical precipitation. Furthermore,
> no experimental work will be done in connection with his fellow-
> ship after the present year. The money which he has given in con-
> nection with the smoke fellowship for the next two years is to be
> devoted to publicity work solely.[134]

Bradley also reported Strong's suggestion that R. B. Mellon be invited to
serve as a Research Corporation director. "I have often felt that this would be
a very good thing to do," he added, "but personally I have been unable to
reach Mr. Mellon in order to discuss this with him, as he did not wish to
become mixed up in the controversy."[135] In April 1913 the executive committee asked Walcott to extend the invitation.[136]

Meanwhile, Cottrell continued to play a key role in the negotiations. On a
short visit to Pittsburgh on June 13, he inspected the experimental unit at the
Bureau of Mines. "Then," he wrote in his diary, "[I] called at University of
Pittsburg[h] Lab & had a long Conference with Bacon on precipitation matters."[137] Bacon believed that a satisfactory agreement between the two groups
could be reached, and Cottrell "promised to take the matter up with the Research Corporation."[138] Back in New York on June 14, he discussed the situation with Goetze over lunch at the Engineers' Club. Several days later he

attended a meeting of Research Corporation's executive committee and reported the results of his Pittsburgh conversations.[139]

Making the situation more urgent was the Pennsylvania Railroad's strong desire to reduce the smoke produced by its locomotives. In the view of company engineer D. F. Crawford, efficient combustion was only part of the answer, especially because starting the fires was necessarily an inefficient, smoky process.[140] He believed that coal-burning steam locomotives remained more economical than a wholesale shift to electric traction. But public concern over air pollution made locomotive smoke a pressing problem, one that he had long tried to solve. "During the last fifteen years," he wrote: "I have examined drawings and patents of many devices which were supposed to eliminate smoke, and made personal observations of their performance. Unfortunately, but very few of these were even promising...."[141]

More was at stake, however, than just Crawford's professional interest:

> The Pennsylvania Railroad System has devoted a great deal of attention, and expended a large amount of money in experimenting with and developing, either on its own account, or in co-operation with representatives of other railways, or the technical societies, devices which gave promise of reducing the smoke from locomotives....[142]

In short, the Pennsylvania Railroad was eager to pursue any method that genuinely promised to reduce smoke. While Research Corporation and Duncan's group were still negotiating, a measure of forbearance was in order. But the Pennsylvania Railroad was definitely not neutral about the issue, prompting Bradley to write Walcott: "I understand that the Pennsylvania Railroad Co. is anxious to go ahead with their work of installing the process, in case an amicable arrangement can be reached between the parties concerned."[143]

In July 1913 Cottrell again went to Pittsburgh, this time for an extended series of meetings that he recorded in his diary:

> Sat[urday,] July 19/13
> Arrived Pittsburg[h] ... & went to Fort Pitt Hotel thence to B[ureau] of M[ines] & examined treater.... Saw smoke tests in P.M. on the treater.... Today's papers spoke of demonstration made day before at Duncans. Strong came down to Hotel in evening & talked with us until a late hour about their work.

Sun[day,] July 20/13

Got up rather late. Went with Strong out to Nesbits & had long talk with him about Duncan matters. Fellows 49% divided 15% each to Strong, Benner, Nesbit & 4% to Shuey.

Benner & Nesbit signed release of same to Duncan for public good. Nesbit now tied up to some extent with some outside interest but relations here not very clear.

Left Nesbits about 6 Strong having left earlier & went to Duncans finding R. K. and wife & brother Norman all on porch. Had half hours chat with all three & then others withdrew & had talk with Duncan over present situation.

Expressed regret for Scott & Lyons expressions and explained they [were] not in position to speak for [Research] Corporation. Discussed question of turning over to the R. C. their pat[ent]s & question of R. C. giving free licenses in Pittsb[urgh] district and suggested as preferable the licensing on same basis as elsewhere but devote the profits (net) to some local institution such as the university or library or other similar public cause. This at once appealed to Duncan as "awakening an industrial conscience." He suggested a school for stokers, &c.

He emphasized his want of something in writing to vindicate himself at any time that any question of his personal integrity or fairness in this matter should come up from any side.

Returned to Hotel 11 PM & had short chat with Bradley & Strong & then to bed.

Monday[,] July 21/13

AM Bureau [of] Mines. . . . Lunch there & discussed Duncan situation with technical committee & emphasized my desire that they do not drag into any discussion of the situation the R.C. relationship &c nor champion what they might feel my or its case in the matter but keep clear of any possible criticism of Bureau using its influence in matters not properly in its field.

Went at 2 PM to see Hammerschlag [*sic*] (Dir[ector,] Carnegie School) & had short chat with him on Duncan situation & other matters.

Thence to Chancellor McCormac[k']s office at Univ. of Pittsb[urgh] where Bradley joined me & we had long chat on Duncan situation &c. Explained to McCormac[k] the project for R. C. to handle all the patents & charge same royalties in Pittsburg[h] district as elsewhere but return net profits from here to local institutions such as university, library, or others as might be decided upon. This met his hearty approval.

Back to hotel & after dinner (rather late) went out to Nesbits with Bradley & met Strong there by appointment.

Discussed whole situation[, with] Nesbit telling of his negotiations with some outside parties who might employ him & Strong at $10,000 per yr between them but mentioned no names. He expressed himself as very ready to come with the Res. Corp....

Tues[day,] July 22/12 [*sic*]

...Called on J. M. Searle with Bradley & discussed smoke situation & he told us of later developments in Penn R.R. matter & Benner's talk at Sewickely & Crawford's dissaproval [*sic*] of same &c....

Bradley & I then went to meet Hammerschlag [*sic*] by appointment at the school & from thence with he & Mrs. H. to their home for dinner & and later had long talk over Duncan situation &c....

Wed[nesday,] July 23/12 [*sic*]

To Bureau in AM.... Searl[e] & 3 inspectors called 9:30. Bradley showed them tests of treater. Called up Duncan & suggested coming over but he suggested going with him in new auto he was testing so he called about 10:30 AM. Asked him if he cared to see tests but he wanted to test auto & so declined & we drove until train time 12:30 PM when he left me at P&LE Sta. We discussed situation again.

Duncan referred to relations with Ba[e]keland as contrasted to those with Res Corp and asked if I though he would have gotten the same fair treatment from me & my associates. This insinuation I promptly resented & Duncan as promptly withdrew as far as our mutual personal relations were concerned. I then pointed out at some length how real legal infractions of contractual relations gradually shaded off into mere evasions of law & then into sharp practice & then into questions of Business Ethics & business etiquet [*sic*] & finally mere matters of general "taste."

I then detailed the Parsons & Sir Thomas Oliver incident emphasizing it as representing how the conditions impressed even his best friends and urged him to talk with Parsons on the subject.

He asked me specifically to write him a letter which he might have for record to confound any charges of unfairness in regard to this matter which might later arise and I undertook to write him something which would put the matter straight but emphasized the need of caution in the phrasing of this to prevent its ever being used in patent litigation which might arise out of the two sets of patents. To this course he assented but urged that the letter be clear & unequivocal.[144]

In less detail, Duncan's view of the encounter with Cottrell also survives. On July 25 Duncan wrote Bacon:

> Dr. Cottrell called to see me at my home last Saturday (19th) and spent the whole evening. He saw me yesterday, as well, and I drove him down to the station. He acknowledges in the plainest way [that] we have done no injury to him or any of them and assures me that he will write me a letter plainly stating this. He tells me, as well, that he has taken the matter up very seriously with certain of the Research Corporation and also with the officials down at the Bureau of Mines; and from what he has told me I judge that we shall have no more of *that*. If he writes me a frank, manly letter completely disclaiming and denying the truth of the allegations set in motion against me at the Bureau of Mines and elsewhere, I shall, I think, let the matter wholly drop, for I shall then be protected against any attack that comes to my knowledge.[145]

In September 1913 Strong delivered to Bradley a typescript draft, implementing the agreement that Cottrell and Duncan had negotiated. According to the draft, Strong and Nesbit's patent rights would be assigned to Research Corporation "without any limitation whatever," and "the net income resulting from the application of the process of electrical precipitation in the state of Pennsylvania be used for ... the development of the process...."[146] Also according to the draft, on October 1, 1913, Strong would begin working for Research Corporation to "study the recent development of the process," while Nesbit would "continue until February, 1914, in putting the [Pittsburgh] patents in as good a condition as possible," after which he too would join Research Corporation.[147]

But the negotiations dragged on, probably due to Nesbit's belief that he had been unfairly treated at the Mellon Institute. Hoping that R. B. Mellon himself would be able to resolve the issue, Nesbit prepared a detailed account of his work on electrostatic precipitation.[148] Because it is one of the few sources offering an insider's view of the Pittsburgh program, I quote from it at length:

> At the time of my appointment as Electrical Engineer, in July 1912, Dr. Bacon outlined definitely my work in connection with the study of Electrical Precipitation as a means of securing relief from the smoke nuisance and at the same time stated the Mechanical Engineering study of the problem was already at work under the supervision of Mr. Bellows.[149]
>
> Dr. Bacon mapped out the working hours in the laboratory from 8.00 A.M. till 12.00 noon, from 1 P.M. till 5 P.M., also the teaching requirements within this schedule of hours. He stated that the vacation periods consisted of six weeks during the summer, two weeks at the holidays, and one week in the spring at the time of the University recess.
>
> Dr. Bacon said that I would be entitled to this vacation schedule, and further agreed that I should have a vacation of two weeks in October 1912, should I be able to secure my release from the Westinghouse Electric Company so as to begin my duties on two day's notice.
>
> I arranged matters satisfactorily with the Westinghouse Company on July 15th and entered upon my duties at the Research Laboratory on July 17th, on a contract for one year.
>
> October passed and no vacation was allowed me. Christmas vacation came and I was sent to Washington D.C. to confer with Hodges and Hodges with reference to our patent applications.
>
> I returned from Washington the night before Christmas. The day after Christmas I was told to keep the investigation work rushing as rapidly as possible.
>
> In January 1913, Dr. Duncan notified both Dr. Strong and myself that our salaries were to be raised to a yearly basis of $3000 in appreciation of the results we had obtained. This increase in salary went into effect February first 1913.
>
> Dr. Duncan told me, at the time of this announcement, that if I kept the work moving during the established vacation periods, it was to be understood that I was to have full recess time during the existence of the fellowship, or else full compensation for the same.
>
> During the removal of the laboratory to its present site, in March 1913, I was directed to continue my work either in the smoke house, the University laboratory or wherever most convenient.

On May 1st. 1913, Dr. Bacon allotted the completion of my work on the report or monograph on the Precipitation of Smoke to Dr. Strong and transferred me to the Mechanical Engineer's report, then being drafted by Messers Straub and McBride.[150]

On account of Mr. Straub's resignation going into effect on June first, Dr. Bacon said that the replies to the objections filed to our patent applications by the patent examiner could be postponed until a later date, and that I should spare no effort or expense to make the Mechanical Engineer's report as reliable and valuable as possible and get it into shape with all the speed I could muster.

... On one occasion during the summer of 1913, Mr. Phillips[151] came up to the Institute for a conference with regard to my work. At a later date, both Mr. Phillips and Mr. Hicks came to the Institute for a similar conference.

The conferences had to do with the situation as regards our patents.... I promised Mr. Phillips and Mr. Hicks that I would not desert my post, but would stick to the work, notwithstanding inducements which had been made me relative to electrical precipitation projects.

... The first draft of the complete Mechanical Engineer's report was ready in December 1913, and [I] immediately set to work preparing the replies for the objections filed against our patent applications.

These replies were worked up as fully and truthfully as could be considering the interruptions made in my progress in the smoke house by another fellowship.

During this last spring vacation, Dr. Bacon sent me to Washington to confer with Hodges and Hodges in regard to the filing of our replies to the examiner's objections.

During the interview with the patent examiners, who had charge of our applications, additional objections were filed, and upon returning home to work up our replies I found my experimental outfit in such damaged shape as to cause a delay of six weeks. As a result of this delay, I was forced to extremes in working up my replies, which were only completed a week ago.

Duncan's death in February 1914 complicated the situation, because it left Nesbit dependent upon Bacon's recollections of what Duncan may or may not have said regarding Nesbit's vacation time. Thus after Nesbit wrote Bacon on May 1, 1914 (the date that Nesbit's smoke fellowship officially ended),

Bacon responded: ". . . I know of no arrangement whatever that was ever made with you by the administration of the Institute whereby you were to receive any extra pay."[152] At that point Nesbit apparently decided to hold out for financial compensation via the patents for which he and Strong had applied.

Actually, the year 1915 began on a hopeful note for Research Corporation. In February the technical efforts of the two groups were featured at a special session of the Midwinter Convention of the American Institute of Electrical Engineers in New York. Cottrell himself offered an historical overview, and Strong, Nesbit, and Bradley presented additional papers.[153] The whole event had a high profile. "The large lecture hall of the United Engineering Societies Building was filled," noted one account: "Many members of the American Institute of Mining Engineers were present, following a cordial invitation extended to them. President P. M. Lincoln of the American Institute of Electrical Engineers presided."[154] Both Strong and Bradley used motion pictures and lantern slides to illustrate their remarks, and Bradley offered an experimental demonstration.[155]

In his remarks, Cottrell commented that "a method of coöperation between the Research Corporation and the Mellon Institute had been effected."[156] Several months later Bradley made a similar comment at a meeting of the New York Section of the American Electrochemical Society held at the time of the National Exposition of Chemical Industries in New York. After describing the generosity of the Mellon brothers in establishing the Mellon Institute, he told the assembly: "Mr. [R. B.] Mellon likewise has generously donated to the Research Corporation the results obtained by the Smoke Fellowship."[157]

Despite such pronouncements, however, the situation remained unsettled. On March 30, 1915, Strong forwarded yet another draft agreement for Research Corporation to consider.[158] Now the transfer of patent rights was to be accompanied by one-time payments of two hundred dollars to Strong and the same amount to Nesbit, for each patent. In addition, there would be annual grants of one hundred and fifty dollars to Strong and the same amount to Nesbit, again for each patent.

Meanwhile, the prospect of formal interference proceedings loomed. At issue were the rights to an important new type of electrode design. In Cottrell's earliest work, the collecting electrodes had been vertical metal plates (with the discharge electrodes suspended between pairs of plates) — a design that continued to be used. But Schmidt's work at Riverside led to a second type of electrode design, in which the collecting electrodes were vertical pipes (with the discharge electrodes suspended along the axis of each pipe).[159]

Even as late as May 1915, Bradley reported to Strong that he was still seeking an informal solution:

> Dr. Bacon recently wrote to me concerning the Patent Office interference between you and Nesbit on the one hand and Schmidt and [G. C.] Roberts on the other. He made what I consider to be an excellent suggestion for avoiding the expense and "red tape" of a Patent Office interference, and which I presume he has taken up with either you or Nesbit. The suggestion is that you and Nesbit, and Schmidt and Roberts present proofs as to priority to him (Dr. Bacon) and me as an independent committee, we to examine the proofs for the purpose of deciding as to who really had priority.[160]

Strong replied: "Your plan of taking the interference case up with Dr. Bacon sounds all right. . . . I shall be very glad to cooperate in any way that opportunity may offer."[161]

Probably due to Nesbit's continued resistance, however, the Patent Office began a formal interference proceeding.[162] Handling Research Corporation's side was Washington patent attorney Clinton P. Townsend. Considerable effort went into collecting appropriate testimony,[163] and in his report at the annual stockholders meeting on February 16, 1917, Goetze expressed optimism:

> Messrs. Byrnes, Townsend & Brickenstein, Patent Attorneys, who were retained by us sometime ago . . . have conducted one important patent interference . . . and have successfully prosecuted the case to such a point that we confidently expect to obtain a very broad decision in our favor.[164]

Finally, at a June meeting of the executive committee he announced the desired result: "An important patent interference was decided in favor of Messrs. Schmidt and Roberts as against Messrs. Strong and Nesbit by the Patent Office."[165]

Just to round out the story, despite the smoke fellowships not being renewed after 1914, the University of Pittsburgh's School of Engineering continued the technical work. In 1922 R. B. Mellon funded R. J. McKay's trip to survey smoke abatement efforts in England, and in 1923 Harry Bertine Meller became head of smoke studies at the Mellon Institute.[166]

As for Nesbit, his commercial efforts continued to disconcert the Research Corporation engineers. Thus E. P. Dillon reported to the directors on January 17, 1919: "We have experienced some competition in electrical precipitation. . . . We were subjected to competitive tests with [F. W.] Steere and with Nesbit at a plant of the Aluminum Company of America, and won out over both of them. . . ."[167] A year later, however, Dillon told the directors that the matter had at last been settled:

> Mr. Nesbit . . . gave us an opportunity to join the Western Precipi-
> tation Company in examining all of his patent material. We paid
> $1,000 on an option to purchase this material, if desirable, and
> upon examination found there was nothing in Nesbit's ideas that
> would be to our advantage to purchase. This in our opinion clears
> up the Nesbit situation conclusively, and we look for no further
> difficulty from this source.[168]

Organizational Changes and the Beginning of Hooker's Presidency

While interacting with the Pittsburgh group, Research Corporation took several steps to establish more securely the technical basis for its work. One was to formalize its presence beyond the New York City region, with the Pittsburgh region being an example. As mentioned, the company arranged for Lyon to look after its interests there, and toward the end of 1915 the company formally established a branch office.[169]

Research Corporation also responded by strengthening its commitments to the pursuit of research on electrostatic precipitation and to the patenting of practical results. The company put Strong on its payroll, thus bringing the principal Pittsburgh researcher into its own sphere of operations. It insti-tuted agreements with all its employees whereby it retained control over any improvements they might devise.[170] In 1916 the company established a labora-tory in Brooklyn aimed "toward a more thorough understanding of the techni-cal features of electrical precipitation, as well as toward the practical and commercial application of the same."[171] It established a patent department which, as Goetze reported, "has gone over several hundred ideas emanating from the personnel, to determine their value to the art of electrical precipita-tion and their patentability."[172] Finally, it revised its earlier agreement with Western Precipitation. Byrnes, Townsend, and Brickenstein would now serve both organizations as "common counsel by whom all patent applications . . . coming within the scope of the agreement of February 4, 1914, shall be filed and prosecuted to completion" and by whom "all interferences and litigation concerning said patent applications" shall be conducted.[173]

In short, Research Corporation strengthened the technical basis for its work through vertical expansion. It expanded forward (toward its markets), by establishing regional branch offices, and it expanded backward (toward its "raw materials," the inventions on which its business was based) by establish-

An engineer and founder of one of the first electrochemical
plants in the U.S., Elon H. Hooker became the first president
of Research Corporation in January 1915.

ing its own development laboratory and by increasing its control over the
patenting process. The general pattern was not new within the electrical industry. Nevertheless, Research Corporation's early history clearly illustrates
how the production of technologically complex goods (electrostatic precipitators) in a competitive situation spurred vertical expansion.[174]

Research Corporation also strengthened its position by rationalizing its
organizational structure. One important step was the report that Bradley prepared in the spring of 1916. Due to the company's rapid growth, he believed
"that it is no longer possible or desirable for a few individuals to look after all
of the details, and the necessity has therefore arisen for creating an efficient
organization and system."[175]

In his view, the solution lay in dividing the company's work into departments along well-defined functional lines with the heads of each department
reporting directly to the chief engineer (that is, to Bradley himself). The divisions included executive (Bradley's office), commercial, engineering, draft-
ing, research, legal and patent departments. Within the engineering department, Bradley proposed a division of labor: one member of a three-man

technical committee would focus on engineering development (Fischer); another, construction (Landolt); and the third, testing (Heimrod). Finally, Bradley proposed to increase still further the size of the technical staff, stating: "The work has suffered more or less in the past, due to an insufficient force of engineers, and it is therefore recommended that this force be made adequate at the earliest possible moment."[176]

In addition to rationalizing the organizational structure, Bradley proposed that Research Corporation assume more of the financial responsibility associated with installing the precipitators. Because their own engineering staffs were capable of carrying out the work, large companies desiring precipitators needed little more than plans and technical advice. But small companies, as Goetze noted, were a different matter:

> In the smaller corporations . . . which do not maintain engineering staffs and with whom the Research Corporation is coming more and more in contact, the desire seems to be for a service by the Research Corporation which will control and direct the entire process of testing and installing the Electrical Precipitation Apparatus. . . .[177]

Unstated in Bradley's report was the assumption that the project engineers would remain dominant within the firm. Authority would be kept in the hands of the chief engineer, and expansion would mean expanding the engineering staff. Even though the report was accepted, however, the firm's reorganization did not stop there, and the project engineers were not left with the upper hand. Instead its first president, Elon H. Hooker, increasingly set the firm's overall tone.

Hooker had not been able to accept the firm's presidency in 1912 because of his duties as the national treasurer for Theodore Roosevelt's Progressive Party. In January 1913 Research Corporation's board of directors made a formal effort to elect him, but still he declined, saying that other commitments prevented him from devoting sufficient time to the firm's affairs.[178] As a result, Research Corporation remained without a president until January 15, 1915, when Hooker finally agreed to serve.[179]

Although he was an engineer, Hooker brought to Research Corporation not so much an emphasis on the technical work as an overall commitment to sound management. Thus he supported Bradley's proposed reorganization, but he also arranged for an additional evaluation. Specifically, in March 1917 he asked Theodore E. Knowlton — a civil engineer known both to him and to others at Research Corporation — "to undertake . . . an administrative audit" of the firm, explaining: "We desire to learn from an outside source what would constitute a suitable constructive policy for the business development of the Corporation and how our present administrative force may be altered or supplemented to best achieve this end."[180]

In his report, Knowlton identified what he saw as Research Corporation's most significant shortcomings. One was the confusion engendered by the firm's two main purposes — making a profit through its business activities, on the one hand, and using those funds to support research, on the other. The firm also tended to spread itself too thin, by undertaking too many installations at once. A third shortcoming was not having some one person to coordinate all the engineering work. In practice, technical authority was split between Bradley (and his staff) and the board of directors (notably, Goetze).

Although Knowlton did little to address the firm's philanthropic goals, he did make several recommendations regarding its business activities. He agreed with Bradley that Research Corporation itself, not its clients, should assume full responsibility for the construction costs and that the firm should perform its technical research at its own laboratory rather than at each installation site. He also suggested that the firm survey previous clients to see how its services could have been rendered more satisfactorily. Most importantly, he believed that the firm should hire a professional manager who would occupy a position in the corporate hierarchy midway between the chief engineer and the board of directors. "It will be *his* business," Knowlton said of the proposed manager, "to make money, and the business of the Executive Committee, or Board of Directors, to make disposition of profits."[181]

In the wake of Knowlton's report, the company indeed hired a general manager. Meeting at the end of December 1917, the executive committee appointed Bradley to the position for the following year. But at its annual meeting in January 1918 the board of directors chose not to approve Bradley's appointment. Instead, they established a committee consisting of Hooker, Lawrence, and Milton C. Whitaker to evaluate other candidates. The committee's choice was E. P. Dillon, who came to them from Westinghouse. Dillon assumed his post in June 1918, and by the first of July he had revised the company's organizational chart. It now consisted of three major departments: engineering, commercial, and purchasing (each of which was further subdivided into various divisions and sections). Bradley continued to head the engineering department. But his authority over the firm's affairs was no longer as sweeping as it once had been, and in 1919 he left the firm's employ.[182]

During these reorganization efforts, serious consideration was given to expanding the firm's research program. In particular, at the board's annual meeting in 1918, Little proposed that Research Corporation build a research laboratory (as distinct from the firm's development laboratory). Not only would the $400,000 suburban facility provide a place for systematic research on electrostatic precipitation, but it would also house the company's other departments and some of its manufacturing operations. What Little wanted were facilities that expressed more fully the company's increasingly secure institutional identity — which, in his view, was based on research. "A Research Corporation without a research laboratory," he insisted, "is something of an anomaly."[183]

The board, however, chose not to accept Little's proposal. Much of the resistance probably came from Hooker, who tended to view laboratory work with a critical eye. In April 1916, for example, Bradley wrote Walcott that:

> Mr. Hooker desires an itemized statement of the proposed expenditures in connection with the field laboratory at Brooklyn, it being his experience that laboratories generally cost more than one anticipates. He also desires a statement as to the relative value of money spent for a field laboratory as against using the same amount of money for additional engineers.[184]

After the 1918 "no" vote, Little offered to resign from the executive committee, explaining: "I now find myself entirely out of sympathy with the expressed policy of the executive and a majority of the Board on a matter which I regard as vital to the success of the Corporation."[185] Eventually Hooker succeeded in getting him to reconsider, though clearly at a reduced level of influence.[186]

Thus Hooker's leadership led neither to a greater emphasis on the company's technical work nor to a greater emphasis on its own research. Instead, what he did was to rationalize its business activities. His achievement was to ensure that Research Corporation developed what Alfred D. Chandler, Jr., has called "organizational capabilities" — meaning the full set of facilities and skills a firm needs to do its work.[187] Putting this idea back into Hooker's own words, he reported to Walcott toward the end of 1918 "that Research Corporation [now] has a machine capable of handling in a businesslike and thorough way whatever comes to it. . . ."[188]

CHAPTER FIVE

AN ASPIRING
PHILANTHROPIC ORGANIZATION

Although legally established as a business enterprise, Research Corporation was never intended to function like one — at least not wholly, or even primarily. In Cottrell's eyes, profit making was not its main objective; public service was.[1] He hoped Research Corporation would serve the public, first, by evaluating patents and helping to develop those that showed promise, and second, by supporting scientific research.

Ideological Altruism

Given the way the firm had been established, however, it was forced from the outset to emphasize its engineering work. As early as May 1912 the executive committee refused to promote an invention unrelated to electrostatic precipitation, "owing to the pressure of business."[2] Similarly, in its report for 1913 the executive committee emphasized the need "to concentrate the energies of the Corporation almost exclusively upon the development of the Cottrell Process, and to turn this endowment into cash ... before attempting to develop any other fields. ..."[3]

Although its early philanthropic activities were few and far between, Research Corporation was from the outset philanthropic in at least an ideological sense, and here the key word was "altruistic." Speaking positively, "altruism" meant generosity to the point of self-sacrifice, or putting the welfare of others ahead of one's own welfare.[4] At the turn of the century, however, "altruism" usually connoted more than that. For a society so deeply committed to individualism and materialism, the term could sound hopelessly idealistic. Thus a contributor to the *Overland Monthly* noted: "Altruists erect an impossible superstructure upon an imaginary base; [they] build what they want on something they will never get."[5]

The people associated with Research Corporation probably used the term "altruistic" because they wanted to embrace its most general meaning, "of benefit to all," but they would have resisted any suggestion of impracticality. More to the point, they tended to emphasize the term's negative meaning, "of no special benefit to particular individuals." Thus Walcott insisted that the directors and stockholders not be motivated by personal financial gain. "The organization is *purely altruistic*," he reported to the Smithsonian's board of regents in 1912, explaining: "no dividends or interest [will be] paid on the stock, nor any salaries, except to employees, and no Director will be paid as such."[6]

At times, however, it was difficult to maintain this altruistic stance. One example involved Frederick A. Goetze, a member of Research Corporation's board of directors and for many years the chair of its executive committee. In the absence of a president (a position not filled until 1915) and a general manager (a position not filled until 1918), much of the responsibility for overseeing the firm's engineering efforts devolved on Goetze.

Goetze attended the Columbia University School of Mines from 1893 to 1895 and then accepted a university position as assistant superintendent of buildings and grounds, eventually advancing to superintendent. In 1907 he became dean of the applied science faculty. Later he became comptroller (in 1914) and treasurer (in 1916). That last position he filled, with distinction, until his retirement in 1948.[7]

What triggered a reassessment of Goetze's work for Research Corporation was his appointment as comptroller. As he explained to Cottrell in April 1914: "my increased duties . . . make it more and more difficult for me to devote any time to outside activities. . . ."[8] He also told Walcott that the solution lay in finding someone who could pay more attention to the firm's engineering efforts. [9]

So extensive were Goetze's contributions – and so slow was Research Corporation in choosing a president or hiring a general manager – that even Walcott felt uncomfortable. Early in 1913, for example, he wrote Cottrell: "Dr. Goetze has given a great deal of time, thought and energy to the Research Corporation, and it is evident that before long he will have to slow down, or else we will have to ask him to take a permanent position."[10]

Initially, however, Goetze would accept neither a salary nor an honorarium. Thus in November 1914 Walcott mentioned to B. B. Lawrence (Goetze's Columbia colleague and fellow Research Corporation director) that Goetze "would feel very keenly any attempt to place him on a different basis from the other Directors."[11] To this, Lawrence replied: ". . . Mr. Goetze, like all men connected with Universities, is poorly paid. . . . Naturally he feels a certain pride about being on the same basis as the [other] Directors of the Corporation. . . ."[12]

At their November 1914 meeting, the board voted to give Lloyd N. Scott (who served as the firm's secretary as well as a director) an honorarium of $1,000.[13] But Goetze resisted a similar arrangement in his case. Finally, in 1917 and again in 1918 the board voted Goetze an honorarium of $5,000. On that second occasion, however, Walcott offered a resolution preventing a recurrence of such compensation, and soon thereafter the firm hired a general manager.[14]

In addition to setting Research Corporation apart from businesses of the usual sort, the term "altruistic" underscored its kinship to certain other organizations. For example, in an early letter to Smithsonian regent C. F. Choate, Walcott explained Cottrell's intentions in a way that clearly echoed the Smithsonian's mission:

> If the patents offered by Professor Cottrell are to be of any advantage to an individual, I should say that they most certainly should not be accepted; but as the proceeds are to be used for research, *for the increase and diffusion of knowledge and the benefit of man*, I do not see but that it is quite as *altruistic* and probably more beneficial, in the long run, as to give them to the public.[15]

Walcott made a similar comment when he wrote the Deputy Commissioner of Internal Revenue in 1915 to maintain that Research Corporation should not be required to pay the newly instituted federal income tax: "The Research Corporation is as *altruistic* in its objects as the Smithsonian Institution, the Carnegie Institution of Washington, and similar institutions."[16]

Although Research Corporation was exempted from the new federal tax, similar efforts regarding New York State taxes did not proceed so smoothly. John B. Pine (the firm's legal counsel as well as a director) explained to the tax lawyer he consulted that Research Corporation's application for state exemption had been declined "upon the ground that as the corporation was formed under the Business law, it was not classed as a charitable corporation."[17] Along with the precedent of the federal decision, Pine stressed Research Corporation's kinship to universities. For example, he wrote in a subsequent letter: "you will see from the Certificate of Incorporation . . . that it is exclusively an educational corporation . . . organized exclusively for educational and scientific purposes. . . ."[18] But the state's tax law was worded in a way that required a different approach. Thus the tax lawyer replied:

> Article 9 of the Tax Law under which the tax is alleged to be collected does not specifically exempt educational corporations but it places a tax on business corporations and we are contending that the Research Corporation, not being a business corporation, does not come within the scope and intent of the article.[19]

Unfortunately, Research Corporation's activities increasingly resembled those of a business corporation, especially as it assumed more and more of the responsibility for installing precipitators. Thus Scott informed the tax lawyer in August 1917 that Research Corporation was no longer merely sell-ing "the intangible rights or licenses to use our processes" but was also "do-ing an electrical machinery business . . . and selling this equipment. . . ."[20] "We were surprised to learn that the company has gone into the jobbing busi-ness," the tax lawyer replied, "for in so doing it can no longer maintain its claim that it is exclusively a research and scientific corporation."[21] Neverthe-less, the issue remain unresolved "until 1921, [when] the Corporation was advised by Commissioner Merrill that the only way it could obtain exemption would be by a special [legislative] act exempting it from all taxes other than those on tangible property. . . ."[22]

Although the term "altruistic" does not appear in the correspondence with the tax lawyer, the documents do shed light on what those associated with Research Corporation meant by the term. To begin with, they did not — and could not — mean "charitable" in the established legal meaning of the term. By its own admission, Research Corporation was engaged in business activi-ties. Nevertheless, its leaders wanted legal recognition that something else was also involved. In their exchanges with the tax lawyer, the term they tended to use was "educational." But what they had in mind involved not the class-room so much as the laboratory. Research Corporation was like a university — and like the Carnegie Institution of Washington and the Smithsonian — be-cause of its commitment to research. Although not explicitly spelled out, the assumption was that research was inherently altruistic. Thus in casting around for yet another example to clarify his position, Pine cited the *Journal of Bio-logical Chemistry*. "It seems to me," he wrote the tax lawyer, "that the ruling of the [State Tax] Department in the case of the Journal establishes a prece-dent which is applicable to the Research Corporation, and I suggest that you apply . . . for the exemption of the Research Corporation upon like grounds."[23]

Another example that similarly refrained from using the word "altruistic" but still sheds light on its meaning was British physicist Oliver Lodge's essay entitled "Public Service versus Private Expenditure." Although Lodge first presented his remarks as a speech in 1904, Cottrell came across them when they were published by the Fabian Society (a British organization promoting socialism).[24] Lodge's essay, Cottrell wrote to Linn Bradley, "gives a very inter-esting presentation of his ideas upon the same underlying principles on which the Research Corporation is built."[25] He did not indicate which passages of Lodge's essay most impressed him, but it is not hard to identify relevant pos-sibilities.

After explaining that he used the term "corporate" to mean a collective or community approach, Lodge stated his thesis:

> I wish to maintain that more good can be done and greater value
> attained by the thoughtful and ordered expenditure of corporate
> money, than can be derived from even a lavish amount distributed
> by private hands for the supply of personal comfort and the mainte-
> nance of special privileges.[26]

He also made it clear that he considered himself and his audience to be persons of limited means. Then he noted: "The only way probably you and I can
ever become wealthy is by becoming corporately wealthy, by clubbing our
savings and becoming an influence and a power in the land."[27] His examples
included projects that surely caught Cottrell's attention:

> A rich corporation, like a rich man, has great power. Suppose he
> wants to *bring out an invention*, his own or some one else's, he has
> the means. Suppose he wants to *build a laboratory* or endow a uni-
> versity, he can do it.... Without the wealth we are powerless. We
> see so many things that might be done if we had the means: for
> instance ... we would like to *suppress smoke and show how the air
> could be kept pure.* ...[28]

In effect, Research Corporation was founded to give persons of limited
means a way of "clubbing" their resources for the benefit of their community,
thereby fully justifying the designation "altruistic." But even in Cottrell's day
"altruistic" was a formal, ceremonious word. Could Research Corporation move
beyond mere ideology and actually implement its philanthropic goals? Could
the organization — with its strong commitment to business success — also be
made to function altruistically? These are questions to which we now turn.

Evaluating Patents

One of Research Corporation's main philanthropic goals was evaluating
new inventions, and during its early years it evaluated several. These included
John L. Malm's process for treating lead and zinc ores, Friedrich F. Friedmann's
tuberculosis treatment, Charles Marchand's technique for processing beef,
and J. H. G. Wolf's concrete railroad tie. Although none became a source of
additional revenue for Research Corporation, a look at the details is still in
order. On the one hand, the procedures that Research Corporation adopted to
evaluate these (and other) inventions illustrate the larger shift from inventing
as an individual activity to inventing as an organized activity. On the other
hand, the variety of inventions illustrates the complex world of practical re-

search at the turn of the century — the world in which Research Corporation sought to operate.

The main features of the evaluation process emerged rather quickly. As early as October 1912 Cottrell was able to answer a letter of inquiry in a way that sounded genuinely routine. While Research Corporation would give a preliminary screening to all inventions that were brought to its attention, some would be rejected without further consideration. For the others, the next step would be a formal evaluation by Research Corporation's board of directors. Specifically, Cottrell explained:

> ... the procedure has thus far been to refer [the ideas] to a Special Committee of two or three of the Directors who have looked into the advisability of the Corporation accepting the Patents. . . . This report will then be considered by the Executive Committee and finally by the Board, as a whole.[29]

One of the earliest ideas that Research Corporation considered was Malm's process of dry chlorination. Working near Denver and following a pattern not unlike Cottrell's early work on electrostatic precipitation, John L. Malm and his associates had already begun developing the process commercially. "Their plan," Cottrell wrote Walcott in November 1911:

> is to own the properties upon which they intend to operate the process themselves, but they are perfectly willing and desirous that it should be used elsewhere by others, and [they] are I understand ready to offer their patents for this purpose to the Smithsonian in the same way that we are offering ours.[30]

After Research Corporation was established, Cottrell continued to speak favorably of Malm's offer, and in April 1912 he wrote Walcott:

> On my way through Colorado I had opportunity to see Mr. Malm and several of his associates, and they are very much inclined to turn over a considerable part of their patent rights to the Research Corporation. . . . They have a plant about two-thirds completed at Georgetown, some 50 miles from Denver, in the heart of the complex ore region. They have spent about $60,000 in the construction thus far, and are now trying to raise the remaining $30,000 necessary for its completion, together with about as much more for operating expenses to get under way.

> I spent a day at the plant and went over it in pretty thorough
> detail, and was very favorably impressed with the substantial way
> in which it has been constructed thus far and the general good
> engineering sense which seems to have been displayed. I was also
> very favorably impressed with the personality of Mr. Malm and
> those of his associates who seemed to be really in control. I am
> inclined to think they deserve thorough encouragement. . . .[31]

Given the advanced state of the project, however, Walcott wondered if support
from Research Corporation was appropriate. "The Malm matter is an interesting one," he conceded, "but I think all questions involving the aid of enterprises that are [already] on a commercial basis will have to be handled carefully."[32]

Cottrell brought up the Malm process again the following year while lunch-
ing with Goetze.[33] Finally, Goetze found time to investigate the project himself. On a trip west in April 1914 he met Malm and was shown the facilities by
Malm's associate, Stanley A. Easton. After returning to New York, Goetze
reported favorably to the other members of the executive committee.[34]

While Research Corporation deliberated, however, Malm's situation
changed. Specifically, Cottrell wrote Goetze in June 1914 that the work site
had shifted from Colorado to Idaho:

> I am sorry that more definite action could not be taken by the
> Research Corporation in the matter of taking over the Malm pat-
> ents before the present work in Idaho got so well under way, as I
> am afraid that now it may be a rather delicate, if not difficult or
> impossible matter to carry out the plan originally proposed for the
> Research Corporation to secure the Idaho and Montana region.[35]

Cottrell then continued with an assessment of how he hoped Research
Corporation would function. In his eyes, the whole process of devising and
developing new technical ideas remained highly personal. What was needed
was an organization that could meet individual inventors on their own ground:

> I believe that no inconsiderable part of the Research
> Corporation's success is going to be measured by the purely psy-
> chological element of encouragement to the struggling inventor
> and promoter just at the time when a real cordial and hearty show
> of genuine interest in his undertaking will do him the most good.
> The difference . . . between Research Corporation and most other

business corporations should be that the former has a real personality of its own, and that any prospective donors should be made to
feel from the start that it is desired to include them as a part of
such personality as rapidly and as far as circumstances will permit. . . .[36]

From Cottrell's point of view, Research Corporation was too often decid-
ing to withhold the kind of support that he hoped it would freely give. As he
reminded Goetze, he knew quite well:

> that a number, if not the majority, of the Directors of the Research
> Corporation very frankly expressed the opinion . . . that they should
> go very cautiously in the diversion of any considerable energy or
> attention to new possibilities, while those already undertaken [no-
> tably, those involving electrostatic precipitation] were demanding
> as much effort as they naturally will for some time to come.[37]

Cottrell also knew how discouraging these deliberations appeared to Malm.
As he told Goetze, the inventor saw only "the delays, cold formalities or in-
definiteness of the correspondence"[38] — all of which undercut whatever psy-
chological boost Research Corporation might have offered.

Cottrell acknowledged that business organizations of the day often resisted the efforts of inventors to promote new ideas. Although he judged much
of that resistance to be appropriate, he insisted that Research Corporation
had been established to provide an alternative. Using metaphors drawn from
physics and biology, he wrote:

> Action is equal to reaction in mechanics, and the natural and
> necessary enthusiasm of the inventor seems almost infallibly to
> develop the corresponding antitoxine [*sic*] of skept[ic]ism in the
> successful man of business whenever the latter becomes "exposed."
> This is all right . . . , but in the case of the Research Corporation,
> much more than in most business organizations, it must not be-
> come too painfully apparent.[39]

As usual, Cottrell remained optimistic. After all, there remained Malm's
Canadian rights to consider. "I discussed this very briefly with Malm," he
reported to Goetze:

> . . . and told him that one of the main reasons that such a plan inter-

ested me was that it would again emphasize the international character of the movement. . . .

. . . if the [Research] Corporation could take on the Canadian territory, even in lieu of the northwestern states east to, say the Dakotas, it might be a very just and advantageous solution of the present problem.[40]

Yet the executive committee continued to drag its feet. In November 1914 they decided that Research Corporation was still in no position to invest in the Malm process.[41] Nevertheless, Cottrell kept up the pressure. In a letter to Walcott a few weeks later he raised the prospect of an agreement with Malm regarding northern Idaho, and — as had been the case with his letter to Goetze the previous June — he revealed some of his larger hopes for the organization.

Cottrell knew from experience that moving an invention from pilot plant to full-scale operation was a demanding challenge, and he was convinced that such efforts could be facilitated by the right kinds of organizations. Here, of course, he hoped that Research Corporation would play a role, but he never expected it to act alone. Nor did he expect the cooperative efforts to be restricted to partnerships with business organizations. Government organizations should also be encouraged to participate, and in the case of Malm's patent rights he explicitly had in mind the Bureau of Mines.

From Cottrell's point of view, Research Corporation was impeding these cooperative efforts. "In the case of the Malm patents," he explained to Walcott, "the delay in taking any action . . . has considerably embar[r]assed the work I have been trying to do for the Bureau of Mines in this district."[42] As in his earlier letter to Goetze, however, Cottrell remained optimistic. "Even now," he told Walcott:

> I am not at all sure that it would not be to their ultimate financial advantage to turn over Northern Idaho to the Research Corporation on account of the probability of establishment of a Bureau of Mines Experiment Station there in the very near future, and the considerably greater freedom with which the latter could probably push the investigation of these and allied processes if the rights to them in this district were not held in private hands.[43]

On January 15, 1915, the executive committee authorized Cottrell to pursue a possible agreement.[44] In the end, however, nothing resulted. This was apparently due as much to the limitations of the Malm process as to Research Corporation's preoccupation with electrostatic precipitation.[45]

' Nevertheless, he pro-

r American mining jour-
alm was then working)
909, *Mining and Scien-*
ared in 1914, when the
ompany purchased the
he equipment to Idaho.
ere positive, but a 1916
ngly of the opinion that
of anybody."[58]
empted to counter that
Bunker Hill and Sullivan,
arge:

nsideration; the
r busy. . . .
full charge for a

ot one man in evidence
perience in hydrometal-
."[60] In Malm's eyes, the
arlie Chaplin to shame.

ed Malm's process inde-
ut more than just under-
s judgment, the evalua-
something more was in-
Across the board, the

mes "miners learned to
und the turn of the cen-
, and larger-scale under-
hanged this system," so
t technological commu-
the dramatic success of
or copper, it was part of
knowledge in the mining
demonstrated the engi-

ition, the Malm process
rnals. The most notable
ngineering. It began in
Joys of Its Theory, Woes
er who served as presi-
02.[46] Chauvenet empha-
aded "every process in
tion, in solution."[47] The
tion, and along the way

et was concerned about
lly critical of scientists
neering practice. "It is
ion or a series of them,
transformations on the
apervision and product

e appealed for an even
ace and practical engi-
ickle field," he warned,
norant chemist, or the
or was a new breed of
designation Bleecker
n to be known as "unit
mastered these "stan-
ratory process to com-

esponse by Chauvenet
s references elicited a
rticle, he insisted that
nethod in its present
as even more combat-
n under the so-called
he subject. . . ."[53]
y, Bleecker defended
the information avail-
m's failure to publish
lished accounts "are
d been "deemed un-

wise on account of the status of patent applications."[
vided a short article describing the process.[56]

Accounts of Malm's process also appeared in othe
nals. When the Western Metals Company (for whom M
began building the experimental plant in Colorado in
tific Press described the project, and brief notices app
Bunker Hill and Sullivan Mining and Concentration (
plant.[57] Subsequently, Bunker Hill and Sullivan moved
Early reports in the *Engineering and Mining Journal* v
account concluded: "The [company's] staff is now strc
the process cannot be a commercial one in the hands

Malm and his associate, Stephen A. Ionides, att
negative assessment. Although they had been hired by l
Malm pointed out that they had not been placed in cl

> Few of my suggestions or protests received any c
> management seemed only concerned that I appe
>   I proposed that either I be permitted to assum
> stated period . . . or be fired. . . . I was fired.[59]

"At the time of our work," Ionides added, "there was
around the mine or mill who had had any previous ex
lurgy or even a good ordinary education in chemistry
result was a "general farce" that "would put even Cl
The process had no chance."[61]

As far as I can tell, Research Corporation evaluat
pendently of the evaluations in the mining journals. B
scoring the soundness of the executive committee'
tions in the mining journals also demonstrated that
volved than just the details of a particular process
character of American mining was changing.

As Kathleen H. Ochs has pointed out, in earlier
mine by working with experienced miners" but "[a]r
tury, automated tools, new ore-processing technique
ground and open-pit mining methods dramatically c
that "mining engineers gradually became the domina
nity."[62] Although the Malm process did not achieve
the cyanide process for gold or the flotation process
the larger trend toward greater reliance on scientific
industry. Thus the debate over the Malm process

neers' concerns regarding their professional status, not just vis-a-vis skilled miners (as Ochs has indicated) but also vis-a-vis laboratory chemists. Tensions among all these groups created strong cross currents for anyone seeking to evaluate or develop new inventions.

As revealing as the whole episode had been — of Cottrell's hopes as well as trends in engineering — Research Corporation's evaluation of the Malm process never advanced beyond the preliminary stage. Another such example involved an entirely different field. The field was medicine, and the example was a tuberculosis treatment proposed by Friedrich F. Friedmann.

Friedmann was a German medical doctor who claimed to have discovered, in turtles, a non-virulent tuberculosis bacillus suitable for human injections. Because tuberculosis was a serious health concern, the public eagerly grasped at possible new treatments. Thus *The New York Times* placed on the front page of its November 7, 1912, issue a short article describing Friedmann's announcement at a Berlin Medical Society meeting.[63] After that, coverage mushroomed. For example, the account of his arrival in America in February 1913 took the entire first column of the front page and continued on the second page.[64]

Despite strong popular interest in Friedman's treatment, New York City's medical and public health community insisted that the German doctor would have to follow established procedures. At first there seemed to be two ways for him to inoculate American patients legally: he could obtain a special visiting physician's license or he could serve as a consulting physician — without pay — at an established hospital. After due consideration, however, the city's board of health decided it would "not permit him to administer his treatment in any of the hospitals or clinics under its jurisdiction."[65]

Friedmann's situation struck Cottrell as providing an excellent opportunity for Research Corporation to offer assistance. Accordingly, he wrote Walcott on March 6, 1913:

> I have noted with considerable interest . . . the newspaper reports of the work being done by Dr. F. F. Friedmann . . . particularly as the accounts spoke of his having applied for patents both in Europe and America and that he explained this as well as his reluctance to publish details as yet by the statement that it was done primarily to protect the public from unscrupulous exploitation and not in the first instance at least for his own personal gain. As this seemed to indicate just the attitude which the Research Corporation was founded to encourage and develope [sic], I intended to send him . . . some of the literature and call his attention to the

movement, when I suddenly noticed that he had come to New York.

I made some inquiries here among the medical profession and our university medical staffs to find if they took his work seriously or whether it was merely newspaper talk, but those whom I have seen were much in the dark as yet. Of course, his failure to publish anything in recognized medical journals coupled with the prominence the work has received in the public press is not in accord with accepted procedure in medical circles. At the same time, they point out that the general direction in which Dr. Friedmann claims to have attained success is one of the most logical from which to expect new results and that ... the present practical results which he claims and which he has not published would be the rational development of ... earlier published work.

The enclosed clipping from yesterday's San Francisco Bulletin made me bestir myself more actively in the matter. On consulting with some of our university staff last night, I found that they felt this was preeminently a place where Research Corporation could be of great value by offering its services in the matter of administration under such terms and through such channels (as for example, The New York Board of Health, The New York County Medical Society, or, perhaps, best of all, The American Medical Society, or one of its committees) as would make the acceptance or the rejection of the offer clearly determine[d] for the medical public in a way that would obviate further discussion [of] just where Dr. Friedmann and his work stood in the light of professional ethics.[66]

Walcott, in turn, consulted Scott, who replied less favorably:

Mr. [Linn] Bradley and I have discussed this with Mr. [J. B.] Pine, and he states that certain physicians in town, with whom he talked last night, did not think that Dr. Friedman[n] has conducted himself in an ethical and professional way in the matter and there is considerable doubt as to whether he had anything of value. We therefore think, that at this time it will be best to allow these matters to develop in their natural course, and if at some future time it apparently becomes desirable for us to intervene and offer our aid, that we do so.[67]

Apparently Walcott accepted Scott's advice. But Cottrell was reluctant to let the matter drop. Writing Walcott again on March 24, 1913, he explained his more general view (which was similar to the one he also expressed in Malm's case):

> ... that the Research Corporation's opportunities for securing new inventions of importance are going to depend, in perhaps the majority of cases, on its willingness and ability to go into the serious, unprejudiced, but withal friendly and sympathetic, investigation of new discoveries or inventions at a time when this would be most appreciated by their inventors; that is, before they are being taken too seriously or favorably by the public.[68]

Finally, at the very end of the month Cottrell wrote directly to Friedmann, to acquaint him with Research Corporation. He then informed Bradley:

> I am enclosing you herewith [a] copy of [the] letter which I have just written to Dr. Friedmann, as from what you wrote I felt this might perhaps be the best way to get in touch with the situation while at the same time relieving the Research Corporation from taking the initiative. You will notice I have written purely as an individual. I hesitated some time to do even this, but as nothing that I have heard up to date indicated that anything at all was being done toward even looking into the Friedmann matter, I concluded that other affairs were entirely absorbing the available energy and so wrote the enclosed to try to help out.[69]

Although Cottrell remained optimistic "that something of value to the [Research] [C]orporation may still come of this matter," he also wrote Bradley in mid-April 1913 that he understood "the desire of the directors to avoid having the Corporation drawn into any objectionable publicity."[70] Soon afterward, however, the whole situation changed in a way that precluded Research Corporation's involvement. In late April *The New York Times* reported that Friedmann had sold his American rights to the Eisner-Mendelson Company — for $125,000 in cash and $1,800,000 in stock in thirty-six proposed "Friedrich F. Friedmann Institutes" (which would administer his tuberculosis treatment for a fee). The problem was that Friedmann never succeeded in overcoming the skepticism of local public health officials. Thus *The New York Times* reported toward the end of May 1913 that the city had just altered its sanitary code to prohibit the use of live bacilli in human inoculations, which immediately forced the first Friedmann Institute to close its doors. A few weeks later Friedmann returned to Germany.[71]

Despite Research Corporation's limited involvement in both the Malm process and the Friedmann treatment, the cases clearly illustrate the complex world in which Research Corporation operated. Included in that world were engineers and medical doctors, scientists and inventors, vigorous public debates and behind-the-scenes discussions, struggles for professional status and difficult technical problems. The two cases are also useful because they reveal the hopes that Cottrell had for Research Corporation. In effect, he sought to replace himself, as an individual, with a philanthropic organization of a very particular sort. Just as his research colleagues had learned to "ask Cot" about their projects, knowing that he would give freely of his ideas, so Cottrell hoped that Research Corporation would facilitate new developments in science and technology by offering timely advice and support.[72]

Having said all that, however, the fact remains that neither the Malm process nor the Friedmann treatment involved the full set of steps in Research Corporation's evaluation process. Although the Malm process survived the initial screening, it was never really taken seriously by the directors, and the Friedmann treatment failed even to survive the initial screening. Thus we must look elsewhere for good examples of full evaluations.

'Meatox' and Concrete Ties

During the spring of 1912 Walcott received a letter from Charles Marchand, a French chemist living in the United States. Marchand wrote that he had developed a concentrated protein source, a dried preparation of beef fiber that he called "Meatox." After several years of experimentation and expenditures totaling nearly $65,000, he was confident that the product was ready for commercial manufacture. The main problem was the high cost of advertising needed to bring it to market. At the suggestion of General W. H. Forwood (a retired army surgeon whom Marchand considered "one of my intimate friends") he approached Walcott.[73] Marchand reasoned that if the Smithsonian were to conduct the commercial introduction of Meatox, its august reputation would likely circumvent the need for an expensive advertising campaign.

Marchand indicated his willingness to give the Smithsonian the rights to his process. Although his letter to Walcott did not provide technical details, the main feature of the process was the use of hydrogen peroxide as a sterilizer. Hydrogen peroxide had been discovered early in the nineteenth century by the French chemist Louis-Jacques Thenard. At the turn of the century, Marchand developed a way to manufacture it in quantity and began experimenting with it to produce a concentrated protein source.[74]

Walcott was interested, but instead of having the Smithsonian act directly, he forwarded Marchand's letter to Linn Bradley in New York. That referral showed how Walcott hoped Research Corporation would function. As he explained to Marchand, the company "has been recently organized to attend to such matters for the Institution."[75]

Bradley advised Walcott that if Research Corporation were given Marchand's patent rights, several different approaches would be possible: the company could turn around and sell the rights; it could negotiate licenses with another company or companies; or it could itself undertake to manufacture the product. Because of the time and money involved, Bradley recommended against the last approach.[76] Marchand, in turn, resisted the idea of having some other company manufacture his product. He wrote directly to Bradley:

> Regarding your remark that it might be preferable to have the preparation made by a reliable manufacturing chemist, who should pay you a royalty, I will call your attention to the fact that every one of them has a so-called concentrated food of his own to push, and although they are worthless as far as protein content is concerned, yet they sell at a very high price.[77]

Meanwhile, as Goetze later reported at a board of directors meeting, Research Corporation decided to explore the commercial prospects for Meatox via a subcommittee consisting of Walcott and Little.[78] Their first step was to distribute samples for testing. Walcott gave some to C. F. Langworthy, a chemist and chief of nutrition investigation at the U.S. Department of Agriculture (in the Office of Experiment Stations). Little gave some to David L. Edsall, a medical doctor at Harvard and at the Massachusetts General Hospital in Boston. And Goetze gave some to N. B. Foster, a medical doctor at Columbia and at New York Hospital. In addition, Little gave samples to members of his laboratory staff and Walcott gave some to his son, who was suffering from the advanced stages of tuberculosis. The initial results were not wholly favorable. Walcott reported that his samples tasted bad, and Little offered a similar observation. But Marchand was confident that such problems could be eliminated.[79]

For his part, Cottrell facilitated the process through informal discussions as he traveled. In August 1912 he talked with Torald H. Sollmann, professor of pharmacology at Western Reserve Medical Center in Cleveland, and in October he talked with W. F. O'Hara at the Nutrition Laboratory of the Carnegie Institution of Washington in Boston.[80] His efforts in California were even more extensive. In early March 1913 he described to Walcott some recent experiments with Meatox by the Berkeley chemist Henry C. Biddle, relating to the problems of odor and taste. In mid-April he reported to Bradley a discussion about the product's usefulness with M. E. Jaffa, a chemist at Berkeley who specialized in nutrition and who also served as director of the state's food and drug lab. Finally, after several tries, in August he met with Walter C. Alvarez, a promising young internist in San Francisco who later became a leading physician at the Mayo Clinic.[81]

Research Corporation carried out its evaluation of Meatox in a highly charged atmosphere. The overall shift of the American economy from farming to manufacturing brought with it an unprecedented reliance on processed food and drugs. As consumer concerns over food and drug purity increased, the issue became a central feature of the Progressive Movement. The issue was apparent to Marchand, who wrote Cottrell:

> The mere fact that the country is loaded with a lot of fake concentrated foods and invalid foods of all kinds and denominations justifies the S[mithsonian] I[nstitution] in taking up the matter in their hands so as to establish the real value of the Sterilized B[eef] F[iber] for the good of the unsophisticated public, even including some unsophisticated MDs whom [sic] believe that some Peptonized foods are really as represented by their manufacturers.[82]

Writing to Little, Edsall made similar remarks, pointing out how the "food and patent medicine people have bamboozled the sick public, in part through doctors."[83]

Also complicating the evaluation process was the popular image of inventors. Rapid technological change during the preceding decades had placed inventors very much in the public eye. Of course, such attention was often positive. Thus Thomas Edison had been dubbed "the Wizard of Menlo Park," and Cottrell himself could be portrayed along similar lines — so that *The New York Sun* called him the "Smoke Wizard."[84] But the public could also view inventors negatively, as eccentrics or crackpots (or, even worse, as fakirs, charlatans, or quacks).

Cottrell's organizational skills and formal scientific training kept him situated on the positive end of the wizard–crackpot spectrum. As a result, he was able not only to win personal credibility with people such as Walcott but also to influence their perception of other inventors. For example, when the Belgian-born chemist and inventor Leo H. Baekeland was being considered as a possible director of Research Corporation, Cottrell offered a positive assessment:

> Dr. Baekeland is a man of the highest and broadest ideals, with tremendous energy, and knows the patent and technical develop-

ment business from A to Z. He is looked upon, I know, as rather eccentric by many, but I think this is due largely to his perpetual overflow of energy and good humor and it has been my observation that he never lets this interfere with business matters.[85]

Baekeland's ties to Research Corporation went back to the formative months of late 1911 and early 1912, so that Cottrell also noted to Walcott:

You will remember he was one who took a very kindly interest in the work when we were framing the organization, but [he] insisted . . . that his own business; namely, the founding of the General Baekelite Company was driving him so hard . . . that he could not consider taking any formal place upon the new staff.[86]

E. H. Hooker's ties to Baekeland went back even further, to the time when Baekeland helped him develop the Townsend-Sperry process. Thus in 1916, on the occasion of Baekeland's receipt of the Perkin Medal, Hooker offered a flattering, decidedly non-crackpot assessment.[87]

As for Marchand, he was fully aware of the wizard–crackpot spectrum, having already been "burned" by its negative end. Thus one account of his work with hydrogen peroxide noted:

When he had perfected his methods he proudly and joyfully wrote to his former colleagues in France and told them of his plans. His chagrin may be imagined when they wrote to him urging that he not speak seriously of his plans because they believed that people would consider him mentally unbalanced. This rebuff wounded him beyond power to express himself.[88]

In order to succeed with Walcott and the other Research Corporation directors, Marchand had to keep himself on the positive end of the spectrum, and at first all went well. Thus Walcott wrote Cottrell in October 1912 that "Dr. Marchand appears to be genuinely interested in having the R[esearch] C[orporation] develop and profit from his sterilized beef fibre preparation."[89] But then the French chemist took steps that moved him toward the negative end. Specifically, he pushed his ideas too hard and he asked for a salary. As a result, by January 1913 Walcott was losing patience. "I have written Dr. Goetze this morning," he confided to Cottrell, "that I think Marchand is either rattleheaded or very hard up."[90]

Cottrell did what he could to smooth things over. In a letter to Marchand, he frankly explained the first mistake:

> I am afraid that your enthusiasm for a rapid development of the work may already have lead [*sic*] to some misinterpretation of your letter East. . . .
>
> I know from my own experience how very easily these misinterpretations come about and how excessively careful, often to what may appear to be a foolish degree, one must be to avoid them when dealing with a quasi-public organization as in this case.[91]

To Walcott he offered an equally frank assessment of Marchand's request for a salary:

> I find it a little hard to know just how to take him. I think the broader purposes of the movement are what have honestly appealed to him and that if he felt himself financially independent, as I think we all first assumed that he was, he might very likely have waived all consideration of return or compensation for himself. . . .[92]

Little concurred, noting that Marchand's salary request threw doubts on "the merit and field of his preparation."[93] Along different lines, Scott also voiced criticism:

> From my conversation . . . I should judge that Dr. Marchand had looked upon the Research Corporation more in the nature of an organization to put its official stamp of approval on "Meatox" and to assist in its development in such a way that it would be commercially profitable to Dr. Marchand . . . rather than from the view-point of an out and out gift to the Research Corporation for the benefit of science, etc.[94]

In the end, however, Meatox received a thorough and balanced evaluation. As noted, samples of the product were distributed to several reputable researchers for evaluation. Careful attention was also given to how the product might be manufactured. Here the initial focus was the cost of a full-scale production plant. Specifically, in June 1912 Cottrell suggested forming a subsidiary corporation, with independent capitalization in the range of $50,000 to $100,000. A few months later the focus shifted to a more modest level, at which time Cottrell suggested an appropriation of $5,000 for experiments to enable Research Corporation to make a sound decision about full-scale production.[95]

Meanwhile, the subcommittee attempted to gauge the product's commercial prospects, and it was here that their greatest doubts emerged. "To me the important question is that of a market," Walcott explained to Goetze in April 1914: "It seems to me that the Meatox can be made at a reasonable cost, but what has prevented my pushing the matter is our inability to obtain any satisfactory statement that there would be such a demand for the Meatox as to make it a commercial success."[96] Soon thereafter Little wrote that he too had concluded "that it is undesirable for the Research Corporation to undertake the development and introduction of this material," stating:

> Dr. Edsall regards its value as problematical, and I cannot see how it would be as good for convalescents as very finely chopped raw meat. . . . The cost of production is very high and much advertising, and a considerable organization would be required to develop any large business.[97]

Accordingly, toward the end of April 1914 the executive committee accepted Walcott and Little's report, decided against accepting Marchand's offer, and discharged the subcommittee.[98]

Although it did not lead Research Corporation to another profitable patent, Marchand's invention was successfully evaluated: some of the firm's directors agreed to assume responsibility for making the evaluation; they proceeded along lines fully consistent with Cottrell's preference for obtaining the voluntary services of qualified individuals; and they remained sensitive to the firm's economic realities, as well as its altruistic ideology. But clearly it was a cumbersome process that could not be used for more than a handful of inventions at any one time.

A consideration of the directors' role makes the limitations of the process especially clear. Because of Research Corporation's commitment to electrostatic precipitation, its salaried personnel were in no position to assist — at least not to any great extent. Instead, responsibility for conducting the evaluations rested primarily on the shoulders of the directors themselves. But often they too had their hands full. For example, Walcott once wrote Cottrell: "Just now I am very much occupied with various matters pertaining to the [Smithsonian] [I]nstitution, so much so that I can hardly concentrate upon the scheme for working out the business side of the Meatox matter."[99] More generally, Walcott once noted for the benefit of someone whom he hoped to recruit for Research Corporation: "All of the Directors are very busy men."[100]

Another invention that illustrated how the evaluation process worked — and how it depended on the efforts of "very busy men" — was a railroad tie made of reinforced concrete. The inventor was J. H. G. Wolf, a construction engineer with a baccalaureate from the University of Delaware. After meeting Wolf in April 1912, Cottrell wrote Walcott that he was "very favorably impressed with his personality and point of view" and that he saw the project as an opportunity for "coöperation with the Railroads and the cement factories on the one side and the departments of civil engineering in our colleges on the other."[101]

In May 1912 the executive committee authorized Bradley to begin the evaluation process. Wolf himself attended their meeting in December 1912 to offer Research Corporation his patent rights in the northeastern states. Hooker agreed to serve as a subcommittee of one to study the matter further, and at the executive committee meeting in June 1913 he reported that he "favored getting the Railroad Companies, and the principal Cement Companies of the United States to subscribe to a fund for experimenting on ties."[102]

What Hooker had in mind can be seen in a draft document entitled "Agreement for Special Research upon the Problem of Concrete Ties." The document emphasized the need for collaboration, noting that "it is often a burden for a lone organization to conduct a thorough and exhaustive research upon a specific problem."[103] In Hooker's view, Research Corporation's distinctive character made it well suited to lead a cooperative effort involving railroad and cement companies. According to his proposal, each participating company would contribute $1,000 per year to support the work of a special committee of three Research Corporation directors. In return, each company would receive a copy of the committee's final report and would have access to the records of the committee's work. If patentable ideas emerged, Research Corporation would retain ownership, but each participant would be authorized to use them.

By late 1914, tests of Wolf's tie at the Riverside Portland Cement Company were yielding positive results. Nevertheless, Hooker began having second thoughts about the project's scale. At the November executive committee meeting he reported that it might take as long as three years and cost as much as $100,000 — and even then Wolf's tie might not end up being the true solution.[104]

On the strength of Hooker's proposal, the executive committee increased the size of the concrete tie subcommittee to include (along with Hooker) Walcott and a newly elected director, William Barclay Parsons — a Columbia alumnus and a civil engineer with extensive experience in railroad construction.[105] Parsons was a key figure in their plan to convince several major railroad companies to test the tie, but in March 1915 he wrote Walcott a letter of desperation. "I have so much outside work to do," he confessed, "that I am getting to a point where I am stalled"— adding:

> I joined the Research Corporation and the first thing that hap-
> pened to me there was to be put on the Executive Committee and
> on this Tie Committee.
> I will try and get along with it, but I am afraid it is simply a
> physical impossibility.[106]

Walcott's prompt reply made it clear that he viewed overwork as a very real occupational hazard for people such as Parsons and himself:

> I have noted with considerable apprehension during the winter
> that you had a tired, worn look that is not well in a man of your age.
> I do not believe in cutting out and running, but there comes a time
> in every man's life when he must decide whether he will be an
> effective force for the remaining portion of his life or break down
> and become a burden to himself and to all interests with which he
> is connected.[107]

In the end, Parsons stuck to the project, but it fell through anyway, because Research Corporation could not convince enough major railroad companies to help with the tests. Although some of the Eastern railroads expressed interest, upon further consideration they decided that the availability of wooden ties was not as big a problem as they first thought. In the case of the Western railroads, their interest had never been especially strong. For example, one official wrote Walcott in mid-May 1915 to say that Research Corporation's proposal "appears to me altogether too vague and the results too speculative to justify any substantial expenditure by the Southern Pacific Company."[108]

The initial interest of the railroads was rooted in their concerns about the continued availability of inexpensive wooden ties. In her 1971 study, Sherry H. Olson assessed how valid the possibility of a timber shortage really was.[109] All along, the predominant material of America's railroads had been wood as much as iron. Wooden ties quickly came into widespread use and usually needed replacing every six or seven years. During the late nineteenth century, railroads studied various alternatives, but as long as new regions (and their stands of timber) were still being added to the overall system, railroads continued to use wooden ties. Early in the new century, railroad executives became concerned about a possible timber shortage, and they joined with forestry officials to call for conservation measures. However, by 1915 the successful treatment of wooden ties with creosote (which increased their longevity) caused railroads to begin a wholesale changeover, and a true timber shortage never materialized. Thus the solution for the railroads lay not with increasing their wood supply (though that continued to be the aim of forestry officials). Nor did it lie in adopting a new material for ties such as reinforced concrete. Instead, the railroads solved their problem by changing the character of their demand.

Although Olson did not mention Wolf's tie by name, she did discuss concrete ties generally. Her analysis demonstrated that inventions like Wolf's were being evaluated on the basis of systematic research. After several decades of dramatic growth, American railroads had emerged as the nation's primary transportation system. Thus a 1915 handbook on railroad maintenance noted: "Railroad development in this country has reached a stage where it is intensive rather than extensive, and the young engineer is probably more concerned with the study of the improvement of existing lines than the laying out of new roads."[110] With a mature system in place, railroad engineers could no longer proceed "along empirical lines" but would have to turn to "more scientific methods."[111]

The need for systematic research was not lost on Walcott. Even after Parsons became a director, Walcott shared with Scott his conviction that Research Corporation should seek yet another director with the ability to handle new developments in railroad technology: "I think ... we should elect some first-class engineer who understands the maintenance and operation of railways, including electrical operation, if possible."[112] He also explained to railroad executive Julius Kruttschnitt that Research Corporation sought "a man who has expert knowledge of the maintenance and operation of railway lines."[113]

Late in 1914, Otto H. Kahn — a leading member of the banking firm of Kuhn, Loeb, and Company and a financial advisor to railroad tycoon Edward H. Harriman — agreed to become a Research Corporation director. In his letter of acceptance Kahn indicated that his existing commitments would not permit him to take an especially active role. But he expressed his hope that circumstances would at least enable him "to be of some modest service."[114]

Like Walcott, Hooker had a clear vision of what was required for researching the concrete tie. In his case, he emphasized the need "to employ experts and establish a laboratory [at a university] to make a study of the tie situation which would be broad enough to include concrete ties, steel ties, wooden ties or composite ties."[115]

But Research Corporation was not in a position to supervise so comprehensive an effort. Its own engineering staff was largely dedicated to electrostatic precipitation, and its directors faced definite limits to their time. Finally, even if Wolf's concrete tie had succeeded in generating wider interest, Research Corporation lacked the capital required for full-scale development.

Supporting Research

Cottrell's participation in the concrete tie discussions was far less extensive than in the case of Meatox. In 1912 he conferred with Wolf personally regarding tests in California, and in early 1913 he reported to Walcott: "I saw Mr. Wolf a few days ago just as he was leaving for Los Angeles to supervise the definite arrangement for the construction of the first lot of experimental concrete ties."[116] After that his attention was drawn elsewhere, "due to the subject's less intimate connection with the Bureau of Mines' own immediate work."[117]

Yet whenever appropriate, Cottrell voiced the general challenge that Research Corporation faced in bringing new inventions to market. At the same time that Meatox was being evaluated he wrote Walcott:

> While I fully appreciate the difficulties and discouragements we have thus far unearthed in investigating the subject, I do not, by any means, consider these as conclusive. . . . We must expect that most of the matters that come to the Research Corporation will be in a relatively early stage of development, and the success of the Corporation itself will depend largely upon the thoroughness and sagacity used in sifting these and in finding the proper channels for their development.[118]

Walcott likewise recognized the scope of the challenge, writing to Marchand in 1916 that "the development of an idea through the experimental stage to a practical business proposition, is usually a long and expensive process. . . ."[119]

In Marchand's eyes, however, Research Corporation was not fully achieving its philanthropic goal. After the firm decided not to pursue Meatox, he turned his attention to the new problem of processing the liquid wastes generated by wood pulp mills that used the sulfite paper-making process. Fully expecting his latest invention to be commercially successful, he wrote Walcott that he and his co-workers had drawn up an agreement whereby the net income resulting from the invention would be given away once the total reached a million dollars. "When I drew up this binding agreement," he noted:

> I had in mind the Research Corporation as being handicapped in their good work by the limited amount of cash at their disposal,

and you may expect that as soon as I will have closed the deals with
all the sulphite pulp factories, you will be welcome to let me know
what the Research Corporation needs at any time to help along
deserving inventors to complete their inventions at our expense.[120]

Thus Marchand viewed Research Corporation as an admirable attempt that had
fallen short of its intended aim — at least in the case of evaluating inventions.

Much the same conclusion holds true in the case of Research Corporation's
other philanthropic goal, namely, supporting scientific research. Not until the
latter part of 1914 (when the firm's financial situation improved) did the directors begin giving the matter serious attention. Even then they decided that
Research Corporation would base its grants not on profits directly but on the
interest generated by invested profits.

Alternative arrangements were occasionally considered. At a meeting of
the executive committee in November 1915, for example, J. Hennen Jennings
proposed that Research Corporation establish "a department to help municipalities clear up the atmosphere within their boundaries" by approaching the
Carnegie Corporation or other large philanthropic organizations for the necessary funds.[121] The aim of such a department, Jennings noted, would be "to
coordinate the activities of said municipalities . . . and render engineering service at cost plus a reasonable addition for overhead expenses."[122] Yet a consensus remained for Research Corporation to act solely on the basis of its
own resources. Thus Otto Kahn commented at the directors meeting in February 1917 that "he did not believe in soliciting gifts to the Corporation, as it
was unique and inspiring for an eleemosynary institution to be run at a
profit. . . ."[123]

Initially Research Corporation concentrated on applying electrostatic precipitation to meet industrial needs. Other applications were certainly possible. The most notable was the Mellon Institute's emphasis on cleaning up
urban air, and we have just seen how Jennings suggested that Research Corporation do likewise. But the firm continued to focus on industrial needs,
especially those of the metallurgical industry.[124]

Cottrell's preference was for a broader approach. He conceded that some
of the firm's profits could be used for research to benefit the metallurgical
industry, but he reminded Walcott that he had never intended Research Corporation to have such a narrow focus. Nor had he meant the firm to operate
purely as a business:

I realize that it has probably been hard for many of the friends of
the movement and even perhaps for some of the Directors of the

Research Corporation itself to realize always that the mere making of money, no matter for how worthy a cause, was not the sole or perhaps in the end the largest opportunity for good before the Research Corporation. . . .[125]

Generally speaking, Cottrell's preferences were still held in high regard. For example, in the discussion that followed a talk Bradley gave in 1913, O. P. Hood (the chief mechanical engineer at the Bureau of Mines) commented on Cottrell's gift of patent rights: "I wish here to express my deep admiration of the altruistic scheme which is expressed in this Research Corporation."[126] A more prominent instance came during A. D. Little's 1913 presidential address to the American Chemical Society, when he cited both Cottrell and Research Corporation as illustrating "the ideals of service which inspire our profession."[127]

But the most dramatic recognition came on January 15, 1915, when the American Institute of Mining Engineers, the American Electrochemical Society, and the Mining and Metallurgical Society of America co-sponsored a dinner in Cottrell's honor at New York's Plaza Hotel. The evening's toastmaster, Sidney J. Jennings, praised Cottrell as "a very practical idealist"; Walcott made similar remarks; and William L. Saunders (who represented the American Institute of Mining Engineers) described Cottrell's gift of patent rights as "a great service to mankind" and "a wholesome example to present and future generations."[128] Research Corporation's board of directors also made their views known. In an official citation distributed at the dinner they noted: "It was Dr. Cottrell's ideal to render discovery[-]already[-]made the mother of new discovery, and thus contribute to the scientific and technical development of the industrial arts."[129]

Only slowly, however, did Research Corporation implement its goal of supporting research, and its earliest steps emphasized the study of electrostatic precipitation. In November 1915 the executive committee authorized the firm's engineering staff to spend $5,000 for "investigation and experimentation" regarding "the principles in electrical precipitation."[130] Modest support along these same lines was continued in later years, but Hooker resisted expanding the firm's "in-house" research (as in the case of Little's proposal for a more ambitious program at a newly constructed laboratory).

Also at its November meeting the executive committee authorized $1,200 to support the work on fog dispersal that Cottrell had already begun. Years before, Lodge had tried unsuccessfully to use electrostatic precipitation on fog. The problem also interested Cottrell, but not until the Panama-Pacific International Exposition of 1915 did he focus on it.[131]

After establishing the Bureau of Mines' laboratory in San Francisco, Cottrell's main responsibility was assisting the Anaconda Smelter Commission in its investigations. Despite regular trips to Washington, D.C., he did not move there until 1916. That meant he was still in California to help with the Bureau's exhibits for the world's fair that celebrated the opening of the Panama Canal.[132] For him the main opportunity of the fair was access to a million-volt transformer. Had the equipment operated successfully (it never achieved full voltage), fog dispersal might have been one of the fair's most dramatic attractions. Instead, the project was more low-keyed. As the fair drew to a close, the technical details were left in the hands of Kenneth V. Laird under the direction of H. F. Fischer, a Research Corporation engineer.[133]

Despite the early focus on electrostatic precipitation, Research Corporation continued to evaluate other projects. In mid-November 1914, for example, Cornell physical chemist Hector R. Carveth wrote Little to ask that Research Corporation consider making a grant to defray the annual deficit of the *Journal of Physical Chemistry*. Since the journal's founding in 1896 its annual deficits had been met by its editor, Wilder D. Bancroft. But, explained Carveth: "This year he is unable to face the certainty of the deficit; the war has cut off his income."[134] Carveth then reported that Cornell had promised to contribute $750, "if a similar amount can be raised from other sources."[135] He also suggested two possibilities: those who had long been loyal supporters of the journal, or Research Corporation.

Adequate funding for research publications was a timely problem.[136] Rather than become known as a source of publication funds, however, Research Corporation drew a firm line. At their meeting in November 1914 the board of directors resolved "that said Corporation shall not undertake to subsidize Journals or Proceedings not the result of its own activities."[137]

Yet Carveth's request was not ignored. For example, Pine wrote to Little the following day:

> An institution known as "The Wistar Institute of Anatomy and Biology" of Philadelphia, which was organized under a Deed of Trust has a considerable fund which it is able to devote to the publication of scientific journals. In 1908 I drew an agreement between the Institute and the Journal of Experimental Zoology whereby the Institute undertook the publication of the Journal, leaving its management in the hands of its Board of Editors, and I think it possible that the officers of the Institute might be willing to make a similar arrangement in regard to the Journal of Physical Chemistry.[138]

Also writing to Little, Walcott suggested that companies benefiting from research in physical chemistry should be asked to support the journal.[139] In a letter to Charles L. Parsons, who had been secretary of the American Chemical Society since 1907, Walcott added another possibility: "I talked with one of the leading chemists that I met after leaving here, and he said that in his judgment it would be better to merge the Journal of Physical Chemistry into the Journal of the National Chemical Society."[140]

Although Little favored the idea of seeking support from business firms, Parsons did not and quickly replied:

> I feel a delicacy in going out to the chemical industry asking for subscriptions to continue the Journal of Physical Chemistry, as I imagine that Professor Bancroft having been a wealthy man and carried this Journal himself for eighteen years might not like to have his present financial condition too extensively advertised.[141]

Parsons also responded negatively to the idea of combining Bancroft's journal with the *Journal of the American Chemical Society*, because it would entail increasing the subscription list to include all 7,100 members of the American Chemical Society.[142]

In his book on the early history of physical chemistry in the United States, John W. Servos has emphasized another problem with the merger. Bancroft believed that his journal's approach differed from the approach of the physical chemists who served as referees for the *Journal of the American Chemical Society*. Bancroft emphasized the field's ties to chemistry, while the referees for the *Journal of the American Chemical Society* emphasized its ties to physics — and their views were gaining the upper hand.[143] As a result, Bancroft chose to retain control of his journal until the early 1930s, when the Great Depression finally forced him to give it up.[144]

A Fellowship Program

Bolder implementation of Cottrell's eleemosynary hopes for Research Corporation did not come about until 1916. Writing Cottrell in January, Scott identified what he saw as the main barrier to progress, namely, that "the ideal [of public service], unless formulated in concrete terms, is very difficult to incorporate in the every day activities of an organization such as ours, which has commercial dealings with other business organizations."[145] Cottrell replied that he well understood the problems associated with turning ideals into policy:

> Answering your more specific questions as to suggestions for

[a] "mechanism" calculated to guard any particular set of ideals in an organization of this kind: I doubt it being very safe to lay the emphasis on this end of the problem. Ideals are a little too evanescent to get at in that way.[146]

Finally, in December 1916 Pine proposed an annual research fellowship amounting to $2,500, "analogous to those offered on similar competition by the American Academy in Rome in architecture, sculpture, and painting."[147] The idea was discussed at the board of directors meeting in February 1917, at which time Walcott expressed his concern, drawn from his experience with the Carnegie philanthropies, that "it was very hard to make proper allotments of money and difficult to get results. . . ."[148] Nevertheless, the directors decided in favor of the idea and referred it to the executive committee for action.[149]

Writing to Hooker, Cottrell expressed his reservations. Noting that the jury for awarding the proposed fellowship would be composed of officers from several national professional societies, Cottrell pointed out that convening such a jury to evaluate applications would be difficult. Another problem was that exclusive reliance on American societies diminished the international scope he preferred. Finally, he felt uncomfortable with having Research Corporation, which still functioned primarily as a business organization, so closely involved with a philanthropic program. Instead, he suggested that the firm divert some of its profits to the Smithsonian and let them administer the fellowship program — at least the first time around.[150]

By the time Cottrell raised his objections, however, plans for the fellowship program were too far advanced to permit major changes. As announced in the August 10, 1917, issue of *Science*, the fellowship was offered "[f]or the purpose of encouraging scientific research directed to the development of the industrial arts."[151] Applications were due by October 1, and the award was to be made before the year was out.

By mid-November 1917 Scott had forwarded the applications to Walcott, who served on the jury in a dual capacity as president of the National Academy of Sciences and as Secretary of the Smithsonian. To help assess the various projects, Walcott enlisted Paul Bartsch, a curator at the Smithsonian's Museum of Natural History and a professor of zoology at George Washington University. Bartsch, in turn, "interviewed specialists in the various Government bureaus."[152] In mid-November, after the applications had been returned with comments by practitioners in the appropriate fields, Walcott wrote Scott recommending two of them and suggesting that the applications be sent to the other jury members. Julius Stieglitz, who chaired the chemistry department at the University of Chicago and who served on the jury as president of the American Chemical Society, agreed with Walcott's recommendations. So did Hooker (who served on the jury as president of Research Corporation), although he added two more names to the list of finalists.[153]

In mid-December 1917 the jury settled upon Philip E. Edelman as their first choice. Edelman was a twenty-three-year-old resident of St. Paul, Minnesota, who had received a bachelor of science degree in electrical engineering from the University of Minnesota in 1916. His proposed project was a study of how atmospheric electricity affected radio communications. In their assessment, S. W. Stratton and L. W. Austin at the National Bureau of Standards acknowledged the project's importance but noted that many other researchers were pursuing similar projects. "Great results," they concluded, "can hardly be expected unless the applicant conducts his work in some large laboratory, such as those of the Government, or that at Harvard, where he can be in contact with men working along parallel lines."[154]

Edelman agreed to pursue his project in any laboratory that Research Corporation recommended, and he participated in the effort to locate the best site. Scott reported to Walcott that Michael Pupin (who had served on the jury as chairman of the Engineering Foundation) recommended Columbia.[155] But Walcott preferred the Bureau of Standards in Washington.[156] Edelman himself leaned toward Columbia. He had recently visited Harvard and the Bureau of Standards, and he reported both to be "well taken up with training of naval operators and military equipment."[157]

Recognizing how crowded the East Coast laboratories were becoming, Walcott then suggested that Edelman stay at the University of Minnesota, but war mobilization efforts soon reached there as well. In January 1918 Edelman informed Walcott:

> Since last writing to you I have learned that the University of Minnesota has contracted to employ its radio equipment for the instruction of Signal Corps recruits beginning with February and that in the meantime the radio station formerly established there remains dismantled, so that the conditions thereat are none too favorable.[158]

Meanwhile, Walcott developed second thoughts about Edelman. To Hooker he confided at the end of February 1918:

> He gives me the impression that he is for Edelman, first, last, and altogether, and that he is carrying on the investigation for what he can get out of it and not as a contribution to science or to the

subject. In other words his ideals are on a lower plane than we might wish.[159]

A month later B. B. Lawrence offered a similar assessment and recommended that "before awarding another Scholarship more particular inquiry should be made into the man's personality."[160] Walcott quite agreed. "The moral of it is," he replied, "that we cannot accept paper testimony, and in the future must have an applicant personally known to members of the Committee or else interviewed by the Committee."[161]

In hindsight, the fellowship idea was clearly sound, as suggested by the success of the National Research Council's (NRC) postdoctoral fellowship program after World War I. National in scope and viewed favorably by leading researchers and research institutions, the NRC fellowship program enabled recent Ph.D. recipients to spend a year or two extending their research skills before accepting full-time employment, and it quickly became the capstone in the training program for American scientists.[162]

Of course, the Research Corporation fellowships were not aimed at the postdoctoral level, but a more important shortcoming was the way they were awarded. As with the evaluation of inventions, the people responsible for evaluating the fellowship applications were very busy. The process would work, but only if the number of applications remained strictly limited.

In truth, however, what actually brought Research Corporation's fellowship program to an end was the country's entry into World War I. When Edelman seemed likely to be drafted, Walcott contacted Rear Admiral R. S. Griffin, who headed the navy's Bureau of Steam Engineering (an important research agency and one of the government's main agencies for radio research). In the end, Edelman was not exempted from service, but he did continue to work as a radio researcher — in the army's Signal Corps Laboratories. From Research Corporation's point of view, government service disqualified him from receiving the balance of the fellowship. When the time for his discharge approached, he asked to have his fellowship reinstated. By then, however, Research Corporation considered the matter closed — not only for Edelman, but also for the fellowship program as a whole.[163]

Of course, the war disrupted far more than just Research Corporation's new fellowship program. At a meeting of the executive committee in September 1917, Goetze reported that the demand for electrostatic precipitators was declining (at least in some industries), due to a rise in the cost of materials (as a result of the war) or to the higher priority of war-related work. Another problem involved the firm's technical personnel. Scott reported to Walcott in October: "Almost our entire staff of engineers is composed of young men subject to [the] draft. . . ."[164] If the men were called into service, Scott hoped that they would be assigned back to Research Corporation for sulfuric acid production projects or "for precipitation work in connection with the removal of black smoke on merchant vessels to make them less visible."[165]

The onset of the war also affected Research Corporation's leaders. L. N. Scott became an army captain, serving as liaison officer to the Naval Consulting Board. Walcott turned his attention to the National Advisory Committee for Aeronautics (which he helped to establish), and Cottrell pursued war-related work (notably, helium production) at the Bureau of Mines.[166]

W. W. Strong's Laboratory

At the same time that Research Corporation was developing its fellowship program, it was also supporting the work of W. W. Strong, the physicist from the Mellon Institute's smoke program. Strong began cooperating with Research Corporation even before settlement of the patent interference case of Strong and Nesbit vs. Schmidt and Roberts. Thus he wrote Bradley in March 1913: "In order to further the cause of electrical precipitation, I think it to be a wise plan for us to get together rather than to be in the present position."[167] Throughout the negotiations between Research Corporation and the Mellon Institute, Strong continued cooperating. In April 1914, for example, he offered Research Corporation the foreign rights to a newly approved electrostatic precipitation patent. "Should your company care to carry this application to foreign countries," he wrote Hooker, "I would be glad to aid you. Personally I am only interested in this country at present."[168]

Of the various people we have met so far, Strong had probably the most direct ties to the new developments in physics. After graduating from Dickinson College in 1905, he received his doctorate from the Johns Hopkins University in 1908 for research conducted under the direction of Joseph Sweetman Ames. Strong remained at Johns Hopkins for three more years, working as a research assistant for Harry C. Jones, a physical chemist whose spectroscopic studies were funded by the Carnegie Institution of Washington.[169]

Although Strong's service with the Mellon Institute formally ended on July, 1, 1913, he continued working on electrostatic precipitation. In 1912, while still at the Mellon Institute, he formed his own company. Located in his hometown of Mechanicsburg, Pennsylvania, the Scientific Instrument and Electrical Machine Co. advertised its willingness to make a wide range of apparatus, including electrostatic precipitators.[170]

During the 1914–1915 academic year Strong served as an instructor at the Carnegie Institute of Technology, where he hoped to continue his research. He wrote Bradley in April 1915: "I have also had some conferences with Dean [John H.] Leete and he seems very favorably disposed to research work at the Institute. A new 200,000 volt 100 K.W. transformer is being put in here so that advantages are exceptional. . . ."[171]

However, parental health problems drew him back to Mechanicsburg. To accommodate Strong's family obligations, Research Corporation decided to give him a salary and allow him to study electrostatic precipitation in his hometown. By early 1916 his research there was under way, though he noted: "The experimental work being done now is of a very preliminary character" — because he was still using relatively low voltages.[172]

The research Strong had in mind was a "Study of Pure Gases that are usually encountered in Precipitation Work."[173] The gases included sulfur dioxide, carbon dioxide, and water. He planned to examine how each gas, separately, affected the precipitation process, under various conditions. He would then subject different mixtures of these gases to a similar series of studies. He said by way of summary:

> Now I should like very much to get complete data for curves and tables on all gases, etc. under all conditions that are met with in practice for say all size of pipes, plates, etc. for voltages from 25,000 to 100,000 — for various temperatures, moisture content, fume content, etc.[174]

Strong made it clear that he was taking a distinctive approach, one that he considered highly advantageous:

> I feel like insisting upon our ideal location here as soon as we get the [new high voltage] experimental equipment. I am certain that the work can be carried out more cheaply here than anywhere else for we already have the building and some apparatus for this very purpose. I feel it to be absolutely impossible to do this kind of work in a commercial installation and in a University it is very hard to work with obnoxious gases [such as sulfur dioxide] and fumes.
>
> My central aim is to be able to build a precipitation chamber of the smallest practical size that will handle the fumes at a maximum velocity as cheaply and effectively as possible. Certain elements as gas velocity, effect of temperature, ionization and dryness are very important. All this field can easily be investigated so that nothing will be left for guess work.
>
> I feel that eventually it will be comparatively easy to put in an

automatic regulating device that will make arcing and localization of corona almost impossible.[175]

Above all, his approach was analytical and comprehensive. He wanted to break down the gas stream into its essential components, study each component individually and then in mixtures with other components, break down the operating conditions into *their* essential components, and then study each condition across the full range of its values. He expected to leave nothing to what he called "guess work," by which he probably meant the experience-based intuition that engineers and other technologists employed. His approach also stressed the design of small-scale precipitators with minimal adjustment needs. Finally, he planned to keep his organizational overhead as limited as possible.

But Strong was not the only one studying electrostatic precipitation. So too were W. A. Schmidt and his colleagues at the Western Precipitation Company. By April 1916 Schmidt had learned of Strong's efforts, and made it clear to Bradley that Western Precipitation would not be caught napping:

> We are at present reconstructing our physical laboratory for the purpose of installing a complete precipitation apparatus. We hope to be able to carry out some interesting experiments. You will learn of this work through the office bulletins.[176]

Schmidt also indicated that he viewed Strong's approach as subject to definite limitations. Earlier Bradley had given him a paper by Strong, and he now replied with a general assessment:

> The paper is very interesting but it does seem to me that Strong puts too much assurance on his fundamental assumptions. It strikes me very much like calculations where the first factors are assumed and the computations are then carried out to the tenth decimal place.
>
> Please understand this is not a condemnation. There is no method available by which to criticize the accuracy or inaccuracy of Strong's conclusions. His discussion, of course, is academic. The factors entering into precipitation are so numerous and involved that it is difficult to trace back the effect of any one factor through our experience, in such manner as to make it possible to pass judgment on computations such as Strong's.[177]

In reply, Bradley signaled his basic agreement:

> Of course, the discussion, as you say, is academic and it is not
> possible for us at the present time to check back from our experi-
> ence in the field, and furthermore, what you state . . . regarding
> fundamental assumptions and computations to the tenth decimal
> place, is correct.[178]

He also confirmed that Research Corporation indeed planned to support
Strong's work, but he assured Schmidt that "it is distinctly not our intention
to establish and maintain permanently a strictly research laboratory."[179] Instead, Research Corporation sought "a field laboratory for field investigations,"
with the idea being to transfer to it "this work which Strong is now doing . . . if
experience indicates that it is worth while."[180] Finally, with regard to Schmidt's
own research plans Bradley noted: "We should be very pleased to learn of the
work from time to time as you have promised."[181]

Clearly at stake here were two distinctive approaches to research. Strong's
approach was based on comprehensive analysis in the laboratory, while
Schmidt's was based on the performance of full-scale devices in the field. The
two approaches may have involved similar experimental equipment, but Strong
and Schmidt arrived at their similar end points via two different routes. For
Strong, the laboratory apparatus represented the greatest complexity with
which he was willing to treat each idealized factor, while for Schmidt the laboratory apparatus represented the minimum simplification he was willing to
make of equipment in actual use. In other words, where Strong favored scaling up the idealized process as little as possible, Schmidt favored simplifying
the commercial process as little as possible.

To summarize, Schmidt's approach can be labeled "engineering research"
and Strong's, "scientific research." Thus one of Schmidt's colleagues at Western Precipitation suggested that a friendly rivalry existed between two types
of researchers trying to understand electrostatic precipitation:

> The engineers, on the one hand, have designed and built precipita-
> tors. . . . The physicists and laboratory investigators, on the other
> hand, have been more concerned with the fundamental principles
> involved. . . .[182]

"Of these two groups," this colleague concluded, "the engineers have made
much the better progress."[183]

The approaches taken by Schmidt and by Strong involved yet another
difference. Even though the experimental equipment in each case might appear similar, the two were not embedded in similar organizational structures.

Schmidt's work was one aspect of a well-established, full-scale company. By contrast, Strong's efforts were part of one individual's research agenda, funded by Research Corporation. This difference was clear to Bradley, who noted in his letter to Schmidt that the value of Strong's work would likely be conditional: "it may be, if work similar to what Dr. Strong is now doing is *properly directed* and his reports *properly analyzed* that considerable value may be obtained."[184]

Strong's increased attention to war-related work complicated the contrast but by no means undermined it. Alongside his studies of electrostatic precipitation, he submitted reports for ideas that he believed would be useful to the military. Yet even here his distinctive approach was apparent. For example, he believed that the lack of organizational complexity in his undertakings would enable him to develop his ideas more inexpensively than the military.[185]

Bradley replied that he had contacted Walcott regarding Strong's war-related work. He also described a new reporting procedure that he wanted Strong to adopt:

> . . . I am enclosing herewith several patent memoranda blanks which I would like to have you make dilligent [*sic*] use of in preparing memoranda of either patentable or non-patentable ideas, either based upon pure science or upon the engineering phases of the work, giving proper data, sketches, etc., as early as possible. Immediately upon filling out these patent memoranda, please send them to me in order that I may go over them with others here and send those which seem to hold promise of something patentable, to our patent attorney for his attention and possible action.[186]

Later in the month, Walcott wrote Bradley that he had contacted Cottrell regarding the value of Strong's work. Cottrell's response echoed Bradley's. In Walcott's words (as reported to Bradley):

> . . . [Cottrell] thinks that Dr. Strong's academic work and dreams may lead to some very interesting and useful work for the Corporation, if properly checked and guarded from the practical side through the New York office.[187]

At this stage, however, Walcott rejected the idea of formal arrangements with the government.[188]

In the months that followed, Bradley attempted to integrate Strong's work more effectively with Research Corporation's overall program. For example, he encouraged additional contact between Strong and other Research Corporation personnel.[189] At Bradley's request, Strong was now submitting a steady stream of patent memoranda. With these and many other such memoranda to process, Bradley commented to Strong: "I have recently been devoting considerable time and attention to our files upon patent subjects and have been rearranging the classification."[190]

As America's wartime activities increased, so did the challenge of organizing individual efforts and managing the sheer volume of research-related information. After the declaration of war in April 1917, Bradley asked A. F. Meston to contact Strong and explain in more detail Research Corporation's procedures. Meston informed Strong that his memoranda were being indexed and filed "in a manner which will let us use them as we find opportunity."[191]

Meston also indicated that Research Corporation was again approaching the government with regard to some of Strong's ideas. But he made it clear that success would require further procedural changes on Strong's part:

> I have noticed in going over these [patent memoranda] that you have been giving considerable thought to the problems incidental to our troubled times and you have suggested means whereby the effect of torpedoes and submarines may be curtailed. . . . I have asked a government expert regarding the use of torpedoes and I have talked to a Patent Attorney regarding the chances of bringing ideas of this kind before Washington authorities, and they did not give a great deal of encouragement. . . . Washington is filled with inventors and the mails are filled with suggestions. It seems that if ideas are not pretty well worked out so they are shown to be practical, they receive little attention from the Naval Advisory Board [*sic*].[192]

The Naval Consulting Board had been created by the secretary of the navy in mid-1915, partially in response to public remarks made earlier that year by Thomas Edison. Serious consideration was given to establishing a naval research laboratory, but the war ended before it was built. Instead, the board's primary wartime activity was screening ideas and arranging for the most promising to be developed. High on the list of military needs was countering the German submarine threat, and the inventor Elmer Sperry, a prominent member of the Naval Consulting Board, experimented with the idea of using steel nets for detection purposes.[193]

In light of these efforts, Strong recognized that his own ideas would have to be developed more fully before presenting them to the government. Additional work, he wrote Meston, would require additional funding:

> I doubt if anything can be done unless there is a patron willing
> enough to push the work to practicality. The government will not
> be likely to do anything unless it is almost a matter of life or death
> and then it is too late. The example of the Monitor [during the
> Civil War] is typical as I see it — and that had to be developed by
> [John] Ericsson.[194]

Of course, as his patron, Strong had in mind Research Corporation. Meanwhile, Meston continued to explore the possibility of bringing Strong's ideas to the government's attention, and in early June 1917 he wrote the Mechanicsburg physicist:

> You will be interested to know that I recently took a number of
> your ideas on submarine nets and torpedoes to Washington and
> presented them to Dr. W. F. Durand for the purpose of ascertaining their merit and to see if there is something that we could do to
> help the present situation.[195]

William F. Durand was a mechanical engineer with a well-established interest in research. He began his career as a naval officer, then retired, received a Ph.D. degree, and served as a professor at Cornell and Stanford. Prior to World War I he turned his attention to aviation, and in 1916 he was chosen to head the National Advisory Committee for Aeronautics. In 1917 Durand also assumed a position on the antisubmarine committee of the National Research Council, the government's new umbrella research agency. Already W. R. Whitney of the Naval Consulting Board had arranged for a cooperative effort at Nahant, Massachusetts, involving GE, AT&T, and the Submarine Signal Company, to experiment with the use of sound waves for detecting submarines. To this work the NRC now added the efforts of academic scientists at New London, Connecticut.[196]

Durand responded via Meston to several of Strong's ideas, but he made it clear that the government's approach was much more extensively organized. For example, with regard to Strong's suggestion of using "microphones for determining the direction of an on-coming torpedo," Meston reported:

> ...Dr. Durand says that you will have to have your ideas more
> detailed before they can receive consideration. He said this particular subject...has been given over to a sub-committee, com-

prising the Research Laboratories of the General Electric Company, the Western Electric Company, the American Telephone & Telegraph Company, and the Underwater Signallying [*sic*] Company. When an array of brains such as this is put to work on a problem you may depend upon it that the field is being pretty well taken care of.[197]

From Durand's point of view, "it is hardly to be expected that individuals working alone will develop methods not already covered by these expert boards."[198] To this, Strong replied:

> I was very glad to learn of your visit to Durand's. Psychologically it is very interesting to me to see the conservatism that is shoved at one who suggests anything new. The public is educated to accept the inventor as a crank — there being but a few exceptions. Then no one at all understands the tremendous amount of testing work required and that you start your invention always as a crude device — the Zeppelin is an example.[199]

Underlying all Strong's interactions with Research Corporation was his great admiration for what Cottrell had tried to accomplish by giving away his patents. [200] At the same time, however, Research Corporation's staff was becoming uncomfortable with their lack of sufficient contact with Strong. "Almost two weeks have gone by since hearing from him, and this is discouraging my endeavors to keep the work of this department properly coordinated," Meston complained to Research Corporation's new general manager E. P. Dillon.[201]

Meston asked Dillon to contact Strong directly, and the result was a letter not from Dillon but from Bradley:

> Dear Dr. Strong:
> I understand that you have recently received a mimeographed copy of the revised organization chart and explanation of the same. You will note that Mr. Meston is in charge of a portion of the work and that we have made other rearrangements as to laboratory, factory, etc. It is the desire of Mr. Dillon that everybody keep in close touch with the New York Office and that in order to carry out the organization plans to the best advantage, you arrange as follows:
> First; that you keep a note book in which will be put all data which covers problems in which the Research Corporation is inter-

ested and that this book be sent to the New York Office at least once a month for inspection.

Second; that you write a weekly report discussing, more or less in detail, the results which you are obtaining and your suggestions for future activities.

Third; that you keep account of the time you put in for Research Corporation, in order that we may bill the government with respect to the same when you do government work, or charge it to our own overhead on problems which are strictly for Research Corporation.[202]

Bradley continued with a proposal that Strong pursue his work at the new site of Research Corporation's laboratory, explaining: "All of our equipment which was formerly in Brooklyn is now on the ground at the new location and in the near future all of our equipment will be moved from Girvin's Philadelphia factory to the building in Jersey City."[203]

The Research Corporation archives include no reply from Strong. Nor have I found any substantive interactions with Strong following Bradley's letter, which suggests that Strong's cooperation did not survive the increased organizational effort required by the wartime projects. But Strong was not silent regarding the forces at work around him. His general views appeared in a book he published in 1920. The relevant chapter was entitled "A Fundamental Philosophy of Research," and it began by situating research in opposition to the materialistic tendencies of the times:

Civilization is not to become the slave of Production. . . . Large cities, railroads, ships and telephones, with enormous multitudes of striving, struggling men, may result in some sort of evolution, but the aim of the research spirit is to direct this very evolution and not to become the slave of supplying the paraphernalia with which innumerable hosts shall live.[204]

Subsequent paragraphs offered a biting critique of organized research. In Strong's eyes, the business sector was corrupt. "[T]he scientist that is directly connected with the business world soon becomes drunken by its materialism."[205] The government sector was also corrupt. "[O]ur patent system is little better than the symbolism of barbarism compared to what it might be."[206] Even the academic sector had been affected:

It is pitiful how apathetic men are to the love of Knowledge. The writer pleaded for means to try the effect of an electric field on light vibrations in his college course in 1903. Not a cent could be gotten. The German Stark (Strong) added lustre to his country by making this discovery.[207]

Making the whole situation worse — and prompting Strong to invoke explicitly religious language — were the organizational tendencies of the Research Revolution:

> . . . people squander enormous sums in futile research. They emphasize publication where the names of "directors" rank first. They emphasize the necessity of spending money in buildings and apparatus and of brass plating these piles of brick and metal with their own names. They fail to appreciate that research accomplishment is a matter of spirit. . . . Only love of research will ever emancipate men to freedom. Only a Christ or a John the Baptist in a wilderness will realize this. Men have never developed any organization that will not eventually strangle and crucify the spirit.[208]

Throughout all this, Strong presented his own, fully democratized, vision for research:

> Society is to permit opportunities of research to all. . . . Religion, philosophy and the research spirit are essentially one. In every man there must be the new birth to the new philosophy. . . . To be common is to drift with the great Gulf Stream on the ocean of life. To be great is to build our own laboratory ship and to sail alone if need be. . . . The tremendous advance in the technique of civilization permits every home to be a laboratory. . . . There does not appear any reason why children in a home should not grow up in the very midst of a laboratory.[209]

He also made it clear that he had attempted to follow his own guidelines. "[The writer's] field of research work," he said of himself, "was selected so that much of it could be done in the home and during spare moments."[210] Research Corporation's organized approach, especially when coupled with the additional demands of wartime projects, worked against his principles. Rather than compromise them further, he ended the collaborative arrangement.

CHAPTER SIX

CONCLUSION

The organization of scientific and technological creativity, on a mass basis, has been one of the most remarkable intellectual accomplishments of the past century and a half. As a vision, organized research claims a long history, dating back at least as far as Francis Bacon's *New Atlantis*, published posthumously in 1627.[1] In his utopian novella, the English philosopher–scientist imagined a European ship being blown off course by a vast storm in the Pacific and landing on the previously unknown island of Bensalem. There the travelers learned about Salomen's House, devoted to the creation of knowledge through experimentation and to the application of that knowledge for the betterment of humanity.[2]

From the outset, Bacon's vision enjoyed a loyal following, especially among members of the Royal Society of London (established in 1662). But organized research was all too easy for others to dismiss. An early example came from the satirical pen of Jonathan Swift in his 1726 novel *Gulliver's Travels*.[3] After landing on the continent of Balnibari and traveling to its capital city, Lagado, Gulliver visited the Grand Academy, a thinly veiled twin to the Royal Society. There the first researcher he met was attempting to extract sunshine from cucumbers, which was then to be sealed in jars for release on cloudy days.[4] Other researchers at the Grand Academy were engaged in equally absurd and fruitless projects.

Even as late as the early twentieth century it remained possible to deny, in principle, the efficacy of organized research. For example, despite W. W. Strong's association with a variety of research organizations, he remained skeptical of efforts that put organizations ahead of individuals. What finally tipped the scales in favor of widespread social acceptance of organized research were the successful research and development projects of World War II. Thus the full flowering of the Research Revolution came after the war and resulted in what David C. Mowery and Nathan Rosenberg (following Richard R. Nelson) have called "the U.S. national innovation system."[5] On the practical side, society gained the ability to invent, develop, and implement entire technological systems.[6] In addition, basic research was itself transformed into what became known as "Big Science."[7] The overall result was a new environment for research. Composed of hundreds of entities, this organizational infrastructure is committed to training, hiring, and supporting the work of thousands of researchers throughout the better portion of their adult lives.

Research Corporation and American Universities

Research Corporation has successfully maintained a place for itself in the organizational infrastructure for research in the United States. Its place, however, has tended to lie on the periphery. By contrast — as David H. Guston and Kenneth Keniston have noted — "the research universities have been at the intellectual center of this entire enterprise."[8] The centrality of universities can be demonstrated in many ways. But the only other example I shall offer is an exchange that *Time* magazine reported in 1986, between a worried American visitor and his host at an advanced Japanese factory:

> "Gosh, even your industrial design is better than ours."
> "Ah, yes," replied the manager, "but America has treasures
>   that Japan can never hope to possess."
> "You mean our mineral wealth and bountiful farms?"
> "Ah, no. I was referring to Caltech and M.I.T."[9]

Taking an historical approach makes the current status of American universities even more impressive. Before World War I, who would have guessed that universities would later assume such an important role? Indeed, their limitations prior to the war were what motivated Cottrell to turn elsewhere when the time came to give his patents away. Thus Research Corporation was deliberately intended as a far less peripheral organization, not just with respect to its development of electrostatic precipitation but also with respect to its patent services and support for research. Why then after World War II did their relative positions switch — with Research Corporation ending up on the periphery and universities at the center? Here we need to examine closely Research Corporation's evolving relationship with American universities.

Certainly American universities at the turn of the century needed an organization such as Research Corporation. On campuses across the country, research still tended to be supported by occasional gifts earmarked for specific purposes. As universities became more interested in research, however, the inadequacies of the traditional funding pattern became increasingly apparent. What universities required instead was something more regular and less restricted.[10]

For example, at a meeting of the Association of American Universities in 1915, the dean of Berkeley's graduate school, A. O. Leuschner, emphasized the limitations that universities faced: "As a rule, opportunities for research

... exist only through the munificence of benefactors who come to the rescue of an investigator on his personal appeal or on that of the president."[11] While such gifts might work well for one or two extraordinary faculty members, they "are of no avail to [the others] who with a little help might make a distinct contribution to the world's achievements."[12] To Leuschner, the solution was clear: "Every large university ought to set aside annually a sum of $10,000 or more to be appropriated for the promotion of research. . . ."[13]

The situation was complicated by changing campus attitudes toward research. Despite widespread belief that research should remain "pure," more and more university researchers were involving themselves in practical applications — especially in connection with the expanding electrical and chemical industries.[14] Practical applications, in turn, raised questions about patents. Some academics were attracted to patents because of the royalties they promised to generate. If commercial work could have been confined to taking out patents, licensing them, and collecting royalties, then perhaps the controversy would have remained limited. But many academics balked at pursuing their projects through the development and marketing stages (especially if litigation was involved). After surveying the situation, one engineering professor concluded that:

> universities are not and cannot be operated for profit. Neither can they handle development, exploitation, and legal defense of inventions in a business-like way. Sooner or later they find out that this is a special business with undesirable and annoying possibilities.[15]

To illustrate this general situation, we can continue the Berkeley example. While serving on the faculty there, Cottrell experienced firsthand the difficulties associated with applied research. Although he published articles based on his low-temperature apparatus, he found that the "pressure of other duties and lack of facilities" kept him from obtaining commercially useful results.[16] As he turned his attention elsewhere, he first hoped that any patents he might receive would provide the university with additional research funds. But when the time came to give away his electrostatic precipitation patents, he ended up taking a different route.

Another possibility was the one that Leuschner proposed, namely, for the university to earmark more of its own discretionary funds for the support of research. Berkeley established such a fund (administered by the faculty) in 1915. For the first year the budget was only $2,000. Even so, President Wheeler explained in 1916: "A definite extra grant of two or three hundred dollars just at the right time is likely to prove of positive benefit. . . ."[17] Although the budgets were increased for the second and third years (to $3,000 and $4,000, respectively), individual grants remained small. Thus when the program was reviewed in mid-1920, the largest grant had amounted to $1,000 (for G. N. Lewis's low-temperature research).[18]

To bring Research Corporation into the picture more directly, consider the case of T. Brailsford Robertson, the Australian biochemist and Berkeley faculty member who in 1917 isolated from the pituitary gland a growth-enhancing substance that he named "tethelin." Like Cottrell, Robertson first considered giving the university the patent that resulted from his work. When the board of regents hesitated, he turned to Research Corporation, thereby demonstrating the distinctive role that Research Corporation was in a position to play. Robertson proposed what he understood to be an arrangement like the one for the electrostatic precipitator: Research Corporation would provide the financial administration, while the Smithsonian would distribute grants from what Robertson proposed calling "the International Foundation for Medical Research."[19]

Robertson had not come to his proposal out of the blue. Like Cottrell, he had been thinking about how to increase the support for academic research, a goal that he considered essential to the well being of society. "Lacking the spirit of research, a nation or community is merely parasitic . . . ," he wrote in the November 1915 issue of *Scientific Monthly*.[20] To help prevent research dependency he proposed the creation of "legal machinery whereby some proportion, no matter how small, of the wealth which science pours into the lap of the community, shall return automatically to the support and expansion of scientific research."[21]

A year later Robertson continued his line of thinking. In the December 1916 issue of the same journal he exhorted himself and his colleagues to "cut ourselves loose from patronage, and take into our own hands the destinies of our own institution," and to illustrate the principle that "investigation must be made self-supporting" he explicitly cited Research Corporation (along with the Solvay Institute in Brussels and the Institute of Experimental Therapy in Frankfort).[22]

In approaching Research Corporation with the offer of his patent rights, Robertson was attempting to practice what he preached, and he hoped Research Corporation would act quickly so that tethelin could be made available for the healing of battlefield wounds. But Hooker was not especially interested, nor was Walcott, who explained to Cottrell:

> I feel a good deal toward Dr. Robertson's tethelin patents as I did
> toward medical investigations, when the question came up in 1902

of the Carnegie Institution taking up medical research. I opposed it
& soon the Rockefeller Medical Research Corporation [*sic*] was organized, & all medical problems were referred there. The Research
Corporation has a great field in the applied physical sciences, & I
doubt the wisdom, unless the character of the board is changed, of
taking up anything that has to do with medical questions.[23]

Meanwhile, Berkeley's board of regents decided to accept Robertson's gift
after all, because (unlike the electrostatic precipitator earlier) tethelin seemed
not to require extensive development work. Toward the end of September
1917 Cottrell reported to Walcott "that the matter is working itself out quite
satisfactorily. . . ."[24]

The Presidency of Arthur A. Hamerschlag

Recognizing that the Berkeley situation was far from unique, Research
Corporation noted in a 1917 brochure: "There is an opportunity and a need
for an organization which can act as the intermediary between the inventor
and the manufacturer. . . ."[25] Although it intended to help meet that need, Research Corporation was still devoting itself primarily to the business of electrostatic precipitation. But in 1923 a new brochure proclaimed more positively: "After eleven years of public service, the Research Corporation . . . is
today in a position to act as the intermediary between the inventor and the
manufacturer. . . ."[26]

More than just the passage of time separated the two brochures. The
interval also marked a critical period in Research Corporation's early history
when many of those who had helped establish it began leaving, through changing interests, retirement, or death. Linn Bradley quit in 1919 and H. D. Egbert,
another senior engineer, died that same year. As late as January 1921 Research Corporation still had eight of its original fifteen directors (see Table 4,
page 192, for a full listing). After that, B. B. Lawrence (a director and treasurer) died.[27] Other significant changes came in 1922 when Arthur D. Little (a
director) resigned and J. B. Pine (a director and the organization's legal counsel) died.[28] Finally, and most significantly, E. H. Hooker stepped down as president in January 1923 (although he continued serving as a director and as a
member of the executive committee). In such circumstances, an organization
that wants to survive must demonstrate its resiliency, and under the leadership of its new president, Arthur A. Hamerschlag, Research Corporation did
just that.

Like Hooker, Hamerschlag was an engineer. Unlike him, however, Hamerschlag was also an educator. He grew up on New York's East Side and gradu-

ated from the trade school that Robert S. Auchmuty established in the early 1880s. Hamerschlag also attended classes at Columbia University. After four years of working abroad on engineering projects in Cuba and Mexico he returned to New York. In 1892 Auchmuty's trade school received a sizable endowment from J. P. Morgan and a charter from the state — and Hamerschlag became a consultant for the school. Meanwhile, Morgan also supported a smaller trade school at St. George's Church where he was senior warden. The rector, W. S. Rainsford, chose Hamerschlag for the teaching staff, and in 1893 appointed him the school's superintendent.[29]

Then in 1903 Hamerschlag accepted a new and bigger challenge, that of directing the trade schools that Andrew Carnegie was establishing in Pittsburgh. For nearly twenty years Hamerschlag presided over what became known in 1912 as the Carnegie Institute of Technology. After Carnegie's death in 1919, responsibility for underwriting Carnegie Tech shifted to the Carnegie Corporation, which decided to continue its support but to postpone the funding of additional campus construction. Having spent the previous two decades erecting some twenty new buildings where none had existed before, Hamerschlag resigned. In 1922 he returned to New York, and early the following year he became president of Research Corporation.[30]

The hallmark of Hooker's presidency had been his commitment to business values. Along with being the appropriate basis for conducting Research Corporation's affairs, such values were also central to American culture. At the directors' meeting in January 1921, for example, Hooker pronounced as successful the company's policy of manufacturing the precipitators it installed. Then, in a more general vein, he added: "I presume we would most of us agree that the genius of America today is expressed in her industrial life."[31]

It is not hard to find additional evidence of Hooker's commitment to business values. In 1920 he sought the Republican nomination for governor of New York State, and his public statements during the campaign emphasized his distinctive approach. Thus *The New York Times* reported in April: "[Hooker] advocated reorganization of the State Government to eliminate waste, systematize expenditures, and centralize responsibility...."[32] When he formally announced his candidacy in early May, he expressed his desire to "bring his business training to bear on reducing the cost of living and the cost of government," adding, "the people of the State are entitled to a business-like conduct of their affairs...."[33] His remarks to a Republican club a few weeks later were equally candid: "...if you don't want a business man for Governor you don't want me."[34]

Hooker's business values provided Research Corporation with the style of leadership it needed to achieve its early success. By 1921, however, a new approach was emerging, and a new leader was on the rise. Meeting informally at the end of November 1920, Research Corporation's executive committee tentatively approved the selection of Hamerschlag as a director (subject to his formal election at the next directors' meeting). In addition, the executive committee approved the formation of a special committee "to gather information in regard to the scientific discoveries and inventions lying dormant in the universities and scientific schools of the country."[35] Hamerschlag was named chair of the committee, whose members also included Cottrell and Little.[36]

At the next directors' meeting Hamerschlag's committee made its report:

> We believe that the Research Corporation may successfully serve . . . by acting as a sort of clearing house for inventions, and by providing the necessary contacts between those who have the inventions and those who possess the resources necessary to develop and introduce them.[37]

That same meeting also saw Hamerschlag's formal election as vice-president as well as director.[38]

After becoming president, Hamerschlag promoted the image of Research Corporation as a place "where new ideas are welcome."[39] *The New York Times* reported in April 1924:

> Dr. Hamerschlag made the first public announcement recently that the Research Corporation . . . is now serving as a recognised connecting link between inventors, manufacturers and the Government, having "weathered" twelve years of experimentation.[40]

Although none of the inventions it examined during these years came close to rivaling the electrostatic precipitator in commercial importance, under Hamerschlag's leadership the scale of the search was expanded. "Considerable progress has been made by the Research Corporation in recent years," he wrote in the August 1924 issue of *Chemical Age*:

> It has examined hundreds of patents; it has advised innumerable inventors; it has cooperated with industries in the solution of technical problems . . . and it has served as a link between American inventors who have secured patent protection abroad and who need an agency of this type to bring world-wide attention to their useful solutions of industrial problems.[41]

Finally an article in the December 1924 issue of *American Industries* noted:

> To many people the idea of applying organization to . . . invention
> as carried on by individuals not in the employ of some big corpora-
> tion . . . is a new one. But impossible as it seemed and difficult as it
> is[,] this institution . . . is to-day rendering the free-lance inventor
> many of the same services that the great industrial organizations
> perform for the highly skilled men working in their research labo-
> ratories. . . .[42]

Had Hooker still been president, such pronouncements would have carried little in the way of an academic focus. But for Hamerschlag, academic
values stood on a par with business values. Admittedly, that left him open to
criticism from both camps. In 1928, for example, when a plaque in his honor
was dedicated on the Carnegie Tech campus, F. P. Keppel (the president of
Carnegie Corporation) identified a business-related shortcoming. Although
he admired Hamerschlag's willingness to undertake educational experiments,
Keppel noted that "[h]is ideas of academic finance . . . were not what were
ordinarily called sound."[43] Likewise, Hamerschlag's approach to traditional
campus activities could be criticized. Thus A. W. Tarbell noted: "It was occasionally difficult for him to be patient with the slow processes of committee
study and . . . he cared little for the ceremonies of academic life. . . ."[44]

Yet Hamerschlag was truly committed to higher education and to cooperative efforts between academia and industry. As a result, his pronouncements for Research Corporation carried connotations that similar pronouncements by Hooker would have lacked, thus signaling the distinctive role that
Research Corporation would play in the world of organized research during
the years that followed.

In the 1920s Research Corporation gradually succeeded in its efforts to
support university researchers. The earliest example was Harvey N. Davis's
low-temperature work at Harvard. During World War I the National Research
Council asked Davis, a professor of mechanical engineering, to serve on a
five-member committee to evaluate various processes for liquefying helium,
which brought him to Cottrell's attention. Back at Harvard after the war, Davis
continued his low-temperature work, and he offered Research Corporation
his patent rights to a new method of air liquefaction. At their meeting in
January 1919 the directors authorized Hooker to investigate further, and later
in the year the executive committee authorized a grant of $5,000 "in order
that the President [of Research Corporation] may be more clearly informed
as to the value of this patentable material."[45]

Davis himself was optimistic regarding future results, telling *The New York Times*:

> When our work is completed we hope to have collected enough of the fundamental data bearing on liquid air and the production of oxygen to put the whole industry on an engineering basis.
>
> Much of it is now on a hit-or-miss, experimental basis. As a result the manufacture of oxygen by present methods is immensely wasteful.[46]

The uncertain performance of the economy in the years just after the war led E. P. Dillon (Research Corporation's general manager) to resist further support.[47] Nevertheless, Davis did assign his patent rights to Research Corporation, and Hamerschlag continued to hope that they would prove commercially valuable.[48]

Another early beneficiary was the Smithsonian Institution, which likewise experienced economic problems immediately after the war. Thus Walcott noted in his annual report for 1920: "It is becoming increasingly difficult for the Institution with its extremely limited funds, in the face of greatly increased costs in every phase of its activity, to carry on effective work."[49] A year later he voiced similar concerns:

> It is an unpleasant duty to here record again the pressing need of the Institution for a larger endowment. . . . Almost daily the Institution is forced to forego opportunities for valuable explorations and scientific researches on account of lack of means. . . .[50]

Under Hamerschlag, Research Corporation began assisting. In 1924 the directors approved a grant of $5,000, which the Smithsonian then used to help Robert H. Goddard – a physicist at Clark University – with his pioneering rocket research.[51] The following year Hamerschlag supported another grant to the Smithsonian, establishing what he hoped would become an annual practice.[52] Despite the deaths of both Hamerschlag and Walcott in 1927, Research Corporation continued its support. Thus a grant of $15,000 in 1928 enabled the Smithsonian to extend its research on solar radiation and led to the creation of a Division of Radiation and Organisms in 1929.[53]

Also in 1925 Hamerschlag supported the creation of the Research Corporation Award, to be given to a notable researcher "who has not undertaken the utilization of his research work for his own pecuniary benefit."[54] Several nominees were considered, including the American chemist Edgar Fahs Smith at the University of Pennsylvania and the American geneticist Thomas Hunt Morgan at Columbia. But "after a rather lengthy discussion" the directors chose the American physiological chemist John J. Abel at the Johns Hopkins School of Medicine.[55] Along with a specially designed plaque by sculptor Herbert Adams, Abel received $2,500. "It is only a modest honorarium that is offered with the [Research Corporation Award]," noted an editorial in *The New York Times*:

> not to be compared in amount with the Nobel Prize – but its pur-
> pose looks in the same direction and should be helpful to democ-
> racy in giving recognition to real merit and service. . . .[56]

The next award was not made until 1929, but thereafter the practice became a regular feature of Research Corporation's work.[57]

Although a detailed account of its later history is beyond the scope of this book, one further example of how Research Corporation assisted academic researchers is relevant. By the late 1920s atomic physicists recognized that their next research frontier would be the structure and behavior of atomic nuclei. But existing techniques for pursuing such studies – primarily the use of high-energy particles emitted by naturally radioactive substances – were inadequate to the task. Physicists responded by posing for themselves a tech-nological challenge: could they design and build machines to accelerate par-ticles to high energies? To meet that challenge they invented particle accel-erators and developed them into highly productive research tools. Two of the most important were the cyclotron, developed by E. O. Lawrence at Berkeley, and the electrostatic generator, developed by R. J. Van de Graaff at MIT. In each case, Research Corporation assisted, through grants and through help with the patents.[58] In 1937 MIT went one step further when it arranged for Research Corporation to "handle all legal and commercial aspects of inven-tions assigned to it by Institute inventors."[59]

A 1940 survey offers us perspective on Research Corporation's role. When asked about their patent policies, fourteen out of a total of thirty-nine colleges and universities replied that they had none. Of the others, three relied on Research Corporation (Berkeley and Princeton, along with MIT), while seven relied on their own research foundations.[60] One of the latter was the Wiscon-sin Alumni Research Fund (WARF), established in 1925 on the basis of Harry Steenback's patent for enriching foods with vitamin A.[61] In short, on the eve of America's entry into World War II, Research Corporation's patent services were an important way – though by no means the only way – for institutions of higher education to manage their patents.

An Organizational Experiment during the Progressive Era

During the earliest years of its existence, some people were tempted to view Research Corporation as one of the new philanthropic foundations. For example, an editorial in *The New York Sun* noted:

> On February 16, 1917, the assets of the [Research] [C]orporation in cash and securities were over $217,000. The corporation has therefore a hope, not an unreasonable one it would seem, of becoming the fairy godmother in industrial art in this country, and of doing for the factory what the Carnegie, Rockefeller and Sage Foundations are doing [in other fields].[62]

Carnegie and the others saw fortune-making and philanthropic giving as two separate processes. From the outset, however, Cottrell took a different approach — and that left him open to criticism. For example, in reviewing *Samaritan of Science* (Frank Cameron's 1952 biography of Cottrell) for *Saturday Review*, Boyden Sparkes described an encounter between Cottrell and George Eastman after World War I. Cottrell asked Eastman to help promote the international language, Esperanto, and Eastman refused. Of this encounter, Sparkes wrote:

> Eastman's career and wealth bring into focus the plight of Cottrell during the last third of his life.... Eastman was able to operate as a man of goodwill on a magnificent scale because of wealth derived from a business.... But Cottrell, as a young man, had abandoned his own great chance.[63]

Sparkes considered Cottrell's giving away his patents before reaping a personal fortune to be an act of "premature generosity."[64] Perhaps he also had in mind the contrasting case of Charles M. Hall, the inventor of a successful aluminum manufacturing technique, who willed much of his personal fortune to his alma mater, Oberlin College. At any rate, what Sparkes did say was that by not following the traditional pattern Cottrell had "turned his back on his greatest opportunity to do what he deeply wished to do — serve mankind."[65]

Nevertheless, such assessments and criticisms fall short of the mark. To begin with, Research Corporation never aimed at becoming a large, general-purpose foundation. If anything it was more akin to Carnegie's smaller mission-oriented philanthropic trusts, such as the Carnegie Institution of Washington. Even so, Cottrell deliberately refrained from following Carnegie's lead. Instead of an organizational mechanism to administer a fortune already made,

Cottrell sought something else. When asked why he had not "[sold] the patent rights for electrical precipitation and donate[d] the money to scientific research," he replied that he wanted "to see a new method introduced for the exploitation of patents and new business ideals incorporated in their administration."[66]

Cottrell's intentions with regard to Research Corporation can be understood more clearly in light of the Progressive Movement, a major political development at the turn of the century.[67] Progressivism began as a response to problems in cities across the country. It rose to national importance during Theodore Roosevelt's presidency, and it continued to play an important role in American domestic politics well into the 1920s. Progressives drew heavily on the ranks of the middle class. As a group, they favored more effective government, greater public control of big business, social justice, and voting rights for women. Yet care must be taken not to attribute to them too much unity. Despite the emergence of a separate political party for the presidential election in 1912, the Progressives are better characterized as a diverse set of individuals and groups who worked for reform within the two major political parties. As a result, their success depended on their ability to forge compromises — not only among themselves but also with other players in the nation's political arena.

By today's standards the national legislative achievements of the Progressives — including the Hepburn Act (which gave the federal government greater control over railroad companies), the Meat Inspection Act, and the Pure Food and Drug Act, all passed by Congress in 1906 — may seem modest. But it is important to recognize that we live on the *other* side of the historic divide whereby government has assumed a much greater role in American life. Unlike true conservatives, the Progressives were uncomfortable with the status quo; they wanted change. But they tended to proceed cautiously, steering clear of socialists and other radicals active at the time.

To promote their distinctive approach, Progressives often borrowed from researchers the language of "experimentation." One example comes from a speech Jane Addams gave in 1892 (several years before the Progressive Movement coalesced). In it she discussed her efforts to help the working-class poor in Chicago. At Hull House, the settlement house she established in 1889, volunteers provided a wide range of community services. "The Settlement," she explained, " . . . is an *experimental* effort to aid in the solution of the social and industrial problems which are engendered by the modern conditions of life in a great city."[68]

A second example comes from a speech Theodore Roosevelt gave in 1912 at the National Convention of the newly formed Progressive Party. In discussing the cooperative efforts between Wisconsin and its land-grant college to solve some of the state's problems, he said: "The University of Wisconsin has been more influential than any other agency in making Wisconsin . . . a laboratory for wise social and industrial *experiment* in the betterment of conditions."[69]

A third example comes from a 1914 book by a young political commentator. In *Drift and Mastery*, Walter Lippmann saw science as providing a model for all politicians to follow. "There are people who think that rebellion is an inevitable accompaniment of progress, " he wrote in his conclusion. "I don't see why it should be." Instead, ". . . change becomes a matter of invention and deliberate *experiment*."[70]

Because the language of experimentation resonated so strongly with the empiricism of American popular culture, this approach opened a politically viable middle route for the Progressives. It allowed them to break with conservatives and take issue with existing practices and conditions without appearing radical.

When describing Research Corporation, Cottrell took a similar approach. In 1912 he explicitly characterized the organization as "an *experiment* in public administration of patent rights" (emphasis added). The general problem, in his view, was how best to apply new ideas (especially from academic researchers), to meet the public's need for improved goods and services. Could he devise an organizational means to introduce potentially useful ideas in a timely fashion without compromising the altruistic motives traditionally associated with academia? To answer that question, he established Research Corporation as an "*experiment* in economics."[71]

Far from a one-time occurrence, the language of experimentation appeared repeatedly in connection with Research Corporation. For example, at the dinner held in Cottrell's honor in 1915, F. Austin Lidbury told the assembled group: "we have met to-night to recognize also Dr. Cottrell's eminent services as an *experimentalist* in social science"— with "the particular branch of social science . . . [being] that which embodies the relations between the universities and the technical industries."[72] In its 1917 brochure Research Corporation noted that it "aimed to serve as an *experimental* laboratory in practical economics where altruistic consideration need not be subordinated to the necessity of paying dividends. . . ."[73] And in later years Cottrell himself wrote of Research Corporation's establishment:

> The idea . . . was not merely to produce revenue for scientific research but to act as a sort of laboratory of patent economics and to conduct an *experiment* in patent administration.[74]

Despite the common references to experimentation by the Progressives and by those associated with Research Corporation, using the label "Progressive" in connection with Research Corporation's early history is problematic. The label is probably best reserved for explicitly political events, and Research Corporation's establishment was not explicitly political. Several participants in its early history did possess Progressive political credentials. Holmes, for example, headed the newly formed Bureau of Mines, one of the notable organizational achievements of the Progressive Era, and Hooker served the Progressive Party as its treasurer during the election of 1912 and as chairman of its finance committee thereafter. Nevertheless, I believe we should sidestep the question of whether or not Research Corporation's founders were true political Progressives.

Instead, the more important point is that a spirit closely akin to the spirit that animated the Progressives also animated Research Corporation's founders. Put another way, the ties between the Progressive Movement and Research Corporation were more parallel than causal. Both were expressions of the same basic impulse toward public service.[75]

To see this more clearly, we can return to *Drift and Mastery*. In the chapter entitled "New Incentives," Lippmann discussed the profit motive. He admitted that the pursuit of profits had traditionally represented the defining motive of American businessmen. Also by tradition, however, other facets of American life lay outside the economic arena of profit making. "For in science," he noted, "[as well as in] art, politics, religion, the home, love, education, – the pure economic motive, profiteering, the incentive of business enterprise is treated as a public peril."[76]

What characterized America at the turn of the century was both a dramatic expansion of the profit motive and a probing assessment of how far it could be trusted. Thus Lippmann insisted:

> I am simply trying to point out that there is in everyday life a widespread rebellion against the profit motive. That rebellion is not an attack on the creation of wealth. It is, on the contrary, a discovery that private commercialism is an antiquated, feeble, mean, and unimaginative way of dealing with the possibilities of modern industry.[77]

Finally, he observed: "The change is . . . working itself out under our very eyes. Each day brings innumerable plans for removing activities from the sphere of profit."[78]

Cottrell's intentions for Research Corporation were remarkably similar. In 1912 he mentioned several existing ways in which industry and academia were already cooperating — including the industrial fellowships that R. K. Duncan had established at the Mellon Institute, as well as the private consulting practices of individual faculty members. But he recognized that such practices were "open to the objection of introducing too direct business relations between the academic institutions or the members of their faculties and individual financial interests."[79] In common with existing practices, he hoped Research Corporation would encourage cooperation between academia and industry. Unlike them, however, he hoped Research Corporation would, as a matter of policy, favor the motive of public service over the motive of private profit. He explained:

> The Research Corporation was primarily intended to serve the ever-growing number of men in academic positions who evolve useful and patentable inventions from time to time in connection with their regular work and [who] without looking personally for any financial reward would gladly see these further developed for the public good, but are disinclined either to undertake such developments themselves or to place the control in the hands of any private interest.[80]

The issues of how to encourage the motive of public service and how far the profit motive could be trusted were widely discussed at the time. Consider, as a final example, the essay entitled "For Service Instead of Profit" that Albert W. Atwood published in the December 4, 1920 issue of *The Saturday Evening Post*. Although I have uncovered no evidence to indicate that Atwood had Research Corporation explicitly in mind, his views may be seen as having much in common with Cottrell's. In the course of examining the relationship between profit making and public service, Atwood quoted a university official as saying:

> ... the community *experiments* with the motive of service. It is always *experimenting* here and there, trying out first with this class and then with that, first with one man and then another, whether they or he will work for something besides money; and always the motive is overworked, pushed too far, pushed harder and further than any one motive should be.[81]

That statement seems to capture the essential spirit of Cottrell's hopes for Research Corporation. He intended it as a test, to see if researchers — especially those engaged in applied research — would "work for something beside money" and to see how far "the motive of service" could be followed instead.

Further Historiographic Reflections

At about the same time that I began my study of Research Corporation's early history, a book was published that surveyed the growing interest of American corporations at the turn of the century in scientific and technological research. But my first response to David Noble's *America By Design* was to resist its main story line. Despite the book's wealth of information, its narrative outcome seemed predetermined by Marxist theory. In a capitalist economy the motive of profit making was destined to dominate. Specifically, in the case of research:

> In all of these industries the systematic introduction of science as a means of production presupposed, and in turn reinforced, industrial monopoly. This monopoly meant control not simply of markets and productive plant and equipment but of science itself as well. Initially the monopoly over science took the form of patent control — that is, control over the *products* of scientific technology. It then became control over the *process* of scientific production itself, by means of organized and regulated industrial research. Finally it came to include command over the social prerequisites of this process: the development of the institutions necessary for the production of both scientific knowledge and knowledgeable people, and the integration of these institutions within the corporate system of science-based industry.[82]

Of course, the fact that Noble was able to find considerable evidence for his main premise *is* significant. But due to his prior theoretical commitments, he had no real need to identify motives other than profit making — much less to gauge how strong those alternatives were.

On further reflection, I came to recognize the value of Noble's book. With the rise of big business in the late nineteenth century, research indeed emerged as a valuable economic resource. At first this new resource was situated at some distance from the business world, mainly on campuses across the country. Hence one way for big businesses to proceed was to transfer academic-style research wholesale, by establishing industrial research laboratories as commercial versions of academic science departments. Noble's book also identified a second approach. Along with bringing academic-style research into industry, the process could also be worked in the other direction: industrial problems could be transferred to academia. As examples here, Noble explicitly discussed Duncan's fellowship programs at the Universities of Kansas and Pittsburgh and the relationship of A. D. Little, Inc., to MIT.[83]

Nevertheless, Noble's book still assumed that the profit motive far outweighed the motive of public service. Or, more accurately, the book did not examine other motives or weigh their relative strengths. Instead, its only focus was how corporate capitalism co-opted academic-style research. Yet alternative motives did exist. The turn of the century also saw deliberate efforts to make the fruits of economically significant research serve the distinctive needs of academia. Of course, the early history of Research Corporation provides an example — one that Noble failed to mention. But the real point is that Research Corporation was not an isolated case.

The effort to come up with practices that put other motives into play turns out to be a characteristic feature of the Progressive Era. As a result, an impressive range of alternatives emerged in field after field.[84] No matter how obscure or offbeat such alternatives may seem to us, the sheer fact of their presence merits thoughtful consideration. Put another way, capitalism as a cultural practice did not have, and never has had, just one meaning. Instead, as people in every era have pondered their futures they have drawn on a variety of motives to create a steady stream of alternatives. Some of these alternatives are embraced while others are rejected, resulting in a complex mixture of old and new. Thus capitalism as a cultural practice has been, and continues to be, remade in each generation. The process is not always rational and conscious, but it can always be seen as a process of choosing. Accordingly, to write history in a way that omits or downplays the alternatives that people imagine for themselves and the choices that they end up making obscures rather than clarifies how change takes place.

Applying these issues and concepts to Research Corporation, this book allows us to see multiple motives and alternative approaches and to gauge for ourselves their relative strengths. Based on this case study, an important pattern emerges: when the motives of profit making and public service were both present, they tended to arrange themselves sequentially — with profit making coming first. This is not to say that Research Corporation's commitment to public service was obliterated. Far from it: once the aim of profit making was achieved, the aim of public service could, and did, take center stage. Of course, we can imagine circumstances in which public service would not have had to wait its turn. We can even wish that American society at the turn of the century had not placed so much emphasis on profit making. But apart from what we wish or imagine, good history requires us to characterize the period as accurately as we can. Revealed in Research Corporation's case is the distinctively "emergent" character of public service relative to profit making. If an organization sought to achieve both goals, societal pressures steered it toward succeeding first as a business.

I offer the emergent character of public service when coupled with profit making as an empirical induction, a pattern arising out of the documentary sources. But I also acknowledge that a similar claim about the two motives has long existed as a popular maxim of individual morality. "[I]t is hard for an empty Sack to stand upright," said Benjamin Franklin in the eighteenth century.[85] "Breakfast before ethics," echoed wilderness preservation pioneer Aldo Leopold two centuries later.[86]

In 1911 Theodore Roosevelt offered his own version. Speaking at Berkeley on the topic of "Realizable Ideals," he expressed his irritation with men who exhorted boys in Sunday School classes "not 'to regard their own interests in any way,' [or] to think of 'nothing whatever but others'. . . . "[87] Instead, he continued:

> What is necessary is to tell them that their first duty is to earn their own livelihood, to support themselves and those dependent upon them; but that when that first duty has been performed there yet remains a very large additional duty, in the way of service to their neighbor, of service to the rest of mankind.[88]

Once Cottrell cast his endowment in the form of patents, he probably committed Research Corporation to becoming a successful business first and only later a successful maker of grants. But to end our analysis there would be to leave obscure the larger forces at work. Here I believe we should turn our attention to the *organizational* character of the Research Revolution.

To a degree that Cottrell had not anticipated, business success quickly turned out to require organizational success. His initial preference for administering his gift was a modest organizational structure based on voluntary efforts. At every step, however, the need to become better organized asserted itself. In order to accomplish its business aims, Research Corporation had to hire additional engineers, and their duties and places in the chain of command had to be carefully spelled out. The kind of work the firm undertook had to be extended, both vertically and horizontally, and accommodations had to be made with competitors.

So unexpected was this trend that Cottrell highlighted it in 1932:

> The idea that you can sit back and simply write licenses has been too generally assumed when people discussed the administration

of patents by universities. Even the Research Corporation started with much of this in mind. The thought was to have a small staff confining themselves largely to making licenses, allowing the licensees to make the installations.[89]

Instead, Research Corporation was forced to expand what Alfred D. Chandler, Jr., would have called its "organizational capabilities." Or, as Cottrell also noted in 1932, if an organization committed itself to administering patents, "[i]t cannot avoid being eventually drawn into every phase of the problem."[90]

In short, organizational development at the turn of the century tended to be *thoroughgoing*. Once an idea began assuming an organizational character, it was compelled to become more and more effectively organized. Far from being confined to research organizations, this pressure was quite widespread, leading some historians to make it the basis for an overall interpretation of modern American history.[91]

The trend was certainly clear to Hooker. In a letter he wrote Walcott shortly after the Armistice, he considered various scenarios for Research Corporation's future. One was for the corporation to emphasize its precipitation business and become "a driving, forceful business machine."[92] Another was to emphasize its philanthropic mandate and become a source "for great gifts to be used for beneficient purposes in the field of science."[93] Finally, he wondered if the corporation could become a capstone for the Research Revolution. Could it:

> offer its [organizational] structure . . . to correlate the scientific activities of the country in governmental, industrial and university life, acting as the general manager of the scientific development of the Nation, accomplishing for Science what great railroad and industrial organizations successfully accomplished for Industry on a similar scale? . . . [94]

Having expressed the larger trend, however, Hooker also confessed his uncertainty regarding the "proper and natural relation the Research Corporation might bear to any such movement. . . ."[95] That uncertainty turns out to be important for understanding Research Corporation's later history. So thoroughgoing was the tendency toward organizational development that Research Corporation was unable to play it out to its fullest extent. Instead, toward the end of the twentieth century Research Corporation spun off important aspects of its original mission — first its engineering business and then its patent service operations. Meanwhile, universities did the opposite. Instead of spinning off activities, they took on more and more. Thus universities became the organizations that most fully embodied the tendency of the Research Revolution to be thoroughgoing.

The contrast with universities, I believe, brings into better focus Research Corporation's historical significance. Until universities were ready and willing to assume greater responsibility for the development and marketing of faculty inventions, Research Corporation and a handful of other innovative organizations assumed the responsibility of technology transfer.

Here my assessment can be usefully linked to the larger picture offered by Peter Dobkin Hall. In his 1992 book *Inventing the Nonprofit Sector*, Hall argued that the Progressive Movement was part of "a fundamental restructuring of public life" that began after the Civil War and continued well into the twentieth century.[96] "The ultimate outcome of these efforts," Hall continued, "would be a government . . . whose policies, methods, and personnel . . . were very much the products of privately governed and funded eleemosynary institutions. . . ."[97]

Faced with the twin forces of urbanization and industrialization, Americans in the late nineteenth century perceived a need for change – with "the chief obstacle" being a "lack of suitable organizational vehicles":

> By itself, government was inadequate because it was inherently corrupt and undependable. Business corporations were, in and of themselves, too limited and uncertain in their purposes for responsibilities of such magnitude.[98]

Yet many Americans were uncomfortable with turning to socialism for solutions. "What was needed [instead] was a private-sector alternative. . . ."[99]

Although making empirical generalizations regarding how "Americans" view any given situation is notoriously difficult, in his book *The Public Image of Big Business in America, 1880–1940*, Louis Galambos did undertake such an effort. Through content analysis of publications emanating from various groups (Midwestern farmers, Southern farmers, organized labor, socialist workers, professional engineers, and the Protestant clergy), he established a statistical basis for making comparisons and contrasts. For example, his analysis of *Engineering News* led him to say of the professional engineer at the turn of the century:

> When he concluded that big business posed problems, he looked increasingly to self-reform for solutions. From 1880 through 1902, he had slowly changed his mind about whether the concentration

movement presented a sufficient threat to justify some kind of public or private action; by 1902, he was more convinced than ever
that something had to be done. But the "something" did not nor-
mally involve the federal or state governments; he gave far more
emphasis to individual action by business itself. . . .

Around 1910 the engineer began to feel that self-reform had
workcd.[100]

If we adopt the engineer's point of view, as Galambos articulated it, Research Corporation's establishment in 1912 becomes an expression of their
confidence that the worst excesses of corporate capitalism could be reformed
from within — that public service goals could be successfully added to the
profit-making goals of an engineering business.

Like Hall, Galambos underscored popular resistance to socialism. Socialism may have offered "a logical, clear, and by its own definition complete
ideology . . . ," but: "What was needed in this situation were vague, many-fac-
eted organizations, political ideologies, and symbols."[101]

To complete this train of thought, I wish to invoke one more idea. Writing
in an entirely different context, Richard White has developed the idea of a
cultural "middle ground." His book of that title focused on the interactions of
Native Americans and European Americans in the Great Lakes region, from
the seventeenth century to the War ot 1812, and his thesis was that although
each group wanted to impose its own desires on the entire region, throughout
the colonial era neither was able to do so. This condition transformed the
region into a cultural middle ground. In White's words:

> The middle ground depended on the inability of both sides to
> gain their ends through force. . . . To succeed, those who operated
> on the middle ground had, of necessity, to attempt to understand
> the world and the reasoning of others and to assimilate enough of
> that reasoning to put it to their own purposes.[102]

Returning now to Hall, via Galambos and White, we see that the organizational efforts at the turn of the century involved not just Research Corporation but also "universities, foundations, professional societies, research institutes, and a host of other 'voluntary cooperative' entities."[103] Moreover, these
organizations constituted a cultural middle ground where the motives of public service and profit making could tug and pull on one another with neither
gaining clear-cut dominance and with each having to reach a genuine measure
of understanding of the other. It was precisely the mixed motives in their

missions that enabled Research Corporation and the others to function in this way. But it was the universities, rather than Research Corporation, that ended up as the most successful embodiments of the middle ground.

Along with this general picture of Research Corporation as a transitional organization — taking on the role of technology transfer until universities themselves were ready to assume it — we now have the details recently offered in a pair of articles by David C. Mowery and Bhaven N. Sampat.

One of the articles featured Research Corporation's patent management services after World War II.[104] Immediately after the war Research Corporation concluded that the scale of its patent management services was not sufficiently large to achieve economic success. In 1946 it created a Patent Management Division, and in the following two decades it expanded its operations dramatically by negotating agreements with more than two hundred universities. Although the model it followed was the 1937 agreement with MIT, a dispute over Research Corporation's handling of a particular patent led to a decision by MIT in 1963 to assume full responsibility for managing its own patents. After that, Research Corporation intensified its interactions with its other university clients, through an expensive program of campus visitations.

Meanwhile, its major source of income was based not on the patents administered through the patent agreements but on a handful of donated patents.[105] After the last of these expired in 1975, the continued economic insufficiency of its patent agreements became even more apparent. By then, Research Corporation had begun an outreach program, to help universities manage their own patents. Thus the passage of the Bayh-Dole Act of 1980 represented only a further step in a longstanding trend away from centralized patent management by Research Corporation to localized managment by each university. The final step for Research Corporation came in 1987, when it closed its Patent Management Division and transferred that mission to Research Corporation Technologies.

In their other article Mowery and Sampat explicitly placed Research Corporation's evolution in the context of larger developments in American higher education after World War II. As federal support for research became more and more widely dispersed, and as concerns about participating directly in the patenting process diminished, other universities followed MIT's lead and undertook to manage their own patents. Thus while Mowery and Sampat admitted that "the Bayh-Dole Act accelerated the growth of university patenting," they also insisted that "the 'transformation' wrought by the 1980 Act in fact followed trends that were already well established by the end of the 1970s."[106]

The Breadth and Depth of the Research Revolution

Throughout this book I have sought to place Research Corporation's early history in the context of the Research Revolution. Until now the larger trend has served to help organize and interpret the specific case. But the tie turns out to be reciprocal, so that Research Corporation's early history also offers us a way to explore the breadth and depth of the Research Revolution.

The breadth of the Research Revolution can be measured in several distinct ways. Because it was basically an organizational revolution, perhaps the most obvious measure of breadth involves the concept of "organizational infrastructure," which I mentioned in the opening section of the present chapter but which I have implied all along. The first chapter emphasized the rise of an extensive set of research organizations, and subsequent chapters emphasized the effort that went into establishing one new organization within that larger set. Mentally multiplying the effort to establish Research Corporation times the overall number of organizations in the set provides an estimate of how broad the organizational infrastructure — and the Research Revolution — had become by the early twentieth century.

Of course, research-related organizations necessarily involved intellectual activity. That, in turn, suggests a second way of measuring the breadth of the Research Revolution. Drawing on Thomas S. Kuhn's concept, a field's intellectual coherence is a function of its dominant "paradigm" — by which Kuhn meant the field's "research consensus," a "body of intertwined theoretical and methodological belief that permits selection, evaluation, and criticism," or "a synthesis able to attract most of the next generation's practitioners."[107]

In my account I have not been emphasizing Kuhnian paradigms; however I have mentioned several examples. One was the electromagnetic field theory of James Clerk Maxwell (with Lodge being an early Maxwellian). Another was the idea that substances in solution are electrically charged particles, which has led historians of science to designate many turn-of-the-century physical chemists (including Cottrell) as "ionists."[108] Multiplying the intellectual sweep of one of these paradigms times the number of paradigms that were actively guiding researchers in various fields yields a second estimate of how broad the Research Revolution was.

Research, as I have been discussing it, is technological as well as scientific, and here a concept that has often been used to measure breadth is the concept of "technological systems." Thomas P. Hughes has defined technological systems as "coherent structures comprised of interacting, interconnecting components."[109] Rather than confining their attention to individual components, leading inventors like Edison made their mark by inventing whole series of interrelated components — entire systems. Even before achieving technical success in his Menlo Park lab, Edison "spoke not only of his incandescent lamp but of other envisaged components of his system, such as meters, dynamos, and distribution mains."[110] Time and again, after creating the laboratory prototypes, he went on to develop them for real-world conditions and to promote their adoption in practice on a wider and wider basis (the processes of innovation and diffusion). Thus invention, development, and innovation and diffusion comprise three distinct stages in the overall process of technological change.[111]

As with "organizational infrastructure" and intellectual "paradigms," mentally multiplying the effort required to invent, develop, and introduce the many components of a technological system times the number of systems in operation by the turn of the century gives us a yet another estimate of the Research Revolution's breadth. Nevertheless, one further observation may be required, for breadth of this sort to become fully apparent. Individual tools and particular techniques have always existed as components in much larger sets of interrelated tools and techniques. Sailing ships on the European voyages of discovery during the Renaissance, family farms during the American colonial era, cotton-textile mills during the early industrial era, railroads after the Civil War, as well as electric lighting at the turn of the century – all can be seen as examples of technological systems. With the rise of big business, however, more and more systems, each of which had become more complex than its pre-industrial counterpart, also became thoroughly dependent on each other. Thus Ruth Schwartz Cowan has noted:

> Early in the nineteenth century the process of industrialization
> had appeared . . . as a rather discrete undertaking. . . . By the end
> of the century, virtually all Americans must have been aware that it
> had become something vastly different: a systematic undertaking
> that had created interlocking physical and social networks in which
> all Americans – rich or poor, young or old, urban or rural – were
> increasingly enmeshed.[112]

So extensive have our technological systems become that most of us probably find it hard to picture a place to which we could not drive or fly, or in which we could not use a telephone, electric lights, gas stoves and so on. In my study of Research Corporation's early history, however, I caught a glimpse of such a place.

After the discovery of gold in 1848, California was rapidly settled by European Americans and was soon granted statehood. These and later developments put considerable pressure on local Native American populations. Of course, the pattern was one that had been repeated many times since the first British settlements along the Atlantic coast. By the early twentieth century, however, many Americans realized that this time was the last. Hence the public appeal of a statue exhibited in San Francisco as part of the Panama-Pacific International Exposition of 1915. Depicting "an exhausted Indian on horseback, slumped forward as if on the edge of collapse," it was entitled simply *The End of the Trail*.[113]

Behind such expressions of mass sentiment lay a gritty reality. For example, in the San Francisco Bay area at the same time as the exposition, the last of California's Yahi Indians was dying of tuberculosis; his passing would come in 1916. For several years he had been under the care of Berkeley anthropologist Alfred L. Kroeber. Years later Kroeber's wife Theodora wrote a book about the experience, entitled *Ishi in Two Worlds: A Biography of the Last Wild Indian in North America*.[114]

In the 1870s the remnants of the Yahi responded to devastating European-American raids by going into hiding. For decades, settlers in the vicinity of Mount Lassen saw only occasional hints of their presence. But in November 1908 a party of surveyors stumbled onto the Yahi camp and took as souvenirs all the movable items they found. That disruption was the final straw. The sole remaining band of Yahis was permanently broken up. The elderly soon died, and Ishi was left as the lone survivor.

In 1911 Ishi entered a European-American settlement, turned himself in, and came under Kroeber's care at Berkeley's Museum of Anthropology. At the time, anthropology was a relatively new field of research. Its origins as a profession lay almost wholly within the nineteenth century, and it had been a department of study at Berkeley only since 1901. But the point of including Ishi's story here is not really to bring anthropology into the picture — though its rise illustrates the growing breadth of the Research Revolution. Instead, the point involves the moment in time when the surveyors disrupted Ishi's camp, despite its being uphill and well-hidden from Deer Creek.

Far from being an accident, that moment shouts out the physical breadth of America's technological development at the turn of the century. Hungry for electrical power, Californians were building hydroelectric facilities up and down the Sierras, and these facilities relied on flumes to create heads of water. The surveyors who stumbled onto Ishi's camp were engineers sent by the Oro Light and Power Company, which anticipated building yet another flume. The path that they were surveying was well-removed from Deer Creek because the path of the flume would be well-removed.

Here, then, is the punch line: by 1910, California's electrical system had become so extensive that it flushed out the last known Native American still living completely within a stone-age culture. The very same technological system that enabled Cottrell to develop his electrostatic precipitator simultaneously eliminated Ishi's traditional world, thus demonstrating that no one in the United States could live in total isolation from the new technologies.

Reaching into the Natural World

So far we have been looking at the breadth of the Research Revolution, measured in terms of organizational infrastructure, intellectual paradigms, and — most notably for Ishi — technological systems. Yet there was more to the Research Revolution than breadth alone. It also had depth.

To explore the depth of the Research Revolution, I shall draw on the concept of applied science via an analogy. The Smithsonian's Museum of Natural History once featured an exhibit on the Bering Sea Eskimos.[115] The material artifacts had been collected just before the Yukon gold rush ushered in massive change, and what most impressed me were the ceremonial masks. Designed to look like animals, each mask also had on it a small human face which represented the animal's spirit. If an Eskimo hunter was respectful of an animal's spirit, the spirit might reveal itself to the hunter — with the face in the mask evincing the moment of revelation.

All along I had known that Cottrell's invention was an example of applied science. Using the conceptual tools of physics and chemistry, Cottrell "reached into" industrial smoke, not just mentally but also physically.[116] While we could describe his act as "applied science," I wish to emphasize the "reaching into" process.

In the course of studying Research Corporation's early history I had come across several other applied science breakthroughs. Cement, for example, had been used by engineers for centuries. But Portland cement was different. To produce it, researchers in the nineteenth century "reached into" traditional cement. They identified the various components and then optimized the composition and percentage of each. Similarly, iron and steel had long been produced. Yet only in the nineteenth century did researchers "reach into" these materials, analyzing their components and redesigning the mixture. More than that, from Sherry H. Olson's book I learned that railroad companies had "reached into" their other basic material, wood, and applied similar methods to determine which types of wood were best suited for which purposes.[117]

As these ideas came to me during the Christmas holiday of 1997, I took a break from my work to join my family at my brother's home in Indianapolis. The drive from Rochester lasted most of the day, and full darkness arrived well before I crossed the Indiana state line. By then I had been in my car so long that I was no longer pursuing any particular train of thought. Instead, I was focused on the road — a focus narrowly defined by the cones of my headlights and by lights in the distance.

What ensued was something I am tempted to call "an epiphany at 65 m.p.h." I was passed by an eighteen-wheeler with a shiny steel tank. No longer pin-points in the distance, the lights on the rig became full-scale features, and behind the mud flaps I could see the rapidly rolling tires. It was then that the face on the mask appeared. Virtually every aspect of the world within my focus — the rubber tires, the molded contours of the lights, the steel tank, the concrete highway, the reflective surface of the signs — had been produced by the "reaching into" process I was discovering in my Research Corporation study. Researchers had "reached into" the materials of the natural world and reordered them — not just at the level of their visible, surface features, but all the way down to the molecular level. What allowed me and that truck driver to race across the Indiana countryside in the dark was the amazingly deep control our culture has acquired over concrete, rubber, plastic, steel, and so forth.

I know that specific individuals could be associated with the development of these materials, but I also know that the overarching control I recognized that night extends far deeper than individuals acting alone. Only an organized effort — indeed, only the coordinated efforts of many organizations over multiple generations of people — could lead to the construction of interstate highways, the building of vehicles, and the daily operation of the system as a whole.

At stake here is the realization that science and technology have acquired a fundamentally new methodological principle during the past hundred and fifty years. Since the time of the ancient Greeks, science has been based on words and mathematics, while technology has been based on craft techniques. In each case, the result (from our point of view) was a genuine degree of understanding and control of nature. But that understanding and control (again, from our point of view) was relatively shallow. During the Renaissance, craft techniques became a part of the scientific enterprise, resulting in genuinely experimental methods. At the same time, the verbal and mathematical techniques of traditional scholarship became important to technology. Thus human understanding and the control of nature deepened.

The Research Revolution marks a further advance. With the rise of an organized approach to the creation of new knowledge, policymaking became part of the process. Far from being a "necessary evil" or something ancillary to the "real" effort, the devising of appropriate policy has become one of the most important means by which our culture is achieving an even deeper understanding and control of nature.

Cottrell's Vision

Like our automotive transportation system, computers also lie beyond the reach of individuals acting alone. The only route to modern computers is the route defined by complex organizations whose actions are guided on the basis of appropriate policy. With so much attention being given to organizations and their policies, however, we may tend to lose sight of the people who still compose our organizational engines of change. Hence the appeal of a book Tracy Kidder published in 1981. Telling the story of the engineers who designed a new computer for the Data General Corporation, Kidder put a human face on the organized creation of new technology.

Had economist John Kenneth Galbraith written a foreword to Kidder's book, he might have noted how it illustrated his concept of "the technostructure" — which he defined as all the people within an organization who make key decisions in designing complex products.[118] In Kidder's story, key decisions regarding the new computer were made not just by the company's president, the vice-president of engineering, and the director of the project, but also by the project engineers. Yet Kidder's emphasis differed significantly from Galbraith's. Where Galbraith would have seen decision-makers shaping policy, Kidder saw, in the same situation, human beings engaged in a creative effort. Instead of writing about "the technostructure," he gave the group a different designation. He called his book *The Soul of a New Machine*.[119]

In 1930 the inventor Michael Pupin explored a similar idea. In an essay entitled "Machine Industry and Idealism" in Charles A. Beard's *Toward Civilization*, Pupin wrestled with the question of why he had left Serbia and come to the United States in 1874. Just after World War I he was invited back to his native country to assess the condition of war orphans. While traveling, he met a peasant who was guiding an oxcart to Belgrade, and in their conversation Pupin remarked that he had once been in a similar position. The peasant then exclaimed: "Oh, how could you desert your lovely animals and run away to the land of machines?"[120]

"I did not answer his question," Pupin confessed in the essay, "but I have been thinking about it ever since...."[121] His arrival in the United States just after the Civil War gave him a firsthand look at a striking series of new technological developments: elevated railroads, the Brooklyn Bridge, Bell's telephone, Edison's phonograph and incandescent lights, the steel mills of Pittsburgh, and so forth. However, he could not treat these observations as strictly material, because the peasant had not treated them as strictly material. Thus Pupin wrote:

> [The peasant] knew that back of these American machines, and
> back of our proverbial hustling and hurry, there is a gentle spirit

which he had not observed among the great folk of Europe whom he had seen in Serbia during the war.[122]

Moving on to his own assessment, Pupin noted that what I have been calling the Research Revolution was motivated by the "unselfish search of the eternal truth."[123] He then invoked language much like Kidder's:

> Every mediaeval cathedral has a soul; it is a part of the soul of its designer and of the souls of the pious men who built it. So every modern machine has a soul; it is a part of the soul of its inventor and of the patient souls of the men who developed it.[124]

Similarly, our assessment of the Research Revolution need not be limited to material considerations alone but may also be extended to spiritual considerations, which brings me back to Cottrell and his vision for Research Corporation.

When I went to Tucson during the summer of 1994 for a final round of work with Research Corporation's early records, I was still resisting the topic of Cottrell's vision. In fact, all along I had shied away from taking a biographical approach. Cottrell's life had been described in Cameron's *Samaritan of Science,* and my unsuccessful search for the documents on which Cameron based his book suggested that a more comprehensive treatment was not feasible. Besides, my dissertation had been an exercise in biographical writing, and I wanted to try my hand at something different. Of course, an organizational approach required taking a close look at key individuals. In Research Corporation's case, that certainly included Cottrell. But that also included Walcott and Hooker, Bradley and Schmidt, Holmes and Duncan, Little and Goetze, etc.

Early on, I had no difficulty in keeping the focus off Cottrell. As I extended my research beyond the company's earliest years, however, I changed my assessment. Viewing him merely as one of several key founders no longer worked. Instead, he emerged as a moral authority to whom others deferred, year after year, throughout the 1920s, the 1930s, and most of the 1940s.

One sign of the continued high regard with which Cottrell was held by his colleagues came in the form of the Perkin Medal, presented to him at the Chemists' Club on January 17, 1919.[125] So important was the medal within the profession that A. D. Little characterized it as "the Badge of Knighthood in American Chemistry."[126] Established in 1906 in honor of William H. Perkin (the British chemist whose work in the mid-nineteenth century established the basis for the coal tar dye industry), the award had been made annually since 1907. Although sponsored primarily by the New York Section of the Society of Chemical Industry, also represented on the selection committee were the American Chemical Society and the American Electrochemical Society.[127]

In Cottrell's case, the presentation address was given by Charles F. Chandler, who had likewise presented most of the earlier awards. Born in 1836, Chandler was a highly respected elder statesman from the earliest years of America's Research Revolution. A founder and long the dean of Columbia's School of Mines, he had strengthened the role of chemistry in the curriculum. His other activities after the Civil War included helping establish the American Chemical Society, actively serving as an industrial chemist, and helping New York City's board of health set vigorous standards. In presenting the 1919 award, he emphasized Cottrell's work with electrostatic precipitation and briefly described Cottrell's other professional achievements.[128]

A year later the American Chemical Society awarded Cottrell its Willard Gibbs Medal, and in making that presentation Willis R. Whitney elected "to preach a brief sermon" on the importance of Cottrell's ideals.[129] "I choose to call attention to your *process* rather than your product," Whitney began, speaking directly to Cottrell:

> I believe that the *way* you have done things is even more important than the actual things themselves. Our country might get along without the particular products of your effort, but it could not get along without men personifying your procedure. We are not so much interested in recovery of fumes, the abatement of the smoke nuisance, . . . in the production of helium, or any other of the definite undertakings which are attributed to you, though these are in themselves very valuable, but rather we exalt that human *quality* which insures advanced undertakings of public welfare and interest. You are one of those who intelligently decline to proceed along entirely old paths but map out and push along new ones. . . . Your work in the West and your radical undertaking in the East, in establishing the Research Corporation, together constitute a trail blazer which calls attention to the possibilities of coöperative research. . . . You have set an example not only in accepting the responsibility of such public work, but your patient persistence in carrying out your own plans with support which only your well-known integrity, industry, and enthusiasm could insure, forms a new high plane of activity for the emulation of the American chemist.[130]

Meanwhile, Cottrell's influence continued to be felt at Research Corporation. Earlier in the chapter we saw how he was a member of the committee that Hamerschlag chaired in 1920–1921. Another example came during a directors' meeting shortly after Hamerschlag's death in 1927. As recorded in the official minutes, Hooker read aloud a letter from Cottrell "in which he outlined his ideas, particularly the desirability of giving as much attention as possible to the altruistic aims of the Corporation."[131] This letter was probably the one that Cameron quoted at length in *Samaritan of Science*. Specifically, Cottrell noted:

> [Hamerschlag] never lost sight of the fact that the development of new projects was, after all, the ultimate object of the Corporation and even in the hardest times of making both ends meet [he] kept also driving ahead on new lines. In the early history of the Corporation a feeling grew up that perhaps it was most expedient to concentrate nearly the entire attention on the precipitation work, viewing other and newer projects as distinctly incidental until a surplus or reserve of, say half a million to a million should be built up, and then turn more definitely to the projects of new inventions.
>
> Personally I was always a half-hearted supporter of this policy but time has since demonstrated that if we are to make the Research Corporation serve the central purposes for which it was created, we must not let the mere running of its established and already income-producing lines of activity absorb all or even the larger part of the interest and attention of the management.[132]

Here again was Cottrell's acceptance of the profit motive, as well as his insistence that the profit motive be used to facilitate a larger aim, namely, the pursuit of new projects. That emphasis on new projects demonstrated his entrepreneurial bent. Once an enterprise was well under way and the need for risk-taking passed, the time had come for the entrepreneur to move on to new challenges. Like other entrepreneurs, and despite his long service at Berkeley and at the Bureau of Mines, Cottrell was uncomfortable with organizational permanence. "No laboratory lasts more than . . . twelve years," he once said, ". . . after twelve, thirteen years every laboratory goes dead. It ought to be cleaned out, started over again, like you do in a garden."[133] Similarly, he hoped Research Corporation would act in an entrepreneurial fashion, by moving beyond the precipitation work and actively seeking new inventions to promote.

From that point of view, Cottrell endowed Research Corporation not only with patents but also with a vision. One facet of Cottrell's vision was his assumption that new ideas *could* be made to pay off. As straightforward as the assumption sounds, its boldness becomes clear in light of Research Corporation's subsequent patent experiences. Using rough figures, only about one in ten patents gets licensed, and only about one in a hundred earns royalties. Research Corporation was organized to help inventors work these odds in their favor — to help them become the one-in-ten or one-in-a-hundred long shots.[134]

Another facet of Cottrell's vision was that Research Corporation should concentrate on inventions with clear social utility that might not otherwise be developed commercially. Further, he believed that the income derived from commercially successful patents should be channeled into research grants, thereby helping to support the kind of activities that gave rise to the patents in the first place. In short, the profit-making process could (and should) be harnessed to serve the public good, by fostering socially useful inventions and new basic research.

Analyzing Cottrell's vision also reveals a very distinctive approach to research. In his own work the boundaries between discovery and invention, between basic research and practical applications, between individual achievement and organized cooperation all remained quite fluid. Cottrell believed that such fluidity could (and should) be encouraged as a matter of deliberate policy.

Hence Cottrell's larger importance for Research Corporation comes into focus: as an individual he held personal views that also served as touchstones for the on-going formulation of policy. He *embodied* the ephemeral link between individual values and organizational policy.

That same quality could be seen in Cottrell's relationship with the larger community of researchers. On February 23, 1937, he was presented the Washington Award at a meeting of the Western Society of Engineers in Chicago. Although administered by the Western Society of Engineers, several other engineering societies formally cooperated in making the award. These were the founder societies, who viewed themselves as comprising the heart of the American professional engineering community: the American Society of Civil Engineers, the American Institute of Mining and Metallurgical Engineering, the American Society of Mechanical Engineers, and the American Institute of Electrical Engineers. The selection committee representing these societies recommended Cottrell on the basis of his "social vision in dedicating to the perpetuation of research the rewards of his achievements in science and engineering."[135]

Cottrell chose as the topic for his acceptance speech "the social responsibility of the engineer," and his starting point was Thorstein Veblen's 1921 book *The Engineers and the Price System.*[136] Veblen was a Norwegian-American economist who had devoted his career to understanding the economic changes brought on by the rise of big business. Although Veblen recognized that engineers comprised a relatively small social group, he knew they played a vital role in the overall process of industrialization — which, in turn, gave them responsibility for social leadership. To this, Cottrell agreed: "There is sound wisdom in Veblen's exhortation of the scientists and engineers to take a more active interest . . . in [the acute social and economic problems facing the world to-day]."[137] Of the individual scientist or engineer, Cottrell had said:

> He is under less direct pressure than the business management to act exclusively under the profit motive, but is distinctively associated in everybody's mind with the function of service.[138]

Finally, he offered Research Corporation as an example of what social responsibility looks like.

After Cottrell's death in 1948, when the time came to prepare an entry on his life and career for the *Biographical Memoirs of the National Academy of Sciences* (to which Cottrell had been elected in 1939), the assignment went to Vannevar Bush, an electrical engineer and the leading research policymaker of his generation. From his position on the faculty at MIT during the interwar years (and as MIT's vice president after 1932), Bush came to Washington, D.C., in 1939 as president of the Carnegie Institution of Washington, a position he held until his retirement in 1955. Concern about the state of America's preparedness for World War II prompted him to help mobilize the country's researchers — first as chair of the National Defense Research Committee (created by President Franklin D. Roosevelt in 1940) and then as director of the Office of Scientific Research and Development (created by Roosevelt in 1941). Finally, for a decade after the war Bush played a leading role in making support for scientific and technological research a central aspect of American federal policy.[139]

What Bush featured in the opening sentence of his entry on Cottrell was the citation of the Washington Award, and he further remarked:

> The social philosophy underlying the Research Corporation was never better stated than by Dr. Cottrell himself in 1937, in his address "The Social Responsibility of the Engineer". . . . [140]

To express Cottrell's core ideal more concretely, Bush then quoted directly from the 1937 address. Of Research Corporation and a newly formed "offshoot," Research Associates, Inc., Cottrell had written:

> . . . they are frankly willing to risk or even sacrifice on occasion
> possible legitimate profits from the licensing or operation of pat-
> ents or developments if thereby a more important public service
> can be rendered. . . .[141]

As I put all these things together, I was reminded of Salomen's House, the organization that Francis Bacon envisioned at the end of the Renaissance. In large measure, Salomen's House has been materially realized in the form of the Research Revolution. Nevertheless, the creation of new knowledge remains a complex and demanding spiritual process. No matter how sophisticated our research organizations become, policy remains linked to the visions of individuals and to the challenges that individuals face in handling mixed motives. More than merely being tolerated, these features of our organizations should be encouraged, not just because they are good things in and of themselves (though I suspect they are) but also because they are essential for the continued unfolding of the Research Revolution.

At a time when the value of research for its own sake — for spiritual purposes, for the good of the soul — is being challenged, the case of Cottrell and the early history of Research Corporation should remind us to leave room for new visions and mixed motives under the hoods of our organizational machinery. Likely, there is no going back to a world where people are not immersed in a vast continuum of organizations. But for our own sense of well-being we should try to hear the human voices that still vivify our organizations and give meaning to their policies. If we succeed, then we shall have held onto one of the most important bases we have for the cultivation of wisdom.

Table 1: The Original Board of Directors

William L. Dudley
T. Coleman du Pont
Frederick A. Goetze
Elon H. Hooker
J. Hennen Jennings
Charles Kirchhoff
Benjamin B. Lawrence
Arthur D. Little
John B. Pine
Mark S. Reardon, III
Lloyd N. Scott
Charles A. Stone
James J. Storrow
Elihu Thomson
Charles D. Walcott

Table 2: The Original Board of Directors — Listed by Class

CLASS OF 1913	CLASS OF 1914	CLASS OF 1915
T. Coleman du Pont	Frederick A. Goetze	William L. Dudley
Arthur D. Little	Benjamin B. Lawrence	Elon H. Hooker
Mark S. Reardon, III	John B. Pine	J. Hennen Jennings
Charles A. Stone	Lloyd N. Scott	Charles Kirchhoff
Elihu Thomson	Charles D. Walcott	James J. Storrow

Table 3: The Original Stockholders *(with number of shares subscribed)*

Edward D. Adams	5
Cleveland H. Dodge	5
James Douglass	5
T. Coleman du Pont	5
Frederick A. Goetze	3
Elon H. Hooker	10
J. Hennen Jennings	10
Charles Kirchhoff	3
Benjamin B. Lawrence	7
Arthur D. Little	3
Thomas C. Meadows	5
H. C. Perkins	5
Charles A. Stone	10
James J. Storrow	10
Elihu Thomson	5
Henry R. Towne	5
Charles D. Walcott	5

Table 4: The Board of Directors at the Time Hamerschlag Became a Director, January 1921 *(original directors noted with *)*

John J. Carty
T. Coleman du Pont*
Frederick A. Goetze*
Arthur H. Hamerschlag
Ellwood Hendrick
Elon H. Hooker*
Otto H. Kahn
George F. Kunz
Benjamin B. Lawrence*
Arthur D. Little*
John C. Pennie
John B. Pine*
Howard A. Poillon
Charles A. Stone*
Charles D. Walcott*

[ENDNOTES]

Abbreviations Used in the Endnotes and Bibliography

Cottrell Papers: F. G. Cottrell Papers, Manuscripts Division,
Library of Congress
MI Papers: Mellon Institute Papers, Carnegie Mellon University Archives
RC Archives: Research Corporation Archives
SI Archives: Smithsonian Institution Archives
Smoke Investigation Papers: Mellon Institute of Industrial Research, Smoke
Investigation Activities 1911–1957, University of Pittsburgh Archives
T. Coleman du Pont Papers: Du Pont Presidential Files,
Hagley Museum and Library
USBM Records: Records of the U.S. Bureau of Mines (Record Group 70),
National Archives
USPO Records: Records of the U.S. Patent Office (Record Group 241),
National Archives

AMS: American Men of Science
AMWS: American Men and Women of Science
ANB: American National Biography
DAB: Dictionary of American Biography
DSB: Dictionary of Scientific Biography
NCAB: National Cyclopaedia of American Biography
WWE: Who's Who in Engineering
WWWA: Who Was Who in America
Biog. Mem. NAS: Biographical Memoirs of the National Academy of Sciences
EMJ: Engineering and Mining Journal
JACS: Journal of the American Chemical Society
JIEC: Journal of Industrial and Engineering Chemistry
JSCI: Journal of the Society of Chemical Industry
MCE: Metallurgical and Chemical Engineering
MI Smoke Investigation Bull.: Mellon Institute of Industrial Research,
Smoke Investigation Bulletin
NYT: The New York Times
Trans. AES: Transactions of the American Electrochemical Society
Trans. AIEE: Transactions of the American Institute of Electrical Engineers
Trans. AIME: Transactions of the American Institute of Mining Engineers
USBM Bull.: U.S. Bureau of Mines Bulletin

Notes on Archival Sources

This study draws extensively (though by no means exclusively) on several collections at the Smithsonian Institution Archives.

Record Unit 45 consists of Charles D. Walcott's records as head of the Smithsonian. Because its overall organization is alphabetical by topic, the material on "Research Corporation" came in Box 47. Other relevant material appeared elsewhere (for example, in Box 17, under the alphabetical listing for "Cottrell, Frederick Gardner."). For this collection, there is a published finding aid: James A. Steed, *Guide to the Records of the Office of the Secretary (Charles D. Walcott), 1890–1929* (Washington, D.C.: Archives and Special Collections of the Smithsonian Institution, 1986).

Another important collection was Record Unit 51, which consists of additional documents from the office of the Secretary. When I first began my research, it was designated Record Unit 46TB. Stored in twelve archival boxes, the documents ran from Research Corporation's formative years (including minutes for meetings of the board of directors, the executive committee, and the stockholders) to the late 1950s — though the detailed correspondence thinned out considerably after the early 1920s.

Also at the SI Archives, I consulted Walcott's diaries (located in the Charles D. Walcott Collection, Record Unit 7004) and the Proceedings of the Board of Regents of the Smithsonian Institution (Record Unit 1).

Although not generally open to scholars, Research Corporation maintains an archive of its history. Through the kind efforts of W. Stevenson Bacon, I was permitted to consult the collections most relevant to my study. Especially useful was the material in thirty storage boxes that contain the records of Research Corporation's activities into the 1950s, and the "Publication Archive," which preserves all documents published by the foundation since its inception. Finally, there were minutes for meetings of the board of directors, the executive committee, and the stockholders.

After their first citations, the following archival documents from the SI Archives and the RC Archives are cited in shortened form:

> *Lodge-Cottrell Limited: Pioneers of Electrical Precipitation.* A brochure enclosed in J. E. Schork (president of Research Corporation) to Richard Hodgson, June 5, 1972. Publication Archive, RC Archives.

> "Minutes of Meeting Called at 63 Wall St. N.Y. Feb. 2 1912 for Purpose of Organizing Research Corporation." Box A14, RC Archives.

> "Random Notes by Walter A. Schmidt with Reference to Suit Filed by the Department of Justice against Western, International, Research, and Schmidt." Aug. 21, 1945. Publication Archive, RC Archives.

> Research Corporation Minutes. RU 51, Boxes 3–4, SI Archives (to the end of 1920); RC Archives (after 1920).

> Schmidt, W. A., to J. W. Barker. Mar. 21, 1949. Box A9. RC Archives.

> Scott, L. N. "Notes on the Founding of the Research Corporation." Feb. 27, 1952. Publication Archive, RC Archives.

Second Statement by Warren H. McBryde. Nov. 22, 1948. Box A9. RC
Archives.

Third Statement by Warren H. McBryde. Nov. 22, 1948. Box A9. RC
Archives.

Other archival sources augmented the material from the SI Archives and the RC
Archives. On several occasions I consulted Cottrell's diaries in the Frederick Gardner
Cottrell Papers in the Manuscripts Division at the Library of Congress. Although the
entries were very useful for following his movements and documenting his contacts,
their brevity sometimes made them cryptic, and Cottrell's handwriting was often
hard to read. In addition, the coverage in time was not complete. One group of diaries
dated from the period 1900–1902. The others started in July 1907, with entries on a
regular basis after that. The collection (stored in six archival boxes) also included
some miscellaneous items, one of which was "Inside Doctor Cottrell," P. H. Royster's
recollections of his colleague.

On a less extensive basis, I consulted the records of the U. S. Bureau of Mines
(Record Group 70) and the U. S. Patent Office (Record Group 241) at the National
Archives. Rather than following the details of Cottrell's career at the Bureau of Mines,
I sought documents relevant to the early history of Research Corporation that comple-
mented what I was finding at the SI Archives and the RC Archives. In the case of the
patent records, I concentrated on documents relating to the original precipitator
patent.

Although documents at the Carnegie Mellon University Archives, the University
of Pittsburgh Archives, and the Hagley Museum and Library contained few direct
references to Cottrell or Research Corporation, they shed important light on the
story I sought to tell. The collections in Pittsburgh (the Mellon Institute Papers at
Carnegie Mellon and the records of the Mellon Institute's Smoke Investigation Activities, 1911–1957, at the University of Pittsburgh) offered details on Duncan's urban smoke program. Likewise, the collections in Delaware (primarily the E. I. du
Pont de Nemours and Co. Presidential Files) helped me better understand the DuPont
facilities in California.

NOTES ON BIOGRAPHICAL SOURCES

Despite this book's focus on Cottrell and the individuals most closely associated
with Research Corporation's early history, the narrative also mentions dozens of
secondary characters. Some are truly obscure, while others are quite famous but
make only cameo appearances. To help render more visible the vast social network of
the Research Revolution, I have included their names and cited biographical sources
at appropriate places in the text. Rather than repeating all those citations here, I
offer only an overview.

For Americans who flourished during the early twentieth century, the array of
biographical sources is especially rich. Heading the list are signed entries in the

DAB, the *ANB*, and the *DSB* (as well as the *Biog. Mem. NAS*). Although the *NCAB* entries are unsigned, the series is indexed — making it especially easy to use. *AMS* (which later became *AMWS*) began appearing in 1906, and in 1983 a cumulative index was released for all the editions to that point. Other important sources are *WWE* (which began appearing in 1923 but unfortunately includes no comprehensive index), *WWWA*, and obituaries in *NYT*. Also facilitating biographical research are the following multivolume publications: the *Personal Name Index to "The New York Times,"* the *Biography and Genealogy Master Index*, and the *Biography Index*. More specialized or selective sources of biographical information appear in the "Selected Publications" lists beginning on page 300.

ACKNOWLEDGMENTS

PAGES 5–8

1. For a description of the department's program and facilities — including mention of assistance from Research Corporation — see J. H. Taylor, "A Decade of Optical Physics in a Small Liberal Arts College, *Applied Optics*, 8 (Jan. 1969), 197–202. Research Corporation's publications, in turn, have mentioned the physics department at Rhodes — for example, a photograph atop p. 16 in the Research Corporation booklet *Science, Invention, and Society: The Story of a Unique American Institution* (Research Corporation, 1972), a copy of which is listed in the Library of Congress online catalog.

2. J. H. Taylor, *A Review of the History of Physics at Southwestern* (Memphis, Tenn.: Southwestern at Memphis, Department of Physics, 1972), p. 58.

3. William L. Bowden (president of the college), "Alfred Kelleher," May 31, 1971, quoted in ibid., p. 88.

4. Taylor, *A Review of the History of Physics at Southwestern*, pp. 53–54.

5. "Schmelz 'Saw the Light' of Solar Physics," *The 150th Anniversary Campaign for Rhodes* (Rhodes College, Feb. 1994), pp. 4–5. Also Research Corporation, *Annual Report for 1993*, p. 24.

6. Herbert Childs, *An American Genius: The Life of Ernest Orlando Lawrence* (New York: E. P. Dutton, 1968), especially pp. 166–168.

7. I joined the faculty at RIT's College of Liberal Arts in September 1982 as a member of both the History Department and the Science, Technology, and Society Department. I defended my dissertation, "Merle A. Tuve and His Program of Nuclear Studies at the Department of Terrestrial Magnetism: The Early Career of a Modern American Physicist," in November 1985 and received my doctorate the following May.

8. For our conference papers, see Ellis L. Yochelson, "Andrew Carnegie and Charles Doolittle Walcott: The Origin and Early Years of the Carnegie Institution of Washington"; and Thomas D. Cornell, "Merle A. Tuve's Post-War Geophysics: Early Explosion Seismology" — both in Gregory A. Good, ed., *The Earth, the Heavens, and the Carnegie Institution of Washington* (Washington, D.C.: American Geophysical Union, 1994), pp. 1–19 and pp. 185–214, respectively. Ellis has since published a two-volume study of Walcott's career — see Ellis L. Yochelson, *Charles Doolittle Walcott: Paleontologist* (Kent, Ohio: Kent State University Press, 1998); and Ellis L. Yochelson, *Smithsonian Institution Secretary, Charles Doolittle Walcott* (Kent, Ohio: Kent State University Press, 2001).

CHAPTER ONE—SETTING THE STAGE

PAGES 9–27

1. For example, on Research Corporation's letterhead or its Web site (http://www.rescorp.org).

2. Research Corporation, *Annual Report for 1989*, p. 2.

3. Riley E. Scott, "Interesting Westerners: The Enemy of the Smoke Nuisance," *Sunset: The Pacific Monthly*, 33 (Nov. 1914), 976. For the growing interest of the mining and metallurgical industry in conservation efforts after the turn of the century, see Duane A. Smith, *Mining America: The Industry and the Environment, 1800–1980* (Lawrence: University Press of Kansas, 1987), pp. 81–104.

4. Samuel Haber, *Efficiency and Uplift: Scientific Management in the Progressive Era, 1890–1920* (Chicago: University of Chicago Press, 1964), Chap. 4, "A Normal American Madness," pp. 51–74.

5. Robert H. Moulton, "Turning Smoke into Money: The Origin and Development of the Cottrell Electric Precipitation," *Scientific American*, 119 (July 20, 1918), 50 and 59–60.

6. L. N. Scott to C. D. Walcott, Oct. 29, 1915, Record Unit 51, Box 1, Smithsonian Institution Archives (hereafter RU 51, Box 1, SI Archives — with other SI Archives citations following a similar style). Lawrence's proposal was subsequently carried out by Research Corporation — see Carl W. Ackerman, "Recovering Gold from Smoke," *Journal of the American Bankers Association*, 16 (Aug. 1923), 83; and N. W. Sultzer, "Recovery of Gold at the U.S. Assay Office, New York," *Chemical Age*, 33 (Jan. 1925), 5–8.

7. David E. Nye, *American Technological Sublime* (Cambridge, Mass.: MIT Press, 1994). "The test for determining what is sublime," wrote Nye (p. 16), "is to observe whether or not an object strikes people dumb with amazement."

8. Oliver Lodge, "Foreword," to William E. Gibbs, *Clouds and Smokes: The Properties of Disperse Systems in Gases and Their Practical Applications* (London: J. and A. Churchill, 1924), p. ix.

9. Linn Bradley to C. D. Walcott, Apr. 30, 1913, RU 51, Box 1, SI Archives. The award Millikan received was the National Academy of Science's Comstock Prize — see Robert H. Kargon, *The Rise of Robert Millikan: Portrait of a Life in American Science* (Ithaca: Cornell University Press, 1982), p. 78.

10. H. O. Hofman, *General Metallurgy* (New York: McGraw-Hill, 1913), pp. 858–860; William H. Walker, Warren K. Lewis, and William H. McAdams, *Principles of Chemical Engineering* (New York: McGraw-Hill, 1923), p. 327; and William I. Wyman, "A Record of Achievement," *Journal of the Patent Office Society*, 8 (Nov. 1925), 103–108.

11. R. Ladenburg, "Elektrische Gasreingung (Elektrofilter)," pp. 31–91, in A. Eucken, ed., *Elektrische und Magnetisch Materialtrennung Materialvereinigung*, Vol. 1, Pt. 4, of A. Eucken and M. Jakob, eds., *Der Chemie-Ingenieur: Ein Handbuch der Physikalischen Arbeitsmethoden in Chemischen und Verwandten Industriebetrieben* (Leipzig: Akademische Verlagsgesellschaft, 1934); R. F. Heinrich and J. R. Anderson, "Electro-Precipitation," in Herbert W. Cremer and Trefor Davies, eds., *Chemical Engineering Practice*, Vol. 3: *Solid Systems* (New York: Academic Press, 1957), pp. 484–534; and John Jewkes, David Sawers, and Richard Stillerman, *The Sources of*

Invention (London: Macmillan, 1958), especially pp. 296–298.

12. Harry J. White, *Industrial Electrostatic Precipitation* (Reading, Mass.: Addison–Wesley, 1963), and A. D. Moore, "Electrostatics," *Scientific American*, 224 (Mar. 1972), 46–58.

13. *The National Inventors Hall of Fame* (Akron, Ohio: National Inventors Hall of Fame, 1994), pp. 65–66.

14. See, for example, F. G. Cottrell, "The Electrical Precipitation of Suspended Particles," *Journal of Industrial and Engineering Chemistry* (hereafter *JIEC*), 3 (Aug. 1911), 549. The device was also ineffective with true gases (e.g., sulfur dioxide), as opposed to suspended particles.

15. For a brief overview of Research Corporation's history, see W. Stevenson Bacon, "Research Corporation," in Harold M. Keele and Joseph C. Kiger, eds., *Foundations*, Greenwood Encyclopedia of American Institutions, Vol. 8 (Westport, Conn.: Greenwood Press, 1984), pp. 349–352. Also useful are the Research Corporation booklet *Science, Invention, and Society*; and Gary W. Matkin, *Technology Transfer and the University* (New York: National University Continuing Education Association; American Council on Education; Macmillan 1990), especially Chap. 4, "A Brief History of Patent Policy and Administration," pp. 56–80.

16. "The Research Corporation's Five-Year Program of Postwar Collegiate Research," *School and Society*, 62 (Oct. 20, 1945), 246.

17. Charles H. Schauer, "How Firm a Foundation?" *Physics Today*, 3 (Oct. 1950), 6–11; Charles H. Schauer, "Support for Research," *Sky and Telescope*, 14 (Mar. 1955), 190; Charles H. Schauer, "Research Corporation—Experiment in Administration of Patent Rights for the Public Good," *Research Management*, 5 (July 1962), 229–235; William Gelman, *Science: U.S.A.* (New York: Viking, 1965), pp. 104–105; and Jack W. Powers and David G. Black, Jr., "Research as a Vital Element in the Undergraduate College," *Journal of Chemical Education*, 54 (Sept. 1977), 565.

18. Robert R. Williams, *Williams-Waterman Fund for the Combat of Dietary Diseases: A History of the Period 1935 through 1955* (New York: Research Corporation, 1956); and Richard S. Baldwin, *The Fungus Fighters: Two Women Scientists and Their Discovery* (Ithaca: Cornell University Press, 1981).

19. Charles H. Townes, *How the Laser Happened: Adventures of a Scientist* (New York: Oxford University Press, 1999), p. 114. The patent in question was C. H. Townes, "Production of Electromagnetic Energy," U.S. Patent No. 2,879,439, issued Mar. 24, 1959 (filed Jan. 28, 1958). Although motivated by the development of the ammonia maser, Townes intended the patent to be quite general, with regard to the wavelength (not just microwaves) and the medium (not just ammonia). At the same time, he was also working with lawyers at Bell Labs on a subsidiary patent to cover visible wavelengths. The laser patent was A. L. Schawlow and C. H. Townes, "Masers and Maser Communications System," U.S. Patent No. 2,929,922, issued Mar. 22, 1960 (filed July 30, 1958). Of the two, Townes considered the first to have been more successful. "I had worked assiduously on the maser patent to see that it covered

everything appropriately, and it proved in the long run to do so. But... only the basic idea in our optical maser or laser manuscript was adequately covered in the laser patent application" (Townes, op. cit., p. 116). For this work, Townes became a co-recipient of the 1964 Nobel Prize in physics.

20. On the changing legal environment, see Marion R. Fremont-Smith, *Philanthropy and the Business Corporation* (New York: Russell Sage Foundation, 1972), pp. 3–30; and Thomas C. Reeves, ed., *Foundations Under Fire* (Ithaca: Cornell University Press, 1970), pp. 1–35. On Research-Cottrell, I consulted J. W. Hinkley to the Research Corporation Board of Directors, Feb. 10, 1967, Research Corporation Archives (hereafter RC Archives); and Alexander R. Hammer, "Losers Edge Out Gainers on Amex; Trading Is Active," *The New York Times* (hereafter *NYT*), Sept. 8, 1967, p. 57, col. 2

21. "Can Pollution Pay Off?," *Business Week*, No. 2159 (Jan. 16, 1971), 46–47; John H. Sheridan, "It Wasn't a Mirage That Fooled Him," *Industry Week*, 197 (June 12, 1978), 88–90 and 95–96; Eugene Kennedy, "The Tragedy at Tower No. 2," *NYT Magazine*, Dec. 3, 1978, 54–57f., "Research-Cottrell Turns to Energy," *ENR*, 205 (Sept. 4, 1980), 28–29; and Steven S. Ross, *Construction Disasters: Design Failures, Causes, and Prevention* (New York: McGraw-Hill, 1984), pp. 377–387.

22. W. Stevenson Bacon to Thomas D. Cornell, private communication. Later in the decade, ownership of Research-Cottrell changed hands — see "Research-Cottrell Is Sold," *ENR*, 218 (June 18, 1987), 133.

23. For a discussion of the patent services provided by Research Corporation after World War II, see Vincent Lee McKusick, "A Study of Patent Policies in Educational Institutions, Giving Specific Attention to the Massachusetts Institute of Technology," *Journal of the Franklin Institute*, 245 (Mar. and Apr. 1948), 193–225 and 271–300. On the effects of the Bayh-Dole Act of 1980 (The Patent and Trademark Law Amendments Act), see Henry Etzkowitz and Ashley J. Stevens, "Inching Toward Industrial Policy: The University's Role in Government Initiatives to Assist Small, Innovative Companies in the United States," in Henry Etzkowitz, Andrew Webster, and Peter Healey, eds., *Capitalizing Knowledge: New Intersections of Industry and Academia* (Albany: State University of New York Press, 1998), pp. 215–238. For explicit mention of Research Corporation in the context of universities themselves undertaking technology transfer, see also Rebecca L. Rawls, "University Technology Licensing Set to Rise," *Chemical and Engineering News*, 53 (Aug. 25, 1975), 11–12; "The Invention Game," *Compressed Air*, 91 (Nov. 1986), 10–16; Robert F. Johnston and Christopher G. Edwards, *Entrepreneurial Science: New Links between Corporations, Universities, and Government* (New York: Quorum Books, 1987), p. 42 and p. 137; Matkin, *Technology Transfer and the University*, passim; and Goldie Blumenstyk, "Payoffs from Patents: Rutgers Office Takes an Activist Approach to Commercializing Results of Research," *Chronicle of Higher Education*, Aug. 10, 1994, A27–A28. For discussions of changing university attitudes towards commercial initiatives, see Henry Etzkowitz and Lois S. Peters, "Profiting from Knowledge:

Organisational Innovations and the Evolution of Economic Norms," *Minerva*, 29 (Summer 1991), 133–166; and Roger L. Geiger, *Research and Relevant Knowledge: American Research Universities Since World War II* (New York: Oxford University Press, 1993), pp. 316–320.

24. Research Corporation, *A 75th Anniversary Report* [the foundation's annual report for 1987], pp. 20–25 and pp. 36–37; Matkin, *Technology Transfer and the University*, pp. 103–105; Albert E. Muir, *The Technology Transfer System* (Latham, N.Y.: Latham Book Publishing, 1997), p. 44; and Etzkowitz and Stevens, "Inching Toward Industrial Policy," pp. 232–233. On RCT, see also its Web site (http://www.rctech.com).

25. For an approach to the history of science that emphasizes organizational change, see Joseph Ben-David, *The Scientist's Role in Society: A Comparative Study* (Englewood Cliffs, N.J.: Prentice-Hall, 1971). Both here and in the remarks that follow I make no effort to survey the literature. Instead, I cite the sources that I found especially useful.

26. The "Research Revolution" concept comes to me from conversations with my dissertation advisor, Robert Kargon. For a brief published account, see Robert H. Kargon, Stuart W. Leslie, and Erica Schoenberger, "Far Beyond Big Science: Science Regions and the Organization of Research and Development," in Peter Galison and Bruce Hevly, eds., *Big Science: The Growth of Large-Scale Research* (Stanford: Stanford University Press, 1992), p. 337. The general importance of organizations in modern American history comes to me from Louis Galambos — see especially Louis Galambos, "The Emerging Organizational Synthesis in Modern American History," *Business History Review*, 44 (Autumn 1970), 279–290, and Louis Galambos, "Technology, Political Economy, and Professionalization: Central Themes of the Organizational Synthesis, ibid., 57 (Winter 1983), 471–493.

27. Here I rely mainly on Robert H. Wiebe, *The Search for Order: 1877–1920* (New York: Hill and Wang, 1967), especially Chap. 5, "A New Middle Class," pp. 111–132.

28. George H. Daniels, *American Science in the Age of Jackson* (New York: Columbia University Press, 1968), p. 18.

29. Sally Gregory Kohlstedt, *The Formation of the American Scientific Community: The American Association for the Advancement of Science, 1848–60* (Urbana: University of Illinois Press, 1976), p. 193.

30. *American Men of Science* (hereafter *AMS*), 1st Ed. (1906), p. v.

31. *AMS*, 4th Ed. (1927), p. viii; and *AMS*, 7th Ed. (1944), p. v.

32. Simon Newcomb, "Exact Science in America," *North American Review*, 119 (Oct. 1874), 307. For an assessment of such claims, see Nathan Reingold, "American Indifference to Basic Research: A Reappraisal," in George H. Daniels, ed., *Nineteenth-Century American Science: A Reappraisal* (Evanston, Ill.: Northwestern University Press, 1972), pp. 38–62.

33. For an assessment of Bush's report, see Daniel J. Kevles, "The National Science Foundation and the Debate over Postwar Research Policy, 1942–1945: A Political Interpretation of *Science — the Endless Frontier*," *Isis*, 68 (Mar. 1977), 4–26.

34. For my account of careers I have drawn from Burton J. Bledstein, *The Culture of Professionalism: The Middle Class and the Development of Higher Education in America* (New York: Norton, 1976).

35. Laurence R. Veysey, *The Emergence of the American University* (Chicago: University of Chicago Press, 1965).

36. My assessment here follows Louis Galambos, "The American Economy and the Reorganization of the Sources of Knowledge," in Alexandra Oleson and John Voss, eds., *The Organization of Knowledge in Modern America, 1860–1920* (Baltimore: The Johns Hopkins University Press, 1979), pp. 269–282.

37. Sources I have used here include David F. Noble, *America By Design: Science, Technology, and the Rise of Corporate Capitalism* (New York: Knopf, 1977); Kendall Birr, "Industrial Research Laboratories," in Nathan Reingold, ed., *The Sciences in the American Context: New Perspectives* (Washington, D.C.: Smithsonian Institution Press, 1979), pp. 193–207; and George Wise, "A New Role for Professional Scientists in Industry: Industrial Research at General Electric, 1900–1916," *Technology and Culture*, 21 (July 1980), 408–429.

38. A. Hunter Dupree, *Science in the Federal Government: A History of Policies and Activities to 1940* (Cambridge, Mass.: Belknap Press of Harvard University Press, 1957), p. 151. Another useful source here is Charles E. Rosenberg, "Rationalization and Reality in Shaping American Agricultural Research, 1875–1914," in Reingold, *The Sciences in the American Context*, pp. 143–163.

39. On developments in American private philanthropy at the turn of the century, see Robert H. Bremner, *American Philanthropy*, 2nd Ed. (Chicago: University of Chicago Press, 1988); Joseph Frazier Wall, *Andrew Carnegie* (New York: Oxford University Press, 1970); Peter Collier and David Horowitz, *The Rockefellers: An American Dynasty* (New York: Holt, Rinehart and Winston, 1976); Robert F. Arnove, ed., *Philanthropy and Cultural Imperialism: The Foundations at Home and Abroad* (Boston: G. K. Hall, 1980); Barry D. Karl and Stanley N. Katz, "The American Private Philanthropic Foundation and the Public Sphere, 1890–1930," *Minerva*, 19 (Summer 1981), 236–270; and Robert E. Kohler, *Partners in Science: Foundations and Natural Scientists, 1900–1945* (Chicago: University of Chicago Press, 1991).

40. The existence of a "Research Establishment" became much clearer in the 1920s — see Robert H. Kargon, "The New Era: Science and American Individualism in the 1920's," in Robert H. Kargon, ed., *The Maturing of American Science: A Portrait of Science in Public Life Drawn from the Presidential Addresses of the American Association for the Advancement of Science, 1920–1970* (Washington, D.C.: American Association for the Advancement of Science, 1974), pp. 1–29.

41. For the participation of researchers in the country's war effort, see Daniel J. Kevles, "George Ellery Hale, the First World War, and the Advancement of Science in America," *Isis*, 59 (Winter 1968), 427–437.

42. For a facsimile of Wilson's executive order, dated May 11, 1918, see Helen

Wright, Joan N. Warnow, and Charles Weiner, eds., *The Legacy of George Ellery Hale: Evolution of Astronomy and Scientific Institutions in Pictures and Documents* (Cambridge, Mass.: MIT Press, 1972), pp. 284–285.

43. See, for example, Robert H. Kargon and Elizabeth Hodes, "Karl Compton, Isaiah Bowman, and the Politics of Science in the Great Depression," *Isis*, 76 (Sept. 1985), 300–318.

44. Leon M. Lederman, "An Open Letter to Colleagues Who Publicly Opposed the SSC," *Physics Today*, 47 (Mar. 1994), 11.

45. My use of a case study under these circumstances is not novel. Thus Sally Gregory Kohlstedt has noted in her review article, "Institutional History" – see Sally Gregory Kohlstedt and Margaret W. Rossiter, eds., *Historical Writing on American Science*, published as *Osiris*, 2nd Ser., Vol. 1 (1985), 19: "As the numbers and diversity of institutions increase in the late nineteenth and twentieth centuries, historians seem less able to encompass larger patterns and rely even more on single case studies as a complement to biographical and thematic research."

46. J. A. Holmes, "The National Phases of the Mining Industry," in *Original Communications [to the] Eighth International Congress of Applied Chemistry, Washington and New York, September 4 to 13, 1912* (Concord, N.H.: Rumford Press, 1912–1913), Vol. 26, p. 747.

47. A. D. Little, "The Chemist and the Community," *Science*, 25 (Apr. 26, 1907), 647.

48. Ibid., p. 651.

49. Ibid., p. 650.

50. Holmes, "The National Phases of the Mining Industry" (1912–1913), pp. 735–736.

51. C. D. Walcott, "Science and Service," *Science*, 61 (Jan. 2, 1925), 3–4.

52. A. D. Little, "A Laboratory for Public Service," *Technology Review*, 11 (Jan. 1909), 17–18.

53. Holmes, "The National Phases of the Mining Industry" (1912–1913), pp. 738–739.

54. "To obtain the results desired it is evident that the great masses of humanity have yet to be educated in the scientific method of thought and action. . . . This is the greatest task immediately before us" (Walcott, "Science and Service," 1925, p. 4).

55. J. A. Holmes, "The New Purpose in State Development: The Safeguarding Its Own Future," *Science*, 32 (July 15, 1910), 65–66.

56. A. D. Little, "Organization of Industrial Research," *Proceedings of the American Society for Testing Materials*, Vol. 18, Pt. 2 (1918), p. 22.

57. C. D. Walcott, "Research and the Smithsonian Institution," *The Independent*, 66 (Mar. 18, 1909), 586.

58. Little, "Organization of Industrial Research" (1918), p. 23.

59. C. D. Walcott, "Relations of the National Government to Higher Education,"

Science, 13 (June 28, 1901), 1009. Although Walcott intended his article to help the effort to found a national university in Washington, what emerged instead was the Carnegie Institution of Washington — see Howard S. Miller, *Dollars for Research: Science and Its Patrons in Nineteenth-Century America* (Seattle: University of Washington Press, 1970), pp. 171–172.

60. "We may as well understand that the men of this generation will not mine, extract or use the state's mineral resources in such a manner as to entail financial loss to themselves . . . [so that] any consideration of the doctrine of conservation of resources must be accompanied by equal consideration of the doctrine of conservation of capital, and conservation of human life" (Holmes, "The New Purpose in State Development," 1910, p. 68).

61. A. D. Little, "Industrial Research in America: Presidential Address," *JIEC*, 5 (Oct. 1913), 800.

62. Holmes, "The National Phases of the Mining Industry" (1912–1913), p. 736.

63. Little, "Industrial Research in America: Presidential Address" (1913), p. 793.

64. C. D. Walcott to O. H. Kahn, Dec. 30, 1914, RU 51, Box 1, SI Archives.

65. F. G. Cottrell, "The Research Corporation, An Experiment in Public Administration of Patent Rights," *JIEC*, 4 (Dec. 1912), 865. Cottrell made his remarks at the Eighth International Congress of Applied Chemistry, to the section on "Political Economy and Conservation of Natural Resources," later described as "[a] unique feature on the scientific program of the Eighth Congress" — see Charles Albert Browne and Mary Elvira Weeks, *A History of the American Chemical Society: Seventy-Five Eventful Years* (Washington, D.C.: American Chemical Society, 1952), p. 105. Although the congress opened in Washington, D.C., on September 4, 1912, most of the presentations were made to the 2,500 attendees in New York, September 6–13, 1912. For a general account, see "International Congress of Applied Chemistry," *JIEC*, 4 (Oct. 1912), 706–719.

CHAPTER TWO—A PRACTICAL INVENTION
PAGES 28–50

1. The most complete treatment of Cottrell's life and career remains Frank T. Cameron, *Cottrell: Samaritan of Science* (Garden City, N.Y.: Doubleday, 1952), which has been reprinted by Research Corporation (Tucson, Ariz: 1993). On Cameron, a freelance writer, see *Contemporary Authors*, Permanent Ser., Vol. 1 (Detroit: Gale Research Co., 1975), p. 105. Other accounts of Cottrell include Vannevar Bush, "Frederick Gardner Cottrell, 1877–1948," *Biographical Memoirs of the National Academy of Sciences* (hereafter *Biog. Mem. NAS*), 28 (1952), 1–11; Thomas P. Hughes, "Frederick Gardner Cottrell," *Dictionary of American Biography* (hereafter *DAB*), Supp. 4 (1974), pp. 183–185; Harland F. Manchester, *New Trail Blazers of Technology* (New York: Scribners, 1976), Chap. 1, "The Man Who Lived a Thousand Lives," pp. 1–29;

Harry J. White, "Centenary of Frederick Gardner Cottrell," *Journal of Electrostatics*, 4 (1977/1978), 1–34; and Anthony N. Stranges and Richard C. Jones, "Frederick Gardner Cottrell," *American National Biography* (hereafter *ANB*), Vol. 5 (1999), pp. 569–570. For a list of Cottrell's publications, see Bush, op. cit., pp. 8–ll.

2. John S. White, "The Six Wide-Open Professions: [Pt.] II.–Electricity and the Telephone," *Harper's Young People*, 10 (June 4, 1889), 530. The series' opening installment listed the six as "architecture, railroading, electrical engineering, politics, the ministry, and secondary education" – see John S. White, "The Six 'Wide-Open' Professions: [Pt.] I.–Architecture," ibid., (Mar. 5, 1889), p. 314. White was a successful headmaster of a boys' college preparatory school – see *National Cyclopaedia of American Biography* (hereafter *NCAB*), Vol. 2 (1899), p. 340. For Cottrell's being read to by his Aunt Mame (Mary S. Durfee), see Cameron, *Samaritan of Science*, p. 33.

3. George Makepeace Towle, "Heroes and Martyrs of Invention: Eli Whitney and the Cotton-Gin," *Harper's Young People*, 10 (Dec. 18, 1888), 114. The series was later published as a book by the same title (Boston: Lee and Shepard, 1890). On Towle – a journalist, writer, and lecturer – see Sidney Gunn, "George Makepeace Towle," *DAB*, Vol. 18 (1936), p. 609.

4. George Makepeace Towle, "Heroes and Martyrs of Invention: The Struggles of Charles Goodyear," *Harper's Young People*, 10 (Sept. 10, 1889), 778.

5. Quoted in Cameron, *Samaritan of Science*, p. 21. For more on the *Boys' Workshop*, see ibid., pp. 17–21 and p. 33.

6. For an assessment of Edison as a cultural hero, see Wyn Wachhorst, *Thomas Alva Edison: An American Myth* (Cambridge, Mass.: MIT Press, 1981).

7. Cameron, *Samaritan of Science*, p. 34. For Henry Cottrell's interest in photography, see ibid., pp. 28–29, p. 38, and p. 53.

8. For Cottrell's high school science courses, see ibid., pp. 37–38. On his botany teacher, Margaret W. Wythe, see *AMS*, 9th Ed. (1955), Vol. 2, p. 1259. S. P. Meads was his chemistry and physics teacher. Since the mid-1880s, serious efforts had been under way to strengthen California's public high schools and to coordinate their curricula with the admission standards at Berkeley – see Roy W. Cloud, *Education in California: Leaders, Organizations, and Accomplishments of the First Hundred Years* (Stanford: Stanford University Press, 1952), especially pp. 86–87; and Verne A. Stadtman, *The University of California, 1868–1968* (New York: McGraw-Hill, 1970), pp. 93–95.

9. Cameron, *Samaritan of Science*, p. 41.

10. W. B. Rising to Cottrell, Sept. 1895, quoted in William L. Jolly, *From Retorts to Lasers: The Story of Chemistry at Berkeley* (Berkeley: College of Chemistry, University of California, 1987), p. 31; and in Cameron, *Samaritan of Science*, p. 43. On Rising – an American chemist who joined the Berkeley faculty in 1872 (after receiving his Ph.D. degree in 1871 from the University of Heidelberg, under the direction of R. W. Bunsen) – see *NCAB*, Vol. 25 (1936), p. 38; Henry M. Leicester, "Willard Bradley Rising, 1939–1910," in Wyndham D. Miles, ed., *American Chemists and Chemical*

Engineers (Washington, D.C.: American Chemical Society, 1976), pp. 410–411; and Jolly, op. cit., pp. 19–20 and pp. 262–263.

11. Third Statement by Warren H. McBryde, Nov. 22, 1948, Box A9, RC Archives. McBryde's three statements, each successively longer and more detailed, were probably intended as press releases after Cottrell's death, which had occurred on November 16. Attached to them in the RC Archives was a cover letter, dated March 16, 1950, from the secretary of J. W. Barker (president of Research Corporation) to W. A. Woods, which suggests that McBryde's statements were made available to Cameron at the time he was writing *Samaritan of Science*.

12. Cameron, *Samaritan of Science*, pp. 48–53.

13. Ibid., pp. 76–77.

14. Ibid., p. 64. For an assessment of Jessie Fulton Cottrell's role in her husband's work, see Martha Moore Trescott, *The Rise of the American Electrochemicals Industry, 1880–1910: Studies in the American Technological Environment* (Westport, Conn.: Greenwood Press, 1981), pp. 332–333.

15. Quoted in Cameron, *Samaritan of Science*, p. 82.

16. Quoted in ibid., p. 83.

17. For Whitney's overtures, see ibid., p. 103, p. 108, and pp. 114–115. Instead of Cottrell, Whitney hired William D. Coolidge – see George Wise, *Willis R. Whitney, General Electric, and the Origins of U.S. Industrial Research* (New York: Columbia University Press, 1985), p. 119. Whitney's early career foreshadowed Cottrell's: he pursued his graduate studies in Ostwald's laboratory at Leipzig (1894–1896) and returned to an academic position (at MIT). But where Cottrell left academia for government service, in 1900 Whitney became the first director of General Electric's research laboratory – a position he held until his retirement in 1932.

18. Thus White noted in his 1978 article "Centenary of Frederick Gardner Cottrell" (pp. 25–26): "Cottrell's service as head of the Fixed Nitrogen Research Laboratory was distinguished by the development of one of the most effective and prominent research organizations in the United States. It was large by the standards of the time, with a staff of over 100, and included many outstanding scientists."

19. Thus Bush noted in his account of Cottrell's career, "Frederick Gardner Cottrell, 1877–1948" (1952), p. 6: "One of his main purposes between 1938 and the time of his death was the promotion of additional research organizations and the furtherance of closer co-operation between those already in existence . . . . The informal and unofficial visits to universities which he made during this period in the effort to keep abreast of research developments in virtually all fields, to become acquainted with the investigators concerned and to give such aid as he could, were stimulating to all."

20. For lists of Ostwald's American students, see R. G. A. Dolby, "The Transmission of Two New Scientific Disciplines from Europe to North America in the Late Nineteenth Century," *Annals of Science*, 34 (May 1977), 292; and John W. Servos,

Physical Chemistry from Ostwald to Pauling: The Making of a Science in America (Princeton: Princeton University Press, 1990), pp. 54–55. In his book Servos argued (pp. 95–99) that the demand for undergraduate chemistry courses in American colleges rose dramatically at the turn of the century, that physical chemists were perceived as being well qualified to fill the new faculty teaching positions, and that once they were hired they tended to find the time and resources needed to continue their research. As one of his main examples, Servos discussed the chemistry program at Berkeley, and in that context he mentioned Cottrell – see especially pp. 241–242.

21. F. G. Cottrell, "The Liquid Air Plant of the Chemistry Department, University of California," *California Journal of Technology*, 6 (1905), 3–11; and F. G. Cottrell, "On Air Liquefiers," *Journal of Physical Chemistry*, 10 (Apr. 1906), 264–274. Although the compressor was manufactured locally, the liquefier itself came from London. Another London connection was Cottrell's visit in 1900 to the laboratory of William Ramsay, a British scientist well known for his use of air liquefaction to isolate the inert gases – see Cameron, *Samaritan of Science*, p. 69; and Thaddeus J. Trenn, "William Ramsay," *Dictionary of Scientific Biography* (hereafter *DSB*), Vol. 11 (1975), pp. 277–284. At the turn of the century, air liquefiers were becoming standard pieces of research equipment – see Paul Forman, John L. Heilbron, and Spencer Weart, "Physics *circa* 1900: Personnel, Funding, and Productivity of the Academic Establishments," *Historical Studies in the Physical Science*, 5 (1975), 86–87. The one Cottrell installed at Berkeley was probably the first on the West Coast – see Cameron, op. cit., pp. 113–114.

22. F. G. Cottrell, "Review of Physical Chemistry," *Journal of the American Chemical Society* (hereafter *JACS*), 27 (May 1905), 615–636; F. G. Cottrell, "Recent Progress in Physical Chemistry," ibid., 30 (Feb. 1908), 288–302; and F. G. Cottrell, "Recent Progress in Physical Chemistry," ibid., 31 (Mar. 1909), 394–403. Except for one by G. N. Lewis – ibid., 28 (July 1906), 893–910 – the reviews were all written by Cottrell. They supplemented the journal's regular coverage of American developments. In later years such reviews became the basis for *Chemical Abstracts*, the first volume of which appeared in 1907 – see Browne and Weeks, *A History of the American Chemical Society: Seventy-Five Eventful Years*, p. 337.

23. Cottrell, "Review of Physical Chemistry" (1905), p. 622. For a brief description of Thomson's model, see Emilio Segrè, *From X-Rays to Quarks: Modern Physicists and Their Discoveries* (San Francisco: W. H. Freeman, 1980), p. 104. While traveling in England, Cottrell visited the Cavendish Laboratory at Cambridge and met Thomson, at which time Thomson "expr[essed] his obj[ections] to the 'Energetikers,' " – Diary of F. G. Cottrell, July 15, 1900, F. G. Cottrell Papers, Box 1, Library of Congress (hereafter Cottrell Papers).

24. In *Physical Chemistry from Ostwald to Pauling,* Servos has noted that most of Ostwald's American students refrained from supporting the energeticists (pp. 69–70). On the debate between the mechanists and the energeticists, see also Mary Jo

Nye, *Molecular Reality: A Perspective on the Scientific Work of Jean Perrin* (New York: American Elsevier, 1972); and P. M. Harman, *Energy, Force, and Matter: The Conceptual Development of Nineteenth-Century Physics* (Cambridge, England: Cambridge University Press, 1982), pp. 143–148.

25. Cottrell, "Recent Progress in Physical Chemistry" (1908), p. 288. The review went on to mention Albert Einstein's treatment of Brownian motion.

26. In part, Lewis was hired as Cottrell's replacement – see Servos, *Physical Chemistry from Ostwald to Pauling*, pp. 242–244. On the College of Chemistry, see Edmond O'Neill, "History of the College of Chemistry," *California Engineer*, 2 (Aug. 1923), 3–4 and 10; Arthur Lachman, *Borderland of the Unknown: The Life Story of Gilbert Newton Lewis, One of the World's Greatest Scientists* (New York: Pageant Press, 1955), especially pp. 30–31; Richard E. Powell, "College of Chemistry," in Verne A. Stadtman, ed., *The Centennial Record of the University of California* (Berkeley: University of California Press, 1967), pp. 71–72; and Jolly, *From Retorts to Lasers*.

27. Edwin E. Slosson, *Great American Universities* (New York: Macmillan, 1910), p. 168. On Berkeley during this period, see also Stadtman, *The University of California, 1868-1968*, especially Chap. 13, "Benjamin Ide Wheeler," pp. 179–213.

28. For his father's death, followed shortly by his own marriage, see Cameron, *Samaritan of Science*, p. 109. Cottrell's older brother, Harry, was in no position to help with the family's finances, leaving Cottrell responsible for his mother, his mother's sister (Aunt Mame), and soon thereafter his wife and her sister (ibid., p. 110). For his annual salary, see ibid., p. 95 and p. 110. When Cottrell was promoted to assistant professor in 1906, his salary was raised to $1,400 (ibid., p. 116). By contrast, Whitney was probably offering him $5,000 for the position at General Electric (ibid., p. 115).

29. Quoted in ibid., p. 81. On O'Neill – who joined the Berkeley faculty in 1879 and who served as the College of Chemistry dean from 1901 to 1912 – see *Who Was Who in America* (hereafter *WWWA*), Vol. 1 (1942), p. 917; and Jolly, *From Retorts to Lasers*, pp. 25–30 and pp. 255–256.

30. Thomas P. Hughes, "The Era of Independent Inventors," in Edna Ullmann-Margalit, ed., *Science in Reflection, Boston Studies in the Philosophy of Science*, Vol. 10 (Dordrecht: Kluwer Academic Publishers, 1988), pp. 151–168. See also Thomas P. Hughes, *American Genesis: A Century of Invention and Technological Enthusiasm, 1870-1970* (New York: Viking, 1989), pp. 13–95; and Thomas P. Hughes, "The Evolution of Large Technological Systems," in Wiebe E. Bijker, Thomas P. Hughes, and Trevor J. Pinch, eds., *The Social Construction of Technological Systems: New Directions in the Sociology and History of Technology* (Cambridge, Mass.: MIT Press, 1987), pp. 57–62. Interesting support for Hughes's view has been offered by Naomi R. Lamoreaux and Kenneth L. Sokoloff, "Inventors, Firms, and the Market for Technology in the Late Nineteenth and Early Twentieth Centuries," in Naomi R. Lamoreaux, Daniel M. G. Raff, and Peter Temin, eds., *Learning by Doing in Markets, Firms, and Countries* (Chicago: Uni-

versity of Chicago Press, 1999), pp. 19–60, especially n. 23, p. 39.

31. *NCAB*, Vol. 25 (1936), p. 38. Rising, the entry also noted, "was one of the first to advocate the development of industry through the participation by chemists in the study of industrial problems, leading to the establishment of industrial chemistry as practically a distinct profession."

32. "He was frequently called upon to analyze products, both natural and manufactured, and to serve as a chemical expert in legal cases" (Jolly, *From Retorts to Lasers*, p. 25).

33. Quoted in Cameron, *Samaritan of Science*, p. 110.

34. Second Statement by Warren H. McBryde, Nov. 22, 1948, Box A9, RC Archives. Born in Alabama in 1876, McBryde received his college training in electrical engineering at Alabama Polytechnic Institute (now Auburn University), graduating in 1897. On his life and career, see "W. H. McBryde, 59th ASME President, 1876–1959," *Mechanical Engineering*, 81 (May 1959), 140–141; and *WWWA*, Vol. 5 (1973), p. 470. William C. Peyton, who headed the Peyton Chemical Company, was born in Santa Cruz in 1868. He graduated from University of California in 1887 and was employed for many years as an engineer for the California Powder Works. His father, Bernard Peyton, had served as superintendent of the company's Santa Cruz plant since 1864. In 1900 they both left to establish their own company, the Peyton Chemical Company, to produce (among other things) the acids needed for producing dynamite. On the Peytons, see Arthur Pine Van Gelder and Hugo Schlatter, *History of the Explosives Industry in America* (1927; rpt. New York: Arno Press, 1972), p. 285 and pp. 843–845; and *NYT*, Apr. 5, 1936, p. 10, col. 3. Martinez is located at the eastern end of the Carquinez Straits, along the southern shore.

35. Van Gelder and Schlatter, *History of the Explosives Industry in America*, pp. 282–283, pp. 402–405, pp. 407–408, pp. 420–421, and pp. 497–500. Giant was one of the companies for whom W. B. Rising (the Berkeley chemist) worked as a consultant – see *NCAB*, Vol. 25 (1936), p. 38.

36. Quoted in Van Gelder and Schlatter, *History of the Explosives Industry in America*, pp. 504–505. For DuPont's response to the introduction of dynamite – and for the increasing percentage of DuPont's ownership in the California Powder Works – see ibid., p. 287, p. 402, and p. 502.

37. "The site finally selected for the new Hercules plant was a 21.72 acre tract of land.... Later purchases brought this up to a magnificent tract of 3,000 acres extending for some two miles back into the hills. The Southern Pacific passes in front of it, near the Bay, and the Sante Fé cuts through the plant about a mile further back" (Van Gelder and Schlatter, *History of the Explosives Industry in America*, p. 505).

38. Ibid., p. 175 and pp. 845–849.

39. John K. Winkler, *The du Pont Dynasty* (New York: Reynal and Hitchcock, 1935), p. 145 and p. 241. On Peyton's wife, see also *NYT*, Oct. 8, 1944, p. 44, col. 2.

40. For the significance of the multidivisional structure that DuPont pioneered, see Alfred D. Chandler, Jr., *Strategy and Structure: Chapters in the History of the Indus-*

trial Enterprise (Cambridge, Mass.: MIT Press, 1962), especially Chap. 2, "DuPont — Creating the Autonomous Divisions," pp. 52–113.

41. Alfred D. Chandler, Jr., and Stephen Salsbury, *Pierre S. du Pont and the Making of the Modern Corporation* (New York: Harper, 1971), pp. 93–99; and Van Gelder and Schlatter, *History of the Explosives Industry in America*, p. 508. In 1910 the Peyton Chemical Company was sold to the General Chemical Company of California (ibid., p. 844). In 1912 DuPont responded to the government's successful antitrust suit by reorganizing its California facilities as part of a separate company, called the Hercules Powder Company (ibid., p. 524).

42. "W. H. McBryde, 59th ASME President" (1959), p. 140.

43. Van Gelder and Schlatter, *History of the Explosives Industry in America*, pp. 561–586 and pp. 588–589. For a summary of the different versions of the contact process, see A. E. Wells and D. E. Fogg, *The Manufacture of Sulphuric Acid in the United States*, U.S. Bureau of Mines Bulletin (hereafter USBM Bull.), No. 184 (Washington, D.C.: GPO, 1920), pp. 148–152. The version for which the New Jersey Zinc Company owned the American rights was the Grillo-Schroeder process, in which the catalyst was platinum.

44. David A. Hounshell and John Kenly Smith, Jr., *Science and Corporate Strategy: DuPont R&D, 1902–1980* (Cambridge, England: Cambridge University Press, 1988), especially pp. 21–23. See also Jeffrey L. Sturchio, "Chemistry and Corporate Strategy at DuPont," *Research Management*, 27 (Jan.–Feb. 1984), 10–13. Eastern Laboratory derived its name from the Eastern Dynamite Company, a holding company for DuPont's dynamite manufacturing companies in the Eastern United States — see Van Gelder and Schlatter, *History of the Explosives Industry in America*, pp. 574–576 and pp. 588–589. Apparently, it was Reese who first publicly demonstrated the contact method in the United States — at the Chemists' Club in New York — see Maurice Holland, *Industrial Explorers* (New York: Harper, 1928), p. 306. For Reese's research on the process, see his remarks at the Chemists' Club on February 20, 1903: Charles L. Reese, "The Schroeder Contact Process of Sulphuric Acid Manufacture, [Pt.] (3.) — Experimental Investigations and Observations," *Journal of the Society of Chemical Industry* (hereafter *JSCI*), 22 (Mar. 31, 1903), 351–354.

45. F. G. Cottrell, "The Social Responsibility of the Engineer-II," *Science*, 85 (June 11, 1937), 553. For the request for assistance from the Hercules Works, as well as for Cottrell's subsequent work involving the centrifugal separator, see Cameron, *Samaritan of Science*, pp. 117–118.

46. Writing to J. W. Barker on March 21, 1949 (Box A9, RC Archives), Walter A. Schmidt referred to Miller as a "fairly wealthy friend" of O'Neill. For O'Neill's bringing Cottrell's work to Miller's attention, see also Cameron, *Samaritan of Science*, p. 117. For Miller's work as a consultant and superintendent, see Van Gelder and Schlatter, *History of the Explosives Industry in America*, p. 685. For his participation in the local chapter of the American Chemical Society, see Jolly, *From Retorts to Lasers*, pp. 27–28. On Miller, see also *AMS*, 6th Ed. (1938), p. 979. Cottrell later commented that

Miller "became actively interested in the problem of acid- and smelter-fume control even before any serious consideration had been given to the use of electrical methods and while the work still centered around centrifugal separators" — see "The Cottrell Dinner," *Engineering and Mining Journal* (hereafter *EMJ*), 99 (Jan. 23, 1915), 200. In the Presidential Files of E. I. du Pont de Nemours and Co., Ser. II, Pt. 2, Box 807, Hagley Museum and Library (hereafter T. Coleman du Pont Papers), I found confirmation of Miller's prior interest in the contact method. On June 30, 1903, Miller sent John Bermingham, the president of the California Powder Works, a report that described various features of the Santa Cruz plant — including its Mannheim unit. I thank the Hagley Museum and Library for permission to cite this information as well as information in subsequent notes.

47. The patents were: F. G. Cottrell, "Manufacture of Sulfuric Acid," U.S. Patent No. 866,843, issued Sept. 24, 1907 (filed Jan. 4, 1906); and F. G. Cottrell, "Apparatus for Separating Sulfuric Acid," U.S. Patent No. 866,844, issued Sept. 24, 1907 (filed Jan. 4, 1906).

48. Third Statement by Warren H. McBryde, Nov. 22, 1948.

49. Schmidt to Barker, Mar. 21, 1949.

50. Many of the sources that Cameron consulted are no longer available, and even those were limited, because the great earthquake and fire of April 1906 destroyed the building where Cottrell worked. Although the earliest of Cottrell's diaries in the Cottrell Papers date from the period 1900–1902, the main series does not begin until July 1, 1907.

51. White, "Centenary of Frederick Gardner Cottrell" (1978), p. 5. For spark coils as common laboratory devices at the turn of the century, see Segrè, *From X-Rays to Quarks*, pp. 4–5. Although Cottrell's remarks suggest that using a centrifuge was something he had been considering in the context of another problem — namely, "the amalgamation of black sands" — I have discovered nothing further about it. On White — a Berkeley alumnus (Class of 1928) who also earned his doctorate there (under the direction of E. O. Lawrence), joined Research Corporation's technical staff in 1935, and later became a well-known authority on electrostatic precipitation — see Leon H. Fisher, "Harry J. White," *Physics Today*, 43 (June 1990), 94–95.

52. For acknowledgment of Lodge's earlier work, see Cottrell, "The Electrical Precipitation of Suspended Particles" (1911), p. 542; F. G. Cottrell, "Problems in Smoke, Fume, and Dust Abatement," *Annual Report of the Board of Regents of the Smithsonian Institution . . . for the Year Ending June 30, 1913* (Washington, D.C.: GPO, 1914), pp. 664–666; and F. G. Cottrell, "Electrical Precipitation: Historical Sketch," *Transactions of the American Institute of Electrical Engineers* (hereafter *Trans. AIEE*), 34 (1915), 388–390.

53. For his talk at the Montreal meeting, on August 29, 1884, see Oliver Lodge, "Dust," *Nature*, 31 (Jan. 22, 1885), 265–269; and for his recollections of the trip, see Oliver Lodge, *Advancing Science* (New York: Harcourt, Brace, 1932), pp. 58–64. This

was the first meeting of the British Association for the Advancement of Science to be held outside the United Kingdom.

54. Bruce J. Hunt, *The Maxwellians* (Ithaca: Cornell University Press, 1991), p. 87. On Lodge's career, see also Charles Süsskind, "Oliver Joseph Lodge," *DSB*, Vol. 8 (1973), pp. 443–444.

55. Lodge, "Dust" (1885), p. 266. For an overview of Britain's smoke problems in the 1880s, see David Stradling and Peter Thorsheim, "The Smoke of Great Cities: British and American Efforts to Control Air Pollution, 1860–1914," *Environmental History*, 4 (Jan. 1999), pp. 10–11.

56. Quoted in Lodge, "Dust" (1885), p. 266.

57. "I am not one to decry the applications of science for the benefit of mankind . . . ," Lodge noted in his conclusion, but "the rewards of the pursuit of science for its own sake are transcendental and immaterial, and [are] not to be imagined except by the few called to the work" (ibid., p. 269). In an earlier lecture, to the Royal Dublin Society on April 2, 1884 – see "Dust-Free Spaces," *Nature*, 29 (Apr. 24, 1884), 613 – Lodge similarly distinguished between pure and applied science (and emphasized the former):

> When we began the investigation into the dust-free spaces found above warm bodies we were not only without expectation, but without hope or idea of any sort, that anything practical was likely to come of it: the phenomenon itself possessed its own interest and charm.
>
> And so it must ever be. The devotee of pure science never has practical developments as his primary aim; often he not only does not know, but does not in the least care, whether his researches will ever lead to any beneficial result.

58. For a survey of these historical developments, see J. L. Heilbron, *Elements of Early Modern Physics* (Berkeley: University of California Press, 1982), Chap. 3, "The Case of Electricity," pp. 159–240.

59. For a brief historical survey, see John A. Fleming, "Electrical (or Electrostatic) Machine," *Encyclopaedia Britannica*, 11th Ed., Vol. 9 (1910), pp. 176–179.

60. Lodge, *Advancing Science*, p. 63. On Thomson – Britain's leading physicist at the time (and later Lord Kelvin) – see Jed Z. Buchwald, "Sir William Thomson (Baron Kelvin of Largs)," *DSB*, Vol. 13 (1976), pp. 374–388.

61. Lodge, *Advancing Science*, p. 63.

62. Ibid., p. 62.

63. Ibid., pp. 63–64.

64. Oliver Lodge, "The Electrical Deposition of Dust and Smoke, with Special Reference to the Collection of Metallic Fume, and to a Possible Purification of the Atmosphere," *JSCI*, 5 (Nov. 29, 1886), 575.

65. For a brief account of the early practical work – including the problem of insufficient insulation and a bibliography– see Oliver Lodge, *Electrical Precipitation: A Lecture Delivered before the Institute of Physics* (London: Oxford University Press,

1925), p. 22 and p. 24. See also "A New Application of Electricity," *Engineering*, 39 (June 5, 1885), 627–628; Lodge, "The Electrical Deposition of Dust and Smoke, with Special Reference to the Collection of Metallic Fume, and to a Possible Purification of the Atmosphere," (1886), p. 575; and Lodge, *Advancing Science*, p. 65. For a list of Walker's patents, see Cottrell, "Problems in Smoke, Fume, and Dust Abatement" (1913), n. 1, p. 665. Walker's American Patent was U.S. Patent No. 342,548, "Process of Depositing Solid Particles Suspended in Air or Gas," issued May 25, 1886 (filed July 15, 1885). For the difficulties with lead fumes, see White, "Centenary of Frederick Gardner Cottrell" (1978), p. 4.

66. "James Wimshurst, F.R.S.," *Nature*, 67 (Jan. 15, 1903), 250. On Wimshurst, see also S. E. Fryer, "James Wimshurst," *Dictionary of National Biography*, Supp. for 1901–1911 (1912), pp. 693–694.

67. Letter from W. M. Hutchings, dated June 9, 1895, quoted in Malvern W. Iles, "Methods for the Collection of Metallurgic Dust and Fume," [Columbia University] *School of Mines Quarterly*, 17 (Jan. 1896), 114.

68. Oliver Lodge, "Historical Note on Dust, Electrification, and Heat," *Nature*, 71 (Apr. 20, 1905), 582. This was not the first time that Lodge had acknowledged the work of an earlier researcher. In "The Electrical Deposition of Dust and Smoke, with Special Reference to the Collection of Metallic Fume, and to a Possible Purification of the Atmosphere" (1886), he noted (p. 574): "My attention has just been drawn to a paragraph in 'The Mechanics' Magazine' for November, 1850, wherein it appears that this phenomenon was at that time observed by a Mr. C. F. Guitard; a fact of which I had been quite ignorant."

69. Quoted in Cameron, *Samaritan of Science*, p. 21. The work of Lodge and Walker was covered in the pages of *Scientific American* − a periodical (as we have seen) to which Cottrell had access as a boy. For example, a nearly verbatim version of "A New Application of Electricity" from the June 5, 1885, issue of *Engineering* (Vol. 39, pp. 627–628), appeared as an article with the same title in the June 27, 1885, issue of *Scientific American* (Vol. 52, p. 401).

70. Walter A. Schmidt and Evald Anderson, "Electrical Precipitation," *Electrical Engineering*, 57 (Aug. 1938), 332. On E. P. Lewis − who had been one of H. A. Rowland's graduate students at the Johns Hopkins University, who was one of the mainstays of research in the Berkeley physics department prior to World War I, and who chaired the department from 1918 to 1926 − see *NCAB*, Vol. 22 (1932), p. 411; Donald H. Menzel, "Exum Percival Lewis," *DAB*, Vol. 11 (1933), pp. 213–214; and Robert Wayne Seidel, "Physics Research in California: The Rise of a Leading Sector in American Physics," Diss. University of California 1978, p. 20.

71. Schmidt to Barker, Mar. 21, 1949. On Davidson − who received his Ph.D. degree from Berkeley in 1907 − see *AMS*, 6th Ed. (1938), p. 333. For the title of his dissertation, "Conditions Affecting the Discharge of Electrodes in Phenomena of Ionization," see M. Lois Marckworth, *Dissertations in Physics: An Indexed Bibliography of All Doctoral Theses Accepted by American Universities, 1861–1959* (Stanford: Stanford

University Press, 1961), p. 79.

72. Quoted in Cameron, *Samaritan of Science*, p. 45 (emphasis added). The instructor was Joseph N. LeConte, a mechanical engineer, whose father Joseph was the well-known geologist — see *WWWA*, Vol. 2 (1950), p. 316.

73. Regarding the date of his earliest work with the electrostatic precipitator, Cottrell once referred to "the original laboratory experiments in the spring of 1906" — see his 1911 article "Electrical Precipitation of Suspended Particles," p. 544. But Schmidt later recalled (Schmidt to Barker, Mar. 21, 1949): "Cottrell switched from his work with the centrifuge to electrical precipitation after I left the University..." — which suggests late spring as the time of Cottrell's first efforts.

74. Cottrell, "Electrical Precipitation of Suspended Particles" (1911), p. 543. "In connection with the references which have been made to the corona phenomena observed in electrical precipitation," H. D. Egbert later wrote — in his article, "The Cottrell Precipitation Process and Its Application to Foundry Dust Problems," *Transactions of the American Foundrymen's Association*, 27 (1919), 269 — "it is interesting to note that the corona discharge which is so useful in precipitation work is exactly what the high tension transmission line engineer endeavors in every way to prevent, because to him it represents a distinct loss of power...."

75. For an assessment of Archimedes' discovery, see Arthur Koestler, *The Act of Creation* (New York: Macmillan, 1964), pp. 105–108.

76. For the shift to AC, see Thomas P. Hughes, *Networks of Power: Electrification in Western Society, 1880–1930* (Baltimore: The Johns Hopkins University Press, 1983), especially Chap. 5, "Conflict and Resolution," pp. 106–139.

77. Already we have seen how Cottrell's early life and career were set in the San Francisco Bay area. He was also familiar with the Sierras. The mining company for which he had worked as a consultant was located near Grass Valley, and he and Jessie Fulton were married in Nevada City — see Cameron, *Samaritan of Science*, pp. 109–111.

78. George P. Low, "The World's Longest Electric Power Transmission," *Journal of Electricity, Power and Gas*, 11 (July 1901), 145–168, explicitly mentioned "the powder works at Pinole" (p. 149), though I should add that the company also had its own powerhouse, equipped with a Westinghouse generator (see R. S. Penniman to the stockholders of the California Powder Works, Mar. 15, 1905, T. Coleman du Pont Papers, Box 811). For a map of the route the line followed, see Thomas Commerford Martin, "The Longest Power-Transmission in the World," *American Monthly Review of Reviews*, 25 (Mar. 1902), 306. In his book *P. G. and E. of California: The Centennial Story of Pacific Gas and Electric Company, 1852–1952* (New York: McGraw-Hill, 1952) Charles M. Coleman noted (p. 5):

> [The gold miners] left a vast water system and legal rights to water
> sources; and they left, too, a generation of men who knew how to
> build tunnels, canals, and flumes, how to lay pipe in rugged terrain,
> how to handle water and where to find it. That was a mighty aid to the

electrical engineers when they began to build water-powered plants.

For recent surveys of turn-of-the-century developments in California, see Hughes, *Networks of Power*, Chap. 10, "California White Gold," pp. 262–284; and James C. Williams, *Energy and the Making of Modern California* (Akron, Ohio: University of Akron Press, 1997), Chap. 9, "Hydroelectricity," pp. 168–198. Interestingly, during the same period that Warren McBryde worked for the Peyton Chemical Company he also "was employed by the Yuba Electric Power Company as assistant resident engineer in charge of construction on the Colgate hydroelectric powerhouse" – see "W. H. McBryde, 59th ASME President" (1959), p. 140.

79. Hamilton Wright, "Long-Distance High-Tension Transmission of Power in California," *Scientific American*, 88 (May 16, 1903), 373. Similar comments continued to appear. "The most striking characteristic of the transmissions along the Pacific Coast," observed one editorial, "is the thoroughness with which they have been amalgamated into networks" – see "The Transmission Systems of the Great West," *Electrical World*, 59 (June 1, 1912), 1143. "An imaginative writer," reported Albert W. Atwood, in his article "The Great Snow Machine" – see *The Saturday Evening Post*, 196 (Dec. 1, 1923), 77 – "recently described California as a machine run by sunshine and snow, soon to be the first completely electrically operated state."

80. For a discussion of the work of Hohlfeld and Guitard, see Cottrell, "Electrical Precipitation: Historical Sketch" (1915), pp. 387–388.

81. "W. H. McBryde, 59th ASME President" (1959), p. 140. Rather than the Grillo-Schroeder version of the contact method, the facilities at Pinole (as well as those at Martinez on which McBryde had worked earlier) were based on the Mannheim version – in which the catalyst was iron oxide – see Van Gelder and Schlattcr, *History of the Explosives Industry in America*, p. 508.

82. First Statement by Warren H. McBryde, Nov. 22, 1948, Box A9, RC Archives. Working with documents in the T. Coleman du Pont Papers (Box 811), I have pinned down the dates of Barksdale's visit more exactly. He arrived on June 10, 1905 (H. M. Barksdale to T. C. du Pont, June 15, 1905), and he planned to depart on July 6 (H. M. Barksdale to T. C. du Pont, July 1, 1905). At the time, Cottrell would have been working on the centrifugal separator.

83. In 1903 Barksdale became vice-president in charge of high explosives, and thus he served on the company's newly created executive committee – see Chandler, *Strategy and Structure*, pp. 56–57. On Barksdale at DuPont, see also Ernest Dale and Charles Meloy, "Hamilton MacFarland Barksdale and the Du Pont Contributions to Systematic Management," *Business History Review*, 36 (Summer 1962), 127–152; and Hounshell and Smith, *Science at Corporate Strategy*, especially Chap. 1, "Organizing for Research and Development, 1902–1911," pp. 17–55.

84. Second Statement by Warren H. McBryde, Nov. 22. 1948.

85. Cottrell noted in his article "Electrical Fume-Precipitation," *Transactions of the American Institute of Mining Engineers* (hereafter *Trans. AIME*), 43 (1912), 514–515:

The gases treated contained about 4 per cent. by volume of dry, gaseous sulphur trioxide, and were brought into contact with water, which, combining with the sulphur trioxide, formed a far less volatile sulphuric acid, which immediately separated as a dense white cloud of suspended particles, so fine as to constitute one of the most difficult of all materials to remove by filtration, but easily and successfully precipitated by the electric current.

He added in his 1913 article "Problems in Smoke, Fume, and Dust Abatement" (p. 670): "Current was supplied from three 1-kilowatt 110-volt to 2,200-volt transformers connected in series on their 2,200 volt side to give 6,600 volts." Finally, he noted in his 1911 article "The Electrical Precipitation of Suspended Particles" (p. 545): "This apparatus was of course merely for experimental and demonstration purposes but a still larger unit built for permanent operation and to handle all of the gas from a Mannheim unit has since been installed at this plant and put into steady commercial operation."

86. For a summary of the legal proceedings, see J. A. Holmes, Edward C. Franklin, and Ralph A. Gould, *Report of the Selby Smelter Commission*, USBM Bull., No. 98 (Washington, D.C.: GPO, 1915), pp. 2–4. The Selby smelter was not the only local plant to find itself subject to legal proceedings. For a brief overview, see the section entitled "Cases Near San Francisco," in Charles H. Fulton, *Metallurgical Smoke*, USBM Bull., No. 84 (Washington, D.C.: GPO, 1915), pp. 86–87. For other early cases in the United States, see John E. Lamborn and Charles S. Peterson, "The Substance of the Land: Agriculture v. Industry in the Smelter Cases of 1904 and 1906," *Utah Historical Quarterly*, 53 (Fall 1985), 308–325; M.-L. Quinn, "Industry and Environment in the Appalachian Copper Basin, 1890–1930," *Technology and Culture*, 34 (July 1993), 575–612; and Timothy LeCain, "The Limits of 'Eco-Efficiency': Arsenic Pollution and the Cottrell Electrical Precipitator in the U.S. Copper Smelting Industry," *Environmental History*, 5 (July 2000), 336–351. I thank Richard Newman for bringing LeCain's article to my attention.

87. For a summary of the ways in which the company responded – including explicit mention of Cottrell's efforts – see Holmes, Franklin, and Gould, *Report of the Selby Smelter Commission*, pp. 15–18.

88. Ligon Johnson, "The History and Legal Phases of the Smoke Problem," *Metallurgical and Chemical Engineering* (hereafter *MCE*), 16 (Feb. 15, 1917), 202. Johnson originally presented his paper on January 26, 1917, at the "Symposium on the Smelter Smoke and Fume Problem" sponsored jointly by the New York sections of the American Electrochemical Society and the American Institute of Mining Engineers – see ibid., (Feb. 1, 1917), 128. Also giving papers at the symposium were Linn Bradley and W. W. Strong – see ibid., (Mar. 15, 1917), 336–340; and ibid., (June 1, 1917), 648–652. On Johnson, who served as special assistant to the U.S. attorney general from 1906 to 1914, see *NCAB*, Vol. F (1942), pp. 134. Earlier, while serving as special

assistant to Georgia's attorney general, he had been involved in the case against copper companies at Ducktown, Tenn. An approach similar to the one at Selby was also taken in the case of Montana's Anaconda smelter. In U.S. Bureau of Mines, *Annual Report for 1913*, p. 86, Holmes carefully explained his presence on both commissions: "While [they] are entirely independent of the Bureau of Mines as an organization, the director of the bureau was asked to serve on each of them as an individual, and, with the approval of the Secretary of the Interior, is so doing."

89. Robert E. Swain, "Smoke and Fume Investigations: A Historical Review," *Industrial and Engineering Chemistry*, 41 (Nov. 1949), 2386. As he recalled in his introduction (p. 2384), Swain had known Cottrell since their student days, when he visited Cottrell at Leipzig. Later, as a member of Stanford's chemistry department, he had followed Cottrell's work. "In the Cottrell process . . . ," he wrote in 1923, "we have an admirable conservation measure, as well as a process which is of growing importance in relieving the smoke evil" — see Robert W. Swain, "Atmospheric Pollution by Industrial Waste," ibid., 15 (Mar. 1923), 300. On Swain, see *AMS*, 9th Ed. (1955), p. 1896.

90. M.-L. Quinn, "Early Smelter Sites: A Neglected Chapter in the History and Geography of Acid Rain in the United States," *Atmospheric Environment*, 23 (1989), 1285.

91. John D. Wirth, "The Trail Smelter Dispute: Canadians and Americans Confront Transboundary Pollution, 1927–41," *Environmental History*, 1 (Apr. 1996), 46. For a brief account of the early electrostatic precipitators at the smelter of the Consolidated Mining and Smelting Company at Trail, British Columbia, see Walter A. Schmidt, "Cottrell Processes of Electrical Precipitation," *Transactions of the American Institute of Chemical Engineers*, 8 (1915), 55–57.

92. Cameron, *Samaritan of Science*, pp. 124–130; and White, "Centenary of Frederick Gardner Cottrell" (1978), pp. 7–9. For accounts of Cottrell's work at Selby, see also "The Cottrell Fume-Condensing System at the Selby Smelter," *EMJ*, 86 (Aug. 1, 1908), 242; Cottrell, "The Electrical Precipitation of Suspended Particles" (1911), pp. 545–546; "Electrical Fume-Precipitation: Discussion of the Paper of F. G. Cottrell, p. 512," *Trans. AIME*, 43 (1912), 756–757; and R. Hoffman, "Travels through the United States in Conjunction with the Eighth International Congress of Applied Chemistry at New York, by Members of the Congress," *JIEC*, 6 (Jan. 1914), 61–62. Like the Hercules Works, Selby obtained electric power via the new high-voltage line from the Colgate power plant — see Low, "The World's Longest Electric Power Transmission" (1901), p. 166. One of the line's most notable engineering features was the section that crossed the Carquinez Straits not far from Selby — see George P. Low, "The Great Carquinez Transmission Span," *Journal of Electricity, Power and Gas*, 11 (May 1901), 91–102.

93. Quoted (with emphasis) in William J. Rich to F. G. Cottrell, Mar. 3, 1908, Patent Application for U.S. Patent No. 895,729, Records of the U.S. Patent Office

(Record Group 241), National Archives (hereafter USPO Records).

94. F. G. Cottrell to Commissioner of Patents, Mar. 17, 1908, Patent Application for U.S. Patent No. 895,729, USPO Records.

95. F. G. Cottrell to Commissioner of Patents, Jan. 6, 1908, Patent Application for U.S. Patent No. 895,729, USPO Records. The patents to which Cottrell referred were Jules E. Neher, "Method of and Apparatus for Rectifying Alternating Currents," U.S. Patent No. 548,217, issued Oct. 22, 1895 (filed Aug. 7, 1893); and Adolph Müller, "Transformation of Alternating Currents into Direct Currents," U.S. Patent No. 599,789, issued Mar. 1, 1898 (filed July 30, 1897).

96. F. G. Cottrell, "Art of Separating Suspended Particles from Gaseous Bodies," U.S. Patent No. 895,729, issued Aug. 11, 1908 (filed July 9, 1907). For an early published account, see "Cottrell Process for Condensing Smelter Fumes," *EMJ*, 86 (Aug. 22, 1908), 375–377.

97. Cottrell, U.S. Patent No. 895,729.

98. Ibid.

99. Ibid.

100. F. G. Cottrell, "Effecting Interchange of Electric Charges between Solid Conductors and Gases," U.S. Patent No. 945,917, issued Jan. 11, 1910 (filed July 13, 1908).

101. F. G. Cottrell, "Method of Discharge of Electricity into Gases," U.S. Patent No. 1,067,974, issued July 22, 1913 (filed Nov. 6, 1911).

102. The best overview remains Samuel P. Hays, *Conservation and the Gospel of Efficiency: The Progressive Conservation Movement, 1890–1920* (Cambridge, Mass.: Harvard University Press, 1959). For another approach, see Adam W. Rome, "Coming to Terms with Pollution: The Language of Environmental Reform, 1865–1915," *Environmental History*, 1 (July 1996), 6–28.

103. Martin V. Melosi, "Environmental Reform in the Industrial Cities: The Civic Response to Pollution in the Progressive Era," in Kendall E. Bailles, ed., *Environmental History: Critical Issues in Comparative Perspective* (Lanham, Md.: University Press of America, 1985), p. 502. Another useful introduction is Joel A. Tarr, *The Search for the Ultimate Sink: Urban Pollution in Historical Perspective* (Akron, Ohio: University of Akron Press, 1996), especially Chap. 1, pp. 7–35. In his book, *Smokestacks and Progressives: Environmentalists, Engineers, and Air Quality in America, 1881–1951* (Baltimore: The Johns Hopkins University Press, 1999), David Stradling emphasizes urban air pollution due to coal combustion.

104. Charles S. Howe, "The Function of the Engineer in the Conservation of the Natural Resources of the Country," *Science*, 28 (Oct. 23, 1908), 538. On Howe, see *NCAB*, Vol. 15 (1916), p. 259. On the 1908 White House conference, see Charles Richard Van Hise, *The Conservation of Natural Resources in the United States* (New York: Macmillan, 1910), pp. 5–7. For an introduction to the engineering facet, see

Carroll Pursell, "Conservation, Environmentalism, and the Engineers: The Progressive Era and the Recent Past," in Bailes, *Environmental History: Critical Issues in Comparative Perspective*, pp. 176–197.

105. Howe, "The Function of the Engineer in the Conservation of the Natural Resources of the Country" (1908), p. 547.

106. For an introduction to the nature lovers, see James Penick, Jr., "The Progressives and the Environment: Three Themes from the First Conservation Movement," in Lewis L. Gould, ed., *The Progressive Era* (Syracuse, N.Y.: Syracuse University Press, 1974), pp. 125–127. Also useful here is Robert L. Dorman, *A Word for Nature: Four Pioneering Environmental Advocates, 1845–1913* (Chapel Hill: University of North Carolina Press, 1998).

107. Kevin Starr, *Americans and the California Dream: 1850–1915* (New York: Oxford University Press, 1973), p. 417 and p. 423.

108. A good example would be the "Symposium on Mineral Wastes" sponsored by the American Chemical Society at its meeting in Washington, D.C., on December 27–30, 1911 – see *JIEC*, 4 (Mar. 1912), 160–188. Joseph Holmes opened with remarks on "Carbon Wastes" (pp. 160–164), and at the appropriate time Cottrell spoke on "Mineral Losses in Gases and Fumes" (pp. 182–185). In his introduction to the published proceedings ("Conservation," p. 160), Charles R. Van Hise – a geologist and, since 1903, president of the University of Wisconsin – explicitly linked the symposium to the larger environmental movement via the White House conference and the engineering facet. "It should be realized," he noted, "that the problem of conservation is largely a chemical one" (where "chemical" meant "chemical engineering" as much as anything else), and then he added: "The conservation movement, following the White House conference in 1908, was taken up with great enthusiasm all over the country, and became almost at once a national policy; but the successful solution of the problem of conservation is one which will require the work of the leaders in applied science through many years to come." On Van Hise, see Maurice M. Vance, "Charles Richard Van Hise," *ANB*, Vol. 22 (1999), pp. 219–221.

109. Cottrell, U.S. Patent No. 895,729.

110. F. G. Cottrell, in "Discussion," p. 559, at the end of W. H. Howard, "Electrical Fume Precipitation at Garfield," *Trans. AIME*, 49 (1915), 540–560. Due to their great expense, the wisdom of installing full-scale electrostatic precipitators was not always clear on the grounds of technical considerations alone. Thus, while acknowledging their "technical success," Lawrence Addicks noted – see "Metallurgy of Copper in 1915," *EMJ*, 101 (Jan. 8, 1916), 92: "where no legal questions are involved it is a debatable matter whether the additional recovery above well-designed dust chambers warrants the additional investment and operation cost [of the Cottrell apparatus]."

CHAPTER THREE—AN ELEEMOSYNARY IDEA
PAGES 51–77

1. Cottrell's case was not unique or even especially early. An earlier and more prominent case was that of Elihu Thomson. In the introduction to his book *Innovation as a Social Process: Elihu Thomson and the Rise of General Electric, 1870–1900* (Cambridge, England: Cambridge University Press, 1991), W. Bernard Carlson has noted: "For Thomson and electrical technology in late-nineteenth-century America, the key social organization was the business firm" (p. 8). Yet the increasing importance of organizations did not eliminate the need for talented individuals, leading Carlson to conclude: "The process by which the innovative function was institutionalized was contingent and shaped to a considerable extent by individual inventors, scientists, and managers" (p. 361).

2. On Cottrell's partners and the support they provided, see (in addition to previous notes regarding O'Neill and Miller) "The Cottrell Dinner," *EMJ*, 99 (Jan. 23, 1915), 200; California Alumni Association, *Directory of Graduates of the University of California, 1864–1916* (Berkeley: University of California Press, 1916); "Western Precipitation Corporation," in William Haynes, ed., *American Chemical Industry*, Vol. 6: *The Chemical Companies* (New York: D. Van Nostrand, 1949), p. 475; and Cameron, *Samaritan of Science*, pp. 124–125.

3. "Western Precipitation Corporation," in Haynes, *American Chemical Industry: The Chemical Companies*, p. 475; and Cameron, *Samaritan of Science*, pp. 124–125.

4. On the installation at Balaklala, see Cottrell, "Problems in Smoke, Fume, and Dust Abatement" (1913), pp. 672–678; Cameron, *Samaritan of Science*, pp. 145–146; and White, "Centenary of Frederick Gardner Cottrell" (1978), pp. 9–10.

5. For Burns's assistance, as well as Cottrell's leave, see Cameron, *Samaritan of Science*, pp. 131–132. On Burns, see also "Western Precipitation Corporation," in Haynes, *American Chemical Industry: The Chemical Companies*, pp. 475–476.

6. F. G. Cottrell to Charles A. Kraus, quoted in Cameron, *Samaritan of Science*, p. 138. On Kraus – a chemist, who had been a physics instructor at Berkeley from 1901 to 1904 and who had then gone to MIT – see Martin D. Saltzman, "Charles August Kraus," *ANB*, Vol. 12 (1999), pp. 904–905.

7. Cameron, *Samaritan of Science*, p. 139.

8. For more on the developments involving Schmidt and Speed, see the next chapter.

9. On Penniman, see the following documents in the T. Coleman du Pont Papers, Box 811: T. C. du Pont to E. S. Pillsbury (director of the California Powder Works), Oct. 6, 1903; John Bermingham (president of the California Powder Works) to T. C. du Pont, Oct. 20, 1903; and R. S. Penniman to T. C. du Pont, Nov. 5, 1903.

10. On H. G. Haskell, see *NCAB*, Vol. 47 (1965), pp. 421–422. On J. A. Haskell, see ibid., Vol. 15 (1916), pp. 260–261.

11. For these developments, see Hounshell and Smith, *Science and Corporate Strat-*

egy, especially Chap. 1, "Organizing for Research and Development, 1902–1911," pp. 17–55.

12. Diary of F. G. Cottrell, July 26, 1907, Cottrell Papers, Box 1.

13. Diary of F. G. Cottrell, Aug. 5, 1907, Cottrell Papers, Box 1. Also present at the conference were McBryde and two others.

14. Ibid.

15. Diary of F. G. Cottrell, Aug. 10, 1907, Cottrell Papers, Box 1.

16. See, for example, Diary of F. G. Cottrell, Sept. 6, 1907, Cottrell Papers, Box 1.

17. Diary of F. G. Cottrell, Mar. 24, 1909, Cottrell Papers, Box 1.

18. Ibid.

19. Diary of F. G. Cottrell, Mar. 31, 1909, Cottrell Papers, Box 1. "Discussed patent matters . . . ," Cottrell noted, "& dropped whole matter for present with understanding that there was perfect good feeling on both sides. . . ."

20. Diary of F. G. Cottrell, Apr. 19, 1909, Cottrell Papers, Box 1.

21. Diary of F. G. Cottrell, May 29, 1909, Cottrell Papers, Box 1.

22. Diary of F. G. Cottrell, May 31, 1910, Cottrell Papers, Box 1.

23. Cottrell, "The Research Corporation, An Experiment in Public Administration of Patent Rights" (1912), p. 864.

24. For example, when Andrew Carnegie became a Cornell trustee in 1890 and attended his first trustees meeting, "he had been shocked to discover how very small the salaries of college professors were, even at a relatively well-endowed university such as Cornell" (Wall, *Andrew Carnegie*, p. 870).

25. P. H. Royster, "Inside Doctor Cottrell" (a typescript biographical sketch, ca. 1950), Cottrell Papers, Box 6. On Royster, a chemical engineer, see *AMS*, 6th Ed. (1938), p. 1215.

26. F. G. Cottrell, "Patent Experience of the Research Corporation," *Transactions of the American Institute of Chemical Engineers*, 28 (1932), 222. Although I have not been able to confirm that a formal offer was ever made, the president of Research Corporation noted in the early 1950s that "the Regents declined to accept [Cottrell's patent rights] on the grounds that their charter did not permit such activities" – see J. W. Barker, *Research Corporation (1912–1952): Dedicated to Progress in Education and Science*, (New York: The Newcomen Society in North America, 1952), p. 11.

27. In their formal offer to the Smithsonian Institution (International Precipitation Co. to the Board of Regents of the Smithsonian Institution, Oct. 18, 1911, RU 45, Box 47, SI Archives), Cottrell and his partners noted:

> From the very outset it was understood and informally agreed between these four if the Company's operations should prove technically and financially successful . . . that they would then unite in turning over their holdings to some public institution as an endowment for scientific research. Neither the selection of the institution nor the administrative details were fixed upon at this time, but as all four of the parties were

graduates of the University of California, the latter was naturally in mind
in the first instance.

"[Cottrell] has told me," George W. Gray later reported, "there was in his mind all
along a feeling of obligation to the University of California in whose laboratory he had
worked out this invention. He and his associates early agreed that the University
should share in the ownership of the patents" — see "Science and Profits," *Harpers
Monthly Magazine*, 172 (Apr. 1936), 541.

28. Cottrell, "The Research Corporation, An Experiment in Public Administration
of Patent Rights" (1912), p. 864.

29. Cottrell, "Electrical Precipitation: Historical Sketch" (1915), p. 391. In his
1932 article "Patent Experience of the Research Corporation," pp. 222–223, Cottrell
made the same point:

> We also had the strong feeling as time went on that another danger
> was involved, especially should the experiment prove highly profitable to
> the university and lead to a general emulation of the plan. University
> trustees are continually seeking for funds and in direct proportion to the
> success of our experiment its repetition might be expected elsewhere.
> The danger this suggested was the possibility of growing commercialism
> and competition between institutions and an accompanying tendency for
> secrecy in scientific work.

30. As the official minutes noted: "Unusual enthusiasm was shown throughout the
whole meeting and many new western members were added to the Society, which
now has a membership of over five thousand" — see Charles L. Parsons, "Minutes of
the Forty-second General Meeting of the American Chemical Society," *Proceedings of
the American Chemical Society for the Year 1910*, p. 102, bound with *JACS*, 32 (1910).
For other reports, see "The Wreck of the Special Train of the American Chemical
Society," *MCE*, 8 (Aug. 1910), 446; "The Western Tour of the American Chemical
Society," ibid., (Sept. 1910), 517–518; "San Francisco Meeting of the American Chemical Society," ibid., 538–539; and "American Chemical Society," *JIEC*, 2 (Aug. 1910),
360–361. For a list of meeting locations in this period, see Herman Skolnik and
Kenneth M. Reese, eds., *A Century of Chemistry: The Role of Chemists and the Ameri-
can Chemical Society* (Washington, D.C.: American Chemical Society, 1976), p. 454.

31. For the establishing of the American Electrochemical Society, see Robert M.
Burns, *A History of the Electrochemical Society, 1902–1976* (Princeton, N.J.: Electro-
chemical Society, 1977), pp. 3–6. For the establishing of the American Institute of
Chemical Engineers and its early relations with the ACS, see Terry S. Reynolds, *75
Years of Progress: A History of the American Institute of Chemical Engineers, 1908–
1983* (New York: American Institute of Chemical Engineers, 1983), pp. 3–9. For the
establishing of the ACS divisions, see Browne and Weeks, *A History of the American
Chemical Society,* pp. 81–96; and Skolnik and Reese, *A Century of Chemistry*, pp. 12–
15.

32. F. E. Gallagher, "Division of Industrial Chemists and Chemical Engineers of the American Chemical Society," *JIEC*, 2 (Aug. 1910), 363.

33. Ibid.

34. Parsons, "Minutes of the Forty-second General Meeting" (1910), p. 101.

35. F. G. Cottrell, "The Electrical Precipitation of Suspended Particles," *JIEC*, 3 (Aug. 1911), 542–550.

36. Diary of F. G. Cottrell, Jan. 18, 1911, Cottrell Papers, Box 1. For the idea of turning the rights over to the ACS, see also Cameron, *Samaritan of Science*, p. 153.

37. F. G. Cottrell to J. A. Holmes, Jan. 22, 1911, Records of the U.S. Bureau of Mines (Record Group 70), General Correspondence 1910–1911, Decimal Classification 132, National Archives (hereafter USBM Records, 1910–1911 – with other USBM Records citations following a similar style).

38. Cottrell, "Electrical Fume-Precipitation" (1912), p. 519. On another occasion Cottrell commented similarly that "none of those approached felt that they were in position to undertake the responsibility"– see Cottrell, "Patent Experience of the Research Corporation" (1932), p. 223.

39. On Holmes and the Bureau of Mines, see American Mining Congress, *Joseph Austin Holmes, 1859–1915: A Record of the Tributes Paid . . .* (Washington, D.C.: American Mining Congress, 1915); Philip B. McDonald, "Joseph Austin Holmes," *DAB*, Vol. 9 (1932), pp. 167–168; Dupree, *Science in the Federal Government*, pp. 280–283; William Graebner, *Coal-Mining Safety in the Progressive Period: The Political Economy of Reform* (Lexington: University of Kentucky Press, 1976); Kenneth S. Mernitz, "Governmental Research and the Corporate State: The Rittman Refining Process," *Technology and Culture*, 31 (Jan. 1990), 83–113; and Mark Aldrich, "Preventing 'the Needless Peril of the Coal Mine': The Bureau of Mines and the Campaign against Coal Mine Explosions, 1910–1940," ibid., 36 (July 1995), 483–518. Holmes "was one of the best men I ever ran across," Gifford Pinchot noted in his autobiography, *Breaking New Ground* (New York: Harcourt, Brace, 1947), p. 56. On the Ballinger-Pinchot Affair, see James Penick, Jr., *Progressive Politics and Conservation: The Ballinger-Pinchot Affair* (Chicago: University of Chicago Press, 1968).

40. U.S. Bureau of Mines, *Annual Report for 1911*, p. 4.

41. Included in one of Cottrell's diaries (Cottrell Papers, Box 1) was a postcard to his wife dated Oct. 6, 1910, on which he had written: "My first meeting with J. A. Holmes. Terry Bldg. SF. Oct. 7 1910." On their first meeting see also Cameron, *Samaritan of Science*, pp. 154–158. The aim of the bureau's laboratory in San Francisco was to test fuel oil for the navy, as well as to investigate the effects of smelter fumes, see J. A. Holmes to Secretary of the Interior, June 23, 1911, USBM Records, 1910–1911.

42. F. G. Cottrell to H. F. Bain, Dec. 31, 1910, USBM Records, 1910–1911.

43. Ibid. On Gilbert's basement apparatus, see Grove Karl Gilbert, *The Transportation of Debris by Running Water*, U.S. Geological Survey, Professional Paper No. 86 (Washington, D.C.: GPO, 1914), p. 19; and for a general discussion of his stream

research see Stephen J. Pyne, *Grove Karl Gilbert: A Great Engine of Research* (Austin: University of Texas, 1980), pp. 239–244.

44. H. F. Bain to J. A. Holmes, Jan. 2, 1911, USBM Records, 1910–1911. For Bain's editorials on Holmes's candidacy, see "Bureau of Mines and the Geological Survey," *Mining and Scientific Press*, 101 (July 9, 1910), 37; "Mining Matters at Washington," ibid., (July 30, 1910), 137; and "Bureau of Mines and the Director," ibid., (Sept. 10, 1910), 322. For Bain's editorials involving Cottrell, see "Meeting of the Chemists," ibid., (July 23, 1910), 107; and [No Title], ibid., (Nov. 26, 1910), 696. On Bain — who would himself become director of the Bureau of Mines in 1921, following Cottrell's year as acting director — see *Mining and Metallurgy*, 29 (Apr. 1948), 219–220; *WWWA*, Vol. 2 (1950), p. 37; *NCAB*, Vol. 36 (1950), pp. 291–292; Cameron, *Samaritan of Science*, p. 185; and Clark C. Spence, *Mining Engineers and the American West: The Lace-Boot Brigade, 1849–1933* (New Haven: Yale University Press, 1970), pp. 64-65.

45. F. G. Cottrell to J. A. Holmes, Jan. 11, 1911, USBM Records, 1910–1911.

46. Ibid. In his 1937 article, "The Social Responsibility of the Engineer-II," p. 554, Cottrell recalled: "I was leaving the university faculty for service with the U.S. Bureau of Mines especially on smelter fume problems closely connected with litigation thereon, so it was necessary to completely separate myself from any financial interest bearing on the subject."

47. F. G. Cottrell to J. A. Holmes, Jan. 30, 1911, USBM Records, 1910–1911.

48. Ibid.

49. J. A. Holmes to C. D. Walcott, Feb. 7, 1911, RU 45, Box 47, SI Archives.

50. Ibid.

51. J. A. Holmes, "Preface" to Holmes, Franklin, and Gould, *Report of the Selby Smelter Commission*, pp. xvii–xviii. Holmes's views were not unique. For example, Edward B. Rosa, a physicist who had charge of electrical studies at the National Bureau of Standards, described in his article, "The Function of Research in the Regulation of Natural Monopolies," *Science*, 37 (Apr. 18, 1913), 579–593, how public commissions could serve as alternatives to laissez-faire arrangements, on the one hand, and to regulatory legislation or public ownership, on the other. "The position of the bureau in this matter," Rosa noted (p. 586), "as in so many others, is advisory. It has no authority to enforce its conclusions and no disposition to suggest federal legislation or regulation. It acts as an unbiased coordinating agency. . . ." Similarly, Charles Baskerville, a chemist at the College of the City of New York, noted in the preface to a book he edited, entitled *Municipal Chemistry* (New York: McGraw-Hill, 1910), p. v: "It is believed by the writer . . . that if each city in the United States . . . established a scientific commission of power, unhampered by political, social, religious or official associations, to advise with the authorities on all practical matters, the public weal would be improved in many ways. . . . " Moving beyond these individual examples, what we are seeing here is a sign of the times. "By using experts in all aspects of American life," one scholar has noted, "the progressives expected to bring

the generalized benefits of disinterested science to the entire society" — see John C. Burnham's "Essay" at the outset of John D. Buenker, John C. Burnham, and Robert M. Crunden, *Progressivism* (Rochester, Vt.: Schenkman Books, 1977), p. 20.

52. J. A. Holmes to F. G. Cottrell, Feb. 23, 1911, USBM Records, 1910–1911.

53. F. G. Cottrell to J. A. Holmes, Mar. 19, 1911, USBM Records, 1910–1911.

54. Ibid.

55. Paul H. Oehser, *Sons of Science: The Story of the Smithsonian Institution and Its Leaders* (New York: Henry Schuman, 1949), p. 141. For a brief overview of the organization, see James A. Steed, "Smithsonian Institution," in Joseph C. Kiger, ed., *Research Institutions and Learned Societies*, Greenwood Encyclopedia of American Institutions, Vol. 5 (Westport, Conn.: Greenwood Press, 1982), pp. 439–443. For an assessment of the Smithsonian during the latter part of the 19th century, see Robert V. Bruce, *The Launching of Modern American Science, 1846–1876* (New York: Knopf, 1987), pp. 187–200 and pp. 323–325. Although the Smithsonian continued to be an important organization, what primacy it still retained after 1900 vanished with the formation of the National Research Council in 1916.

56. Theodore Roosevelt to Emma Baker Kennedy, Apr. 28, 1911, in Elting E. Morison, ed., *The Letters of Theodore Roosevelt* (Cambridge, Mass.: Harvard University Press), Vol. 7 (1954), p. 248. In large measure, Roosevelt was singing Walcott's praises because of Walcott's assistance in raising funds for his African expedition. "He's a born administrator . . . ," Powell once said of Walcott — see George Wharton James, "The Father of Conservation and Reclamation," *Twentieth Century Magazine*, 3 (Dec. 1910), 210. On Walcott's career generally, see Ellis L. Yochelson, "Charles Doolittle Walcott: 1850–1927," *Biog. Mem. NAS*, 39 (1967), 471–540 (which includes a listing of Walcott's publications). For the earliest phase of his career, see Ellis L. Yochelson, "Walcott in Albany, New York: James Hall's 'Special Assistant,' " *Earth Sciences History*, 6 (1987), 86–94. For his leadership at the USGS, see Thomas G. Manning, *Government in Science: The U.S. Geological Survey, 1867–1894* (Lexington: University of Kentucky Press, 1967), p. 212, and pp. 218–222. For his role in creating the Carnegie Institution, see Nathan Reingold, "National Science Policy in a Private Foundation: The Carnegie Institution of Washington," in Oleson and Voss, *The Organization of Knowledge in Modern America*, pp. 313–341; and Ellis L. Yochelson, "Andrew Carnegie and Charles Doolittle Walcott: The Origin and Early Years of the Carnegie Institution of Washington," in Good, *The Earth, the Heavens and the Carnegie Institution of Washington*, pp. 1–19.

57. In his 1924 address as retiring president of the American Association for the Advancement of Science, Walcott noted: "I have always had in view the discovery of older and still older evidences of primitive life" — see "Science and Service" (1925), p. 2. Along these lines, during the period when Research Corporation took shape Walcott's summer field trips to the Canadian Rockies yielded one of the new century's most important fossil finds: the rich record of the Cambrian Period preserved in the

Burgess Shale. Walcott began serious fieldwork at the site in 1910, and he continued to collect fossils there for several summers running. For Gould's assessment, see his book, *Wonderful Life: The Burgess Shale and the Nature of History* (New York: Norton, 1989), especially p. 13, p. 24, p. 75, pp. 244–245, and pp. 276–277. In a subsequent essay, "In Touch with Walcott," in his book *Eight Little Piggies: Reflections in Natural History* (New York: Norton, 1993), Gould responded to T. H. Clark's comments on *Wonderful Life*. "Clark kept emphasizing," Gould noted (p. 236), "the immensity of Walcott's empirical work.... And I realized that I had virtually excluded this part of Walcott from my account." But Gould retained his view that Walcott's "Burgess error will stand as his paramount mark upon intellectual history" (p. 236). I thank Robert J. Paradowski for bringing to my attention Gould's subsequent essay.

58. Diary of C. D. Walcott, Oct. 31, 1910, RU 7004, Box 15, SI Archives.

59. J. A. Holmes to F. G. Cottrell, Feb. 23, 1911, USBM Records, 1910–1911. For the earlier letter, which referred to the telephone conversation, see J. H. Holmes to C. D. Walcott, Feb. 7, 1911, RU 45, Box 47, SI Archives.

60. J. A. Holmes to F. G. Cottrell, Feb. 23, 1911, USBM Records, 1910–1911.

61. F. G. Cottrell to J. A. Holmes, Mar. 19, 1911, USBM Records, 1910–1911.

62. "Proceedings of the Board of Regents of the Smithsonian Institution," Feb. 9, 1911, RU 1, SI Archives. Formed in 1894 and consisting of the Secretary and the executive committee, the Smithsonian's permanent committee had "authority to accept for the Institution any property" that was given to further the purposes for which the Smithsonian had been founded (*Annual Report of the Board of Regents of the Smithsonian Institution ... to July 1894*, p. xiii).

63. J. A. Holmes to F. G. Cottrell, April 22, 1911, USBM Records, 1910–1911.

64. C. D. Walcott, "Memorandum: Remarks by Mr. Walcott on the Origin of the Research Corporation," [1915], RU 51, Box 1, SI Archives. The meetings took place on June 16 and 26, 1911 – see Diary of F. G. Cottrell, Cottrell Papers, Box 1; and Diary of C. D. Walcott, RU 7004, Box 15, SI Archives. An imaginative reconstruction, by W. Stevenson Bacon, of the first meeting between Cottrell and Walcott was recounted in *Research Corporation, A 75th Anniversary Report* (1987), pp. 3–7.

65. F. G. Cottrell to J. A. Holmes, Mar. 19, 1911, USBM Records, 1910–1911.

66. Cameron, *Samaritan of Science*, p. 157; and F. G. Cottrell to J. A. Holmes, Aug. 17, 1911, USBM Records, 1910–1911.

67. International Precipitation Co. to the Board of Regents of the Smithsonian Institution, Oct. 18, 1911, RU 45, Box 47, SI Archives. See also some of the documents in Box 17.

68. C. D. Walcott to F. G. Cottrell, Oct. 26, 1911, RU 45, Box 47, SI Archives.

69. *Annual Report of the Board of Regents of the Smithsonian Institution ... for the Year Ending June 30, 1912*, p. xi. On Bacon, see Warren Grice, "Augustus Octavius Bacon," *DAB*, Vol. 1 (1928), pp. 473–474. On Dalzell, see Laura Rundell, "John Dalzell," *ANB*, Vol. 6 (1999), pp. 45–46. On Bell, see Robert V. Bruce, *Bell: Alexander Graham Bell and the Conquest of Solitude* (Boston: Little, Brown, 1973).

70. A. G. Bell to C. D. Walcott, Nov. 8, 1911, RU 45, Box 47, SI Archives. "Personally I feel very favorably toward accepting the proposition . . . ," Walcott wrote in his initial letter to Bell (Oct. 27, 1911, RU 45, Box 47, SI Archives). For Cottrell's meeting with Dalzell, see Diary of F. G. Cottrell, June 18, 1911, Cottrell Papers, Box 1; and C. D. Walcott to John Dalzell, Oct. 27, 1911, RU 45, Box 47, SI Archives.

71. George Gray to C. D. Walcott, Nov. 23, 1911, RU 45, Box 47, SI Archives. On Gray, see H. W. Howard Knott, "George Gray," *DAB*, Vol. 7 (1931), pp. 515–516. "Possessing an eminently judicial mind," Knott noted (p. 516), "Gray combined a thorough knowledge of legal principles and practise with a capacity for applying that knowledge to concrete cases, and his decisions were rarely reversed."

72. C. F. Choate, Jr., to C. D. Walcott, Nov. 25, 1911, RU 45, Box 47, SI Archives. On Choate, see the *NYT*, Dec. 1, 1927, p. 27, col. 5. Regarding the possibility of forming a stock corporation, Cottrell had earlier discussed with Walcott a plan "whereby a corporation would be organized in New York, the whole of whose stock should be held by the Smithsonian" — see F. G. Cottrell to C. D. Walcott, Nov. 3, 1911, RU 45, Box 47, SI Archives.

73. C. D. Walcott to C. F. Choate, Jr., Nov. 27, 1911, RU 45, Box, 47, SI Archives.

74. Diary of F. G. Cottrell, June 26, 1911, Cottrell Papers, Box 1. In the early 1950s Research Corporation's president, J. W. Barker, noted in *Research Corporation (1912–1952)* that "legal advice from Mr. Taft, a Regent of the Smithsonian, convinced Cottrell and Walcott that the Smithsonian charter was not broad enough to carry out such a concept" (p. 11). For a general discussion of Taft's approach to the law, see James David Barber, *The Presidential Character: Predicting Performance in the White House*, 4th Ed. (Englewood Cliffs, N.J.: Prentice-Hall, 1992), pp. 196–197. An example of Taft's patent experience would be his decision in an interference case involving C. M. Hall's patent for producing aluminum — see Junius Edwards, *The Immortal Woodshed: The Story of the Inventor Who Brought Aluminum to America* (New York: Dodd, Mead, 1955), pp. 160–161. "I know very little about chemistry, but I know a good deal about patent litigation," Taft told the group of chemists he had invited to a reception at the White House on September 4, 1912 — see "International Congress of Applied Chemistry," *JIEC*, 4 (Oct. 1912), 710. That Walcott indeed had access to the president was demonstrated by a visit he and his son made. "With Stuart," he noted in his diary entry for Dec. 9, 1911 (RU 7004, Box 15, SI Archives), "called on President Taft in re. Stuart's appointment to *Annapolis*."

75. "Proceedings of the Board of Regents of the Smithsonian Institution," Dec. 14, 1911, RU 1, SI Archives. Their exact phrasing was: "[We] do not deem it expedient for the Institution to become the direct owner of the proposed gift of royalty-bearing patents." They resolved further that the Smithsonian "may properly accept a declaration of trust from the owners of the patents to hold and operate the same in the interest of the Institution, and to pay over to the said Institution the net profits therefrom." The resolutions were also quoted in Cottrell, "The Research Corporation, An Experiment in Public Administration of Patent Rights" (1912), p. 864.

76. C. D. Walcott to F. G. Cottrell, Dec. 15, 1911, RU 45, Box 47, SI Archives.

77. F. G. Cottrell to Erwin Möller, Mar. 7, 1913, RU 45, Box 47, SI Archives. Cottrell also noted that Research Corporation's directors were selected "with the greatest care to insure an organization in both whose ability and integrity everyone could have sufficient confidence to leave matters of detail freely in its hands without hampering the development with any unnecessary formal restrictions which in time might otherwise accumulate to a point to seriously block the wheels of progress."

78. F. G. Cottrell to C. D. Walcott, Jan. 3, 1912, RU 45, Box 47, SI Archives.

79. C. D. Walcott to F. G. Cottrell, Jan. 22, 1912, RU 45, Box 47, SI Archives.

80. C. D. Walcott to F. G. Cottrell, Feb. 6, 1912, RU 45, Box 47, SI Archives.

81. F. G. Cottrell to C. D. Walcott, Jan. 29, 1912, RU 45, Box 47, SI Archives.

82. One writer even called him "The Voice of Research" — see Holland, *Industrial Explorers*, Chap. 9, pp. 149–169. On Little and the company he founded, see also "Arthur D. Little, Inc.," in Haynes, *American Chemical Industry: The Chemical Companies* (1949), pp. 249–251; Eduard Farber, ed., *Great Chemists* (New York: Interscience Publishers, 1961), pp. 1193–1201; Noble, *America by Design*, pp. 124–125; John W. Servos, "The Industrial Relations of Science: Chemical Engineering at MIT, 1900–1939," *Isis*, 71 (Dec. 1980), 530–549; E. J. Kahn, Jr., *The Problem Solvers: A History of Arthur D. Little, Inc.* (Boston: Little, Brown, 1986); and Charles W. Carey, Jr., "Arthur Dehon Little," *ANB*, Vol. 13 (1999), pp. 739–742. A collection of his published articles may be found in the Arthur Dehon Little Papers, Box 3, Library of Congress.

83. For Little's offer — as well as for his presence at the San Francisco meeting — see Cameron, *Samaritan of Science*, p. 162. For the contact between Cottrell and Little at the Indianapolis meeting, see the Diary of F. G. Cottrell, June 30, 1911, Cottrell Papers, Box 1. That meeting was also the occasion for Little's address, "The Earning Power of Chemistry" — see *JIEC*, 3 (Aug. 1911), 598–604 and 610. In a memorandum dated March 15, 1912 ("Organization of Research Corporation," RU 45, Box 47, SI Archives), Walcott noted that Little "was most helpful in getting the Boston people interested."

84. For the names Little suggested, see F. G. Cottrell to C. D. Walcott, Dec. 21, 1911, RU 45, Box 47, SI Archives. For the trip to Boston, see Diary of F. G. Cottrell, Jan. 11 and 12, 1912, Cottrell Papers, Box 1; and Diary of C. D. Walcott, Jan. 11 and 12, 1912, RU 7004, Box 15, SI Archives. On Thomson, see David B. Sicilia, "Elihu Thomson," *ANB*, Vol. 21 (1999), pp. 593–594. On Storrow, see *NCAB*, Vol. 33 (1947), pp. 198–199 — and on his father, see Bruce, *Bell*, pp. 267–268. On Stone, see Thomas P. Hughes, "Charles Augustus Stone and Edwin Sibley Webster," *DAB*, Supp. 3 (1973), pp. 744–747; and on the firm Stone and Webster, see Hughes, *Networks of Power*, pp. 386–390.

85. T. C. du Pont to A. D. Little, quoted in A. Montgomery (Little's secretary) to C. D. Walcott, Jan. 25, 1912, RU 45, Box 47, SI Archives. On du Pont, see Kenneth H. Williams, "T. Coleman Du Pont," *ANB*, Vol. 7 (1999), pp. 130–132.

86. For his agreeing to subscribe to the shares of Research Corporation stock, see T. C. du Pont to C. D. Walcott, Mar. 2, 1912, RU 51, Box 1, SI Archives. For his contribution to MIT, see "T. C. du Pont, '84, gives $500,000," *Technology Review*, 13 (1911), 341; and Samuel C. Prescott, *When M.I.T. Was "Boston Tech," 1861-1916* (Cambridge, Mass.: MIT Press, 1954), pp. 250–251 and p. 257.

87. Margaret Ripley Wolfe, *Lucius Polk Brown and Progressive Food and Drug Control: Tennessee and New York City, 1908-1920* (Lawrence: Regents Press of Kansas, 1978).

88. On Kirchhoff, see Philip B. McDonald, "Charles William Henry Kirchhoff," *DAB*, Vol. 10 (1933), p. 426. Cottrell was introduced to Kirchhoff by B. B. Lawrence – see Diary of F. G. Cottrell, Jan. 19, 1912, Cottrell Papers, Box 1. Regarding the general situation in New York City, David C. Hammack has noted in his book, *Power and Society: Greater New York at the Turn of the Century* (New York: Russell Sage Foundation, 1982), p. 312: "Greater New York attracted disproportionately large numbers of experts, and their numbers encouraged them to specialize and to form professional associations."

89. Meeting of the Board of Directors, Nov. 19, 1914, Research Corporation Minutes (hereafter RC Minutes), RU 51, Box 3, SI Archives. Writing in 1952, Scott recalled that when Cottrell and Walcott first visited him at his office in New York he had recognized Cottrell from their student days at Berkeley (L. N. Scott, "Notes on the Founding of the Research Corporation," Feb. 27, 1952, Publication Archive, RC Archives). On Scott – who began his work for Columbia in association with J. B. Pine (and who later succeeded Pine as the university's main attorney) see also *NCAB*, Vol. 52 (1970), pp. 594–595; and *NYT*, Feb. 20, 1966, p. 88, col. 4.

90. On Hooker and the company he founded, see "Hooker Electrochemical Company," in Haynes, *American Chemical Industry: The Chemical Companies*, pp. 210–215; Robert E. Thomas, *Salt & Water, Power & People: A Short History of Hooker Electrochemical Company* (Niagara Falls, N.Y.: 1955); Thomas P. Hughes, *Elmer Sperry: Inventor and Engineer* (Baltimore: The Johns Hopkins University Press, 1971), pp. 92–93; Martha Moore Trescott, *The Rise of the American Electrochemicals Industry, 1880-1910: Studies in the American Technological Environment* (Westport, Conn.: Greenwood Press, 1981), pp. 81–82; and Terry S. Reynolds, "Elon Huntington Hooker," *ANB*, Vol. 11 (1999), pp. 130–131. Poised geographically between the fresh water of the Great Lakes and the salt mines of western New York, the Hooker Chemical Company used electrical power from Niagara Falls to produce chemicals on an industrial scale. Thus, in striking contrast to the notoriety it has since acquired as a result of the Love Canal controversy, at the time of its founding the company could have been portrayed along the general lines that Nye has described in his book *American Technological Sublime*.

91. F. G. Cottrell to C. D. Walcott, Jan. 30, 1912, RU 45, Box 47, SI Archives. For Cottrell's meeting with Eads Johnson, the secretary of the local Cornell alumni soci-

ety, see also Diary of F. G. Cottrell, Jan. 31, 1912, Cottrell Papers, Box 1.

92. Diary of F. G. Cottrell, Feb. 1, 1912, Cottrell Papers, Box 1.

93. At times Cottrell also stayed at the Hotel Belmont (at 42nd Street and Park Avenue, across from Grand Central Station), which was a favorite of Walcott's. Regarding his professional society memberships, the first edition of *AMS* (1910), pp. 100–101, listed only the American Chemical Society, while the second edition (1921), p. 148, added the Mining and Metallurgical Society of America, the American Institute of Mining Engineers, and the American Electrochemical Society. He was elected a member of the last two in 1912 — see *Trans. AIME*, 43 (1912), lxxiii; and *Transactions of the American Electrochemical Society* (hereafter *Trans. AES*), 23 (1913), 15.

94. "International Congress of Applied Chemistry," *JIEC*, 4 (Oct. 1912), 714. On the new building, see various articles in *JIEC*, 3 (Apr. 1911), 205–210; and Charles F. Chandler, "Chemistry in the United States," ibid., 13 (May 1921), 394. For the contrast to the New York Academy of Sciences, see Simon Baatz, *Knowledge, Culture, and Science in the Metropolis: The New York Academy of Sciences, 1817–1970* (New York: New York Academy of Sciences, 1990), published as Vol. 584 (1990) in the *Annals of the New York Academy of Sciences*, p. 200.

95. F. G. Cottrell to C. D. Walcott, Dec. 24, 1911, RU 45, Box 47, SI Archives. On Goetze, see *NYT*, Mar. 8, 1950, p. 25, col. 1; and *WWWA*, Vol. 3 (1960), p. 331. On his administrative position at the time, see "Goetze Appointed Dean," *NYT*, Nov. 6, 1906, p. 6, col. 3. On Lawrence, see ibid., Jan. 22, 1921, p. 11, col. 4; and Nicholas Murray Butler, "Benjamin Bowden Lawrence, '78 Mines," *Columbia Alumni News*, 12 (Feb. 4, 1921), 265–266. On the School of Mines (later renamed the School of Engineering), see Thomas Thornton Read, *The Development of Mineral Industry Education in the United States* (New York: American Institute of Mining and Metallurgical Engineers, 1941), especially pp. 175–183; and James Kip Finch, *A History of the School of Engineering, Columbia University* (New York: Columbia University Press, 1954), especially Chap. 5, "The Earlier Years at Morningside," pp. 77–91.

96. F. G. Cottrell to C. D. Walcott, Nov. 3, 1911, RU 45, Box 47, SI Archives.

97. F. G. Cottrell to C. D. Walcott, Dec. 4, 1914, RU 45, Box 47, SI Archives.

98. F. G. Cottrell to C. D. Walcott, Dec. 21, 1911, RU 45, Box 47, SI Archives.

99. For the location of Research Corporation's office, see F. G. Cottrell to C. D. Walcott, Feb. 28, 1912, RU 45, Box 47, SI Archives; and F. G. Cottrell to C. D. Walcott, Mar. 10, 1912, RU 45, Box 47, SI Archives.

100. On Pine, see the *NYT*, Oct. 29, 1922, p. 30, col. 2. "It is my belief," Scott recalled in "Notes on the Founding of the Research Corporation" (his 1952 memorandum), "that Dr. Cottrell and Dr. Walcott were referred to Mr. Pine by either Mr. Lawrence or Mr. Goetze."

101. "Minutes of Meeting Called at 63 Wall St. N.Y. Feb. 2 1912 for Purpose of Organizing Research Corporation" — in Cottrell's hand — Box A14, RC Archives. On Jennings, a mining engineer, see Philip B. McDonald, "James Hennen Jennings,"

DAB, Vol. 10 (1933), pp. 55–56. On Dudley, a chemist, see *NCAB*, Vol. 8 (1924), pp. 227–228.

102. F. G. Cottrell to A. D. Little, Jan. 17, 1912, Box A14, RC Archives.

103. The expanded number of directors was mentioned in J. B. Pine to J. H. Jennings, Feb. 9, 1912, Box A14, RC Archives. The official list appears in the brochure, *Research Corporation: Certificate of Incorporation, By-Laws, and Stockholders' Agreement* (New York: Research Corporation, 1912), a copy of which may be found in RU 51, Box 1, SI Archives. During the spring of 1912 Thomas C. Meadows was elected to replace Dudley, while M. Bernard Philipp was elected to replace Reardon. This revised list appeared in Cottrell, "The Research Corporation, An Experiment in Public Administration of Patent Rights" (1912), p. 866. For Meadows' election, see Meeting of the Board of Directors, Mar. 14, 1912, RC Minutes, RU 51, Box 3, SI Archives; for Philipp's, see ibid., May 22, 1912. On Reardon, a lawyer, see *NYT*, Sept. 25, 1919, p. 8, col. 6; on Philipp, a patent lawyer, see *NCAB*, Vol. 26 (1937), pp. 190–191; on Meadows, see *NYT*, May 6, 1935, p. 19, col. 4.

104. An example of Cottrell's use of "Technical Research Company," appeared in F. G. Cottrell to A. D. Little, Jan. 17, 1912, Box A14, RC Archives. Pine's efforts involved an exchange of telegrams with the Corporation Department, in the office of New York's secretary of state, on Jan. 18, 1912 (Box A14, RC Archives).

105. "Minutes of Meeting Called at 63 Wall St. N.Y. Feb. 2 1912. . . ." For Little's suggestion, see F. G. Cottrell to C. D. Walcott, Jan. 20, 1912, RU 45, Box 47, SI Archives.

106. "Minutes of Meeting Called at 63 Wall St. N.Y. Feb. 2 1912. . . ." Subsequently, the secretary of state gave his permisssion to use this new choice (Edward Lazansky to John B. Pine, Feb. 6, 1912, Box A14, RC Archives).

107. Allan Nevins, *Ford: The Times, the Man, the Company* (New York: Scribners, 1954), especially Chap. 13, "The Shadow of Monopoly," pp. 284–322, and Chap. 17, "No Monopoly," pp. 415–446.

108. Fred Howard, *Wilbur and Orville: A Biography of the Wright Brothers* (New York: Ballantine Books, 1987), especially Chap. 38, "The Patent Wars Begin," pp. 327–334, and Chap. 46, "The Aerodrome Affair," pp. 393–402; and Kirk W. House, *Hell-Rider to King of the Air: Glenn Curtiss's Life of Innovation* (Warrendale, Pa.: SAE International, 2003), especially pp. 113-119 and pp. 143-147.

109. L. H. Baekeland, "The United States Patent System, Its Use and Abuse," *JIEC*, 1 (May 1909), 204–205.

110. Quoted in "International Congress of Applied Chemistry," ibid., 4 (Oct. 1912), 710.

111. Quoted in Floyd L. Vaughan, *Economics of Our Patent System* (New York: Macmillan, 1925), p. 72. On William Allen Oldfield, the congressman who chaired the House Committee on Patents, see *NCAB*, Vol. 21 (1931), p. 299. For contemporary assessments of the bill that Oldfield introduced, see Waldemar Kaempffert, "Our Defective Patent System," *Outlook*, 101 (July 6, 1912), 548–551; and L. H. Baekeland,

"The Incongruities of American Patent Litigation," *JIEC*, 4 (Nov. 1912), 785–789. Patent suits were a sore point with Edison. Unpleasant experiences involving the carbon-filament lamp led him to confide in an 1885 diary entry, "A lawsuit is the suicide of time," and later in life he complained: "My electric light inventions have brought me no profits, only forty years of litigation" — quoted in Matthew Josephson, *Edison* (New York: McGraw-Hill, 1959), p. 295 and p. 358.

112. Scott, "Notes on the Founding of the Research Corporation" (1952). Membership Corporations in New York State included hospitals, libraries, cemeteries, historical societies, and other non-profit organizations.

113. Scott, "Notes on the Founding of the Research Corporation" (1952).

114. "Minutes of Meeting Called at 63 Wall St. N.Y. Feb. 2 1912...."

115. A. D. Little to F. G. Cottrell, Feb. 13, 1912, RU 45, Box 47, SI Archives.

116. F. G. Cottrell to J. B. Pine, Feb. 14, 1912, Box A30, RC Archives.

117. J. B. Pine to A. D. Little, Feb. 16, 1912, Box A14, RC Archives. In his letter, Pine elaborated (using citations from the *Federal Reporter* — with volume numbers appearing to the left and page numbers, to the right):

> This view is sustained by a number of decisions. In *Greene v Buckley* (120 Fed. 955) the United States Circuit Court decided in 1902, that "officers of a corporation cannot be held individually liable for the infringement of a patent by the corporation where it does not appear that they committed any act of infringement as individuals, or that the corporation is insolvent."
>
> This ruling was followed in *Hutter v De[Q.] Bottle Stopper Co.* (128 Fed. 283,286) by the U.S. Circuit Court of appeals in 1904. This was an action against a corporation for an infringement of patent, in which the secretary and treasurer, who was also a director, was made a party defendant. The Court dismissed the bill of complaint as to such director in the absence of proof of any infringement by him as an individual, there being no question as to the solvency of the corporation, and used the following language: "The Courts of the Circuit have frequently had occasion to criticise this practice (i.e., of including officers of corporations as defendants in suits for infringement of patent) and have, in some instances imposed costs upon the complainant as a penalty for thus subjecting innocent parties to the expense and annoyance of defending themselves against an unwarrantable accusation." A different rule was laid down in *National Cash Register Co v Leland* (94 Fed. 502), which was decided by only a majority of the Court in 1899 and has since been overruled in numerous instances, one of the latest being *Glucose Sugar Refining Co. v St. Louis Syrup Co.* (135 Fed. 54[0]), decided in 1905. The opinion in this case, after reviewing all the authorities, held that the president of a corporation, not alleged to be insolvent, cannot properly be joined with the corporation as a defendant in a bill for an infringement of a patent by the

corporation, merely because as such president he directs the business of the corporation. A still later case, *Cazier v Mackie* (138 Fed. 654) holds that "An infringement by a corporation gives no right of action against one of its officers, unless he has acted beyond the ordinary scope of his office."

118. J. B. Pine to A. D. Little, Feb. 16, 1912, Box A14, RC Archives.

119. Telegram, A. D. Little to J. B. Pine, Feb. 21, 1912, Box A14, RC Archives. "The latter information is particularly gratifying," Pine replied (Feb. 24, 1912, Box A14, RC Archives), "as I presume that Mr. Stone's decision will have some weight with Mr. Storrow." In a letter to Pine dated March 1, 1912 (Box A14, RC Archives), Little confirmed: "... there is no question but that we have enlisted the interest and cooperation of Mr. Stone and Mr. Storrow." The action taken at the meeting — with Cottrell, Walcott, Pine, Hooker, Jennings, Lawrence, and Scott in attendance — was noted in the minutes for "the preliminary meeting of the Directors of the 'Research Corporation,' held at No. 63 Wall Street, New York, on February 16th, 1912," Box A14, RC Archives.

120. Research Corporation, *Research Corporation: Certificate of Incorporation, By-Laws and Stockholders' Agreement* (1912).

121. Ibid.

122. F. G. Cottrell to C. D. Walcott, Jan. 17, 1912, RU 45, Box 47, SI Archives.

123. The list of stockholders was published in Cottrell's 1912 article "The Research Corporation, An Experiment in Public Administration of Patent Rights," p. 866. For the number of shares in each case, see Meeting of the Board of Directors, May 22, 1912, RC Minutes, RU 51, Box 3, SI Archives.

124. Scott, "Notes on the Founding of the Research Corporation" (1952). The arrangement was one that Scott attributed to Pine.

125. Cottrell, "The Social Responsibility of the Engineer-II" (1937), p. 554.

126. J. B. Pine to Edward Lazansky, Feb. 19, 1912, Box A14, RC Archives. In his 1952 "Notes on the Founding of Research Corporation" Scott commented: "There was some difficulty in getting this rather unique Certificate of Incorporation accepted by the Secretary of State at Albany, New York, but Mr. Pine finally succeeded...."

127. The first official meeting of the board of directors (followed by the first official meeting of the executive committee) came on February 27, 1912 — see RC Minutes, RU 51, Box 3, SI Archives. "Yesterday morning," Walcott wrote his cousin, "Dr. Cottrell and I succeeded in raising a thousand dollars, which, with the fifteen hundred dollars of the day before, completed what was needed for the working fund of the Research Corporation" (C. D. Walcott to F. C. Walcott, Mar. 15, 1912, RU 45, Box 47, SI Archives). For the low level of capitalization and an explanation of Cottrell's reason for it, see Linn Bradley, "Practical Applications of Electrical Precipitation and Progress of the Research Corporation," *Trans. AIEE*, 34 (1915), 423–424. On the difficulties in choosing a president, see F. G. Cottrell to C. D. Walcott, Mar. 1, 1912, RU 45, Box 47, SI Archives.

128. *Annual Report of the Board of Regents of the Smithsonian Institution... for the Year Ending June 30, 1912*, p. 4. As an example of Walcott's letters to individual regents, see C. D. Walcott to George Gray, Mar. 28, 1912, RU 45, Box 47, SI Archives.

129. J. B. Pine to C. D. Walcott, Feb. 28, 1912, RU 45, Box 47, SI Archives.

CHAPTER FOUR–A SUCCESSFUL ENGINEERING FIRM
PAGES 78–115

1. F. G. Cottrell to C. D. Walcott, Mar. 10, 1912, RU 45, Box 47, SI Archives. In his diary entry for February 3, 1912 (Cottrell Papers, Box 1), Cottrell noted: "Showed Jennings & Pine Schmidt's letter on Bradley & discussed him as [an] employee. They [were] very favorably inclined." Then on February 28, 1912, Cottrell wrote Walcott (RU 45, Box 47, SI Archives): "I have wired for Mr. Bradley to come on and expect he is just about leaving Los Angeles today." On Bradley, see *Who's Who in Engineering* (hereafter *WWE*), 4th Ed. (1937), p. 146; and *NYT*, Nov. 1, 1956, p. 39, col. 2. His work for Schmidt was discussed in W. A. Schmidt to J. W. Barker, Mar. 21, 1949, Box A9, RC Archives; and Cameron, *Samaritan of Science*, p. 168. On his official appointment – at a salary of $250 per month for the first six months (and $300 for the second) – see Meeting of the Executive Committee, Mar. 8, 1912, RC Minutes, RU 51, Box 3, SI Archives.

2. C. D. Walcott to F. G. Cottrell, Dec. 15, 1911, RU 45, Box 47, SI Archives. "Called at Edison Co. Offices," Cottrell noted in his diary entry for December 21, 1911 (Cottrell Papers, Box 1), and in the next day's entry he added: "Went to Waterside plant of Edison Co . . . ." On both occasions he talked with Lieb. On Lieb – who was chief electrician for Edison's Pearl Street Station when it opened in 1882, who then for a dozen years represented Edison in Italy, and who subsequently held a leading position in the Edison company that generated electricity in New York – see Paul B. Israel, "John William Lieb," *ANB*, Vol. 13 (1999), pp. 633–634.

3. "Smoke Nuisance Ended," *NYT*, Sept. 5, 1911, p. 8, col. 6. "The Department of Health," that same article noted, "has been vigorously enforcing the law since a year ago last July, when the old law, which was inadequate to give it power, was amended." For a less sanguine view of how effective the city's smoke legislation was, see Samuel B. Flagg, *Smoke Abatement and City Smoke Ordinances*, USBM Bull., No. 49 (Washington, D.C.: GPO, 1912), p. 22. For overviews of the situation in New York, see Payn B. Parsons, "The Smoke Problem; With Some Special Applications to New York City," in Baskerville, *Municipal Chemistry*, pp. 322–336; John Duffy, *A History of Public Health in New York City, 1866–1966* (New York: Russell Sage Foundation, 1974), pp. 523–529; and Stradling, *Smokestacks and Progressives*, pp. 73–75.

4. "Fines the Edison Co. for Smoke Nuisance," *NYT*, Jan. 17, 1911, p. 7, col. 1.

Located at 38th Street and First Avenue, the plant furnished almost 90 percent of the electrical power used in Manhattan and the Bronx.

5. "Engineer's Progress Report," Meeting of the Executive Committee, June 20, 1913, RC Minutes, RU 51, Box 3, SI Archives. For the onset of negotiations, see Meeting of the Board of Directors, Mar. 14, 1912, RC Minutes, RU 51, Box 3, SI Archives. For the details of the contract, see F. A. Goetze to J. W. Lieb, Mar. 27, 1912, RU 45, Box 47, SI Archives. For a description of the project, see Linn Bradley, "The Electrical Precipitation of Suspended Particles by the Cottrell Process," *JIEC*, 4 (Dec. 1912), 908–909. During the summer of 1913 the New York Edison Company succeeded in obtaining a legal decision against the city law prohibiting "dense smoke" — see "Smoke Ordinance Set Aside by Court," *NYT*, July 19, 1913, p. 6, col. 8. But on appeal the city got the law reinstated — see "Court Upholds Smoke Ordinance," ibid., Dec. 6, 1913, p. 19, col. 1. Soon thereafter the New York Edison Company implemented a technique other than electrostatic precipitation — see "Wash Their Smoke to Kill Nuisance," ibid., Dec. 23, 1913, p. 14, col. 4.

6. F. G. Cottrell, "Discussion," p. 496, at the end of Linn Bradley, "Electrical Precipitation of Suspended Particles," *Trans. AES*, 22 (1912), 489–497. The last installation with which Cottrell was personally associated in a technical capacity was the one at Balaklala — see White, "Centenary of Frederick Gardner Cottrell" (1978), p. 10. Bradley's paper also appeared as "Electrical Precipitation of Dust and Fumes," in *Original Communications, Eighth International Congress of Applied Chemistry*, Vol. 26, pp. 471–478; and "The Electrical Precipitation of Suspended Particles by the Cottrell Process," *JIEC*, 4 (Dec. 1912), 908–910. For more on the Raritan installa tion, see Charles H. Aldrich, "Treatment of Silver Furnace Fume by the Cottrell Process," *Trans. AES*, 28 (1915), 119–137. For more on the Garfield installation, see Howard, "Electrical Fume Precipitation at Garfield" (1915).

7. Thus Bradley observed in his article, "Practical Applications of Electrical Precipitation and Progress of the Research Corporation," *Trans. AIEE*, 34 (1915), 423: "our [early] operations were so conducted that no financial obligations would accrue to either the stockholders or the directors. Therefore, one of the requirements of our early contracts was that the client had to pay all expenses incident to our work upon his problem, and in addition thereto had to pay us certain stipulated sums of money for technical services." On the difficulty of standardizing the installations, see "Report of Executive Committee of the Research Corporation for the Year 1913," n.d., RU 51, Box 1, SI Archives; and "The Research Corporation and the Cottrell Process," *EMJ*, 97 (May 30, 1914), 1108.

8. C. D. Walcott to F. G. Cottrell, March 13, 1913, RU 45, Box 47, SI Archives. With regard to costs at Balaklala, Cottrell noted in his 1913 article, "Problems in Smoke, Fume, and Dust Abatement," p. 678: "The gas-treating plant as a whole, including flues, fans, motors, and electrical apparatus, cost, up to the time it was first put in operation, a little less than $110,000."

9. B. B. Lawrence to C. D. Walcott, Nov. 4, 1914, RU 45, Box 47, SI Archives. For the difficulties Research Corporation faced, see *Annual Report of the Board of Regents of the Smithsonian Institution . . . for the Year Ending June 30, 1915*, p. 123. The contract licensed the Anaconda Copper Mining Co. to install precipitators at Anaconda, Mont.; Toole, Utah; Great Falls, Mont.; and East Chicago, Ind. – see Meetings of the Executive Committee, Sept. 30, 1914 and Oct. 5, 1914, RC Minutes, RU 51, Box 3, SI Archives. As of late 1914 the Anaconda Copper Mining Co. was controlled by a holding company, the Amalgamated Copper Company, which in April 1914 had acquired the International Smelting and Refining Company (a development which helped rationalize Anaconda's expanding interests) – see Isaac F. Marcosson, *Anaconda* (New York: Dodd, Mead, 1957), pp. 95–96 and pp. 143–144. On the installations at Anaconda, see Bradley, "Practical Applications of Electrical Precipitation and Progress of the Research Corporation" (1915), pp. 433–436; Frederick Laist, "Changes in Smelting Practice of Anaconda Copper Mining Co.," *EMJ*, 102 (Oct. 7, 1916), 635–638; Swain, "Smoke and Fume Investigations: A Historical Review" (1949), p. 2385; and LeCain, "The Limits of 'Eco-Efficiency' " (2000), pp. 336–351. For the decisions following the contract signing, see Meeting of the Board of Directors, Nov. 19, 1914, RC Minutes, RU 51, Box 3, SI Archives. So peculiar was Research Corporation's full ownership of the original stock issue that Scott continued to worry about it. Finally he "called it to the attention of Dave H. Morris, a lawyer and one of the Directors of the corporation," who took the steps necessary "to legalize this unique set-up" – see Scott, "Notes on the Founding of the Research Corporation" (1952). As a result (Scott continued): "The New York Legislature passed an Act on February 10, 1932, ratifying these acts of the directors. . . ."

10. C. D. Walcott to E. H. Hooker, Dec. 30, 1914, RU 51, Box 1, SI Archives.

11. At its meeting on May 22, 1912, the board of directors resolved (RC Minutes, RU 51, Box 3, SI Archives): "That the work of the Corporation had made it necessary to engage an assistant engineer at $100 per month, and that it was expected that it would soon be necessary to have a representative at each plant at which an installation was in progress of erection." For Bradley's new title – and for a decision to increase further the size of the engineering staff – see Meeting of the Executive Committee, Nov. 18, 1915, RC Minutes, RU 51, Box 3, SI Archives. For the list of personnel, see Linn Bradley, "Proposed Organization for Development of Activities of Research Corporation," Apr. 6, 1916, RU 51, Box 2, SI Archives. For a list of "Salaries: Year Ending December 31, 1916" (Bradley, for example, received $5,000 that year), see Meeting of the Stockholders, Feb. 16, 1917, RC Minutes, RU 51, Box 4, SI Archives. On Fischer (whose name appears as "Fisher") – an electrical engineer with a B.S. degree from Berkeley, who served on the faculty there from 1911 to 1915 – see *WWE*, 3rd Ed. (1931), p. 426. On Hale, see ibid., 4th Ed. (1937), p. 557.

12. C. D. Walcott to E. H. Hooker, Oct. 31, 1914, RU 51, Box 1, SI Archives. "I think you are right in your point of not over-emphasizing the control of any one University

influence in the Corporation...," Hooker replied (Nov. 2, 1914, RU 51, Box 1, SI Archives). The specific context for their exchange was the question of whether or not to make Goetze president of Research Corporation. For the Columbia degrees of the Research Corporation engineers, see Columbia University, *Columbia University Alumni Register: 1754–1931* (New York: Columbia University Press, 1932), passim.

13. Slosson, *Great American Universities*, p. 446. By contrast, Slosson continued (p. 447), the University of Chicago was "a cloister in a city": "The University of Chicago might be anywhere... but Columbia, body and soul, is so thoroughly characteristic of New York City as to be quite inconceivable elsewhere." On Slosson — who in 1902 received his Ph.D. degree in chemistry from the University of Chicago but then embarked on a distinguished career in journalism and popular-science writing — see David J. Rhees, "Edwin Emery Slosson," *ANB*, Vol. 20 (1999), pp. 108–109.

14. In his annual report for 1910–1911 Butler even expressed the view "that it would have been wiser not to establish these undertakings apart from universities, but rather in connection or association with them" — quoted in Columbia University, *The Rise of a University* (New York: Columbia University Press, 1937), Vol. 2, p. 71. On Butler — a major figure in the reorganization of American higher education in the early twentieth century — see Hugh Hawkins, "Nicholas Murray Butler," *DAB*, Supp. 4 (1974), pp. 133–138. For a discussion of Butler at Columbia in this period, see William Summerscales, *Affirmation and Dissent: Columbia's Response to the Crisis of World War I* (New York: Teachers College Press, Columbia University, 1970), Chap. 2, "Academic Managership at Columbia: The Early Butler Years," pp. 18–40.

15. Nicholas Murray Butler, "The University and Industry," *JIEC*, 7 (Dec. 1915), 1071.

16. For the various terms, see Thomas P. Hughes, "The Development Phase of Technological Change: Introduction," *Technology and Culture*, 17 (July 1976), 423–431; John A. Heitmann and David J. Rhees, *Scaling Up: Science, Engineering, and the American Chemical Industry*, Center for History of Chemistry Publication, No. 2 (Philadelphia: Center for History of Chemistry, 1984); and Edwin T. Layton, Jr., "Mirror-Image Twins: The Communities of Science and Technology in 19th-Century America," *Technology and Culture*, 12 (Oct. 1971), 562–580.

17. Bradley, "Practical Applications of Electrical Precipitation and Progress of the Research Corporation" (1915), pp. 422–423 (emphasis added). Bradley may have been paraphrasing L. H. Baekeland, "The Incongruities of American Patent Litigation," *JIEC*, 4 (Nov. 1912), 788. A. D. Little also made similar statements. For example, in his remarks when Milton C. Whitaker was awarded the Perkin Medal — see *Industrial and Engineering Chemistry*, 15 (Feb. 1923), 196 — he noted: "Those of us whose professional activities center in the study, the classroom, or the laboratory are commonly inclined to award a disproportionate need of merit to that one whose discovery of fact, material, or reaction supplies the basis for a great industrial devel-

opment. They seldom recognize or appreciate the obstacles and difficulties along the steep and rocky road, which leads from the laboratory to the plant."

18. For a brief survey of the various early applications, see P. E. Landolt, "Eliminating Waste and Nuisance in Smoke, Fume and Gas," *Chemical and Metallurgical Engineering,* 25 (Aug. 31, 1921), 428–432. It is also worth noting that engineering studies could lead to problems of a more scientific sort. An example would be determining the volatility of metals – see the "Discussion" at the end of Aldrich, "Treatment of Silver Furnace Fumes by the Cottrell Process" (1915), pp. 126–127 and pp. 136–137.

19. Cottrell, "Patent Experience of the Research Corporation" (1932), p. 223.

20. For Bradley's initial recommendation, see Meeting of the Executive Committee, May 2, 1912, RC Minutes, RU 51, Box 3, SI Archives. For Little's report, see Meeting of the Executive Committee, May 22, 1912, RC Minutes, RU 51, Box 3, SI Archives. Presumably, these negotiations involved the Lemp patents.

21. Linn Bradley to A. D. Little, June 25, 1912, RU 51, Box 1, SI Archives. The patents Bradley mentioned were W. R. Whitney, "Purification of Gases," U.S. Patent No. 1,022,012, issued Apr. 2, 1912 (filed Mar. 6, 1911); and W. R. Whitney, "Concentration of Solids in Liquids," U.S. Patent No. 1,022,523, issued Apr. 9, 1912 (filed Apr. 2, 1910). For a description of the former, see "Purification of Smelter Fumes; Removal of Sulphur Dioxide," in the "Recent Metallurgical and Chemical Patents" section of *MCE*, 10 (May 1912), 313. Not only did the description explicitly mention Cottrell's process, but the next patent described (ibid., pp. 313–314) was one of Cottrell's, namely, F. G. Cottrell, "Purification of Gases," U.S. Patent No. 1,016,476, issued Feb. 6, 1912 (filed Feb. 26, 1909).

22. Meeting of the Executive Committee, June 22, 1917, RC Minutes, RU 51, Box 4, SI Archives.

23. The initial letter from GE came with a copy of a similar agreement already reached between GE and Western Precipitation (Arthur A. Buck to Linn Bradley, Jan. 15, 1918, Box A14, RC Archives). After the necessary changes were made, Bradley sent Scott a copy of the final agreement (Linn Bradley to L. N. Scott, June 20, 1918, Box A14, RC Archives). The significance of the Lemp patents to Cottrell's early work was noted in Schmidt to Barker, Mar. 21, 1949; and Cameron, *Samaritan of Science*, p. 124. The patents involved were Hermann Lemp, "Alternating-Current Selector," U.S. Patent No. 774,090, issued Nov. 1, 1904 (filed Dec. 1, 1897); and Hermann Lemp, "Exciting Vacuum-Tubes," U.S. Patent No. 774,138, issued Nov. 1, 1904 (filed Dec. 1, 1897). On Lemp, a naturalized American citizen from Switzerland who had worked with Edison at Menlo Park, see *AMS*, 8th Ed. (1949), p. 1472; and "Henderson Medal Awarded to Hermann Lemp," *Railway Age*, 131 (Aug. 20, 1951), 61 and 64.

24. G. H. Horne, "Electrical Engineering Features of the Electrical Precipitation Process," *Trans. AIEE*, 41 (1922), 810. For brief mention of kenotrons – including their use in electrostatic precipitators – see Kendall Birr, *Pioneering in Industrial*

Research: The Story of the General Electric Research Laboratory (Washington, D.C.: Public Affairs Press, 1957), pp. 46–47 and pp. 100–101. Saul Dushman was the GE researcher then working on the kenotron. Not only did he mention "the *precipitation of dust, smoke, etc.*" as one possible application of the new vacuum tube in his original published description – see Saul Dushman, "A New Device for Rectifying High Tension Alternating Currents: The Kenotron," *General Electric Review*, 18 (Mar. 1915), 167 – but he also had personal contact with Research Corporation's engineers and with Cottrell. "A couple of years ago," he noted, in the "Discussion" at the end of a paper presented by someone else – see H. D. Braley, "Notes on Electrostatic Precipitation," *Trans. AES*, 35 (1919), 233 – "the writer and some of the engineers of the Research Corporation took a number of oscillograms in connection with experiments on smoke precipitation at a round house." Similarly, on another occasion Dushman contributed remarks to the discussion that followed papers by Cottrell and Bradley – see "Electric Smoke and Fume Precipitation before the American Institute of Electrical Engineers," *MCE*, 13 (Mar. 1915), 160 – and that same evening he joined Cottrell, Bradley, and H. V. Welch for supper at the Chemists' Club – see Diary of F. G. Cottrell, Feb. 19, 1915, Cottrell Papers, Box 1.

25. See not only the article – H. A. Winne, "The Cottrell Process of Electrical Precipitation," *General Electric Review*, 24 (Nov. 1921), 910–921 (with the assessment of the kenotron coming on p. 919) – but also the editorial, "Electrical Precipitation," ibid., p. 909. Subsequent issues carried articles about specific applications, including "Electrical Precipitation of Cement Mill Dust," by G. A. Witte, a Western Precipitation engineer – see ibid., 25 (Feb. 1922), 125–128.

26. Meeting of the Stockholders, Feb. 16, 1917, RC Minutes, RU 51, Box 4, SI Archives.

27. Meetings of the Executive Committee, Sept. 27, 1917, Dec. 15, 1917, and Feb. 7, 1918, RC Minutes, RU 51, Box 4, SI Archives. The agreement was terminated in 1919 – see Meeting of the Executive Committee, June 13, 1919, RC Minutes, RU 51, Box 4, SI Archives. In his 1919 article, "The Cottrell Precipitation Process and Its Application to Foundry Dust Problems," H. D. Egbert noted (p. 272): "During the last year or two a high-potential direct-current generator known as the Girvin generator has been successfully used for precipitation work." Later G. H. Horne reported – see his 1922 article "Electrical Engineering Features of the Electrical Precipitation Process," p. 810: "So far as is known, there has been only one serious attempt made to produce a direct-current generator for precipitation work. This was made several years ago by the Girvin Electrical Development Company of Philadelphia, working in conjunction with the Research Corporation of New York."

28. "Practically all of the electrical equipment used in this installation," Schmidt noted in his 1916 account of the International Smelting Company's electrostatic precipitator at Inspiration, Ariz., "was supplied by the Westinghouse Electric & Manufacturing Company" – see Walter A. Schmidt, *Dust and Fume Collection by the Cottrell*

Process of Electrical Precipitation: Results Obtained at Smelter of International Smelting Company [,] Inspiration, Arizona[, and] Factory of Riverside Portland Cement Company[,] Riverside, California (paper presented at a meeting of the American Institute of Mining Engineers, at Globe, Ariz., Sept. 21, 1915; published, Los Angeles, 1916), p. 10. For another source explicitly mentioning Westinghouse equipment, see W. G. Smith and A. A. Heimrod, "Application of the Cottrell Process to the Recovery of Fume from Silver Refining Operations," *Chemical and Metallurgical Engineering*, 21 (Sept. 15, 1919), 362. For the standardized equipment, see the notice headed "Electrical Precipitation of Fine Particles," in the "New Apparatus and Appliances" section of *Electrical World*, 70 (Dec. 1, 1917), 1080. At about the same time, Goetze reported to Research Corporation's executive committee that "the Westinghouse Electric & Manufacturing Company and other electrical manufacturers are also realizing the importance of the field of electrical precipitation as a market for electrical equipment"— see Meeting of the Executive Committee, June 22, 1917, RC Minutes, RU 51, Box 4, SI Archives.

29. H. D. Braley, "Notes on Electrostatic Precipitation," *Trans. AES*, 35 (1919), 199–237; and O. H. Eschholz, "Electrostatic Precipitation," *Transactions of the American Institute of Mining and Metallurgical Engineers*, 60 (1919), 243–279. On Eschholz, see *WWE*, 2nd Ed. (1925), p. 648.

30. Meeting of the Board of Directors, Jan. 16, 1920, RC Minutes, RU 51, Box 4, SI Archives. Girvin's patent was C. W. Girvin, "Art of Electrical Precipitation of Particles from Fluid Streams," U.S. Patent No. 1,252,104, issued Jan. 1, 1918 (filed Mar. 22, 1917). Regarding Chubb, one biographical entry noted: "The Westinghouse scientist was also extraordinarily interested in the field of electrical precipitation and as early as World War I was granted several patents on his work" — see "Lewis Warrington Chubb," in *Biographical Notices of the John Fritz Medallists*, Vol. 2: 1923–1947 (New York, 1947), p. 224. At a joint meeting of the Pittsburgh sections of the American Institute of Electrical Engineers and the American Electrochemical Society in September 1914, Chubb and his Westinghouse colleague Charles L. Fortescue contributed to the discussion following A. F. Nesbit's remarks on electrostatic precipitation — see "The Electrical Precipitation of Smoke, Dust, Etc.," *Electrical Review*, 65 (Oct. 31, 1914), 877.

31. "Random Notes by Walter A. Schmidt with Reference to Suit Filed by the Department of Justice against Western, International, Research and Schmidt," Aug. 21, 1945, Publication Archive, RC Archives. "Dr. Chubb," noted an account of his remarks at the annual meeting of the Edison Electrical Institute in 1937 (see *NYT*, June 3, 1937, p. 27, col. 8), "demonstrated an electric air cleaner which removes about 90 per cent of all particles from the air. Relief from hay fever, asthma and throat irritations was made possible by the device, he said."

32. "Random Notes by Walter A. Schmidt" (1945).

33. The exact nature of the relationship between Research Corporation and the electrical giants was not always clear to outside observers. For example, in the early

1920s a subscriber to the *Engineering and Mining Journal-Press* wrote: "I have been advised from sources which are ordinarily reliable that [Western Precipitation Company and Research Corporation] are owned or at least sentimentally controlled by the General Electric Co. and the Westinghouse Electric & Manufacturing Co. . . ." – see "The Work of the Research Corporation," Vol. 115 (June 16, 1923), 1072. The article included not only the subscriber's remarks but also responses from Cottrell and A. A. Hamerschlag. "With reference to relations of the Research Corporation to such interests as the General Electric and the Westinghouse Electric Manufacturing companies," Cottrell noted (ibid., p. 1073), "the directors and officials of the Research Corporation have been very careful throughout to keep the corporation entirely free from control or domination by any particular set of interests. . . ." Hamerschlag was even more forthright (ibid., p. 1073): "The Research Corporation has no direct affiliation with either the General Electric or the Westinghouse Electric company. It operates entirely independent of them, using the apparatus of both only where it has proved itself to be the best and cheapest for the purpose."

34. On the company, see "Western Precipitation Corporation," in Haynes, *American Chemical Industry: The Chemical Companies*, pp. 474–478. On Schmidt, see *AMS*, 10th Ed. (1961), p. 3587; and *NCAB*, Vol. 50 (1968), pp. 152–153.

35. For a review of the electrostatic method of oil dehydration, see D. B. Dow, *Oil-Field Emulsions*, USBM Bull., No. 250 (Washington, D.C.: GPO, 1926), especially pp. 58–64. The patents – each issued on March 21, 1911 – were as follows: F. G. Cottrell, "Process for Separating and Collecting Particles of One Liquid Suspended in Another Liquid," U.S. Patent No. 987,114 (filed Oct. 12, 1909); F. G. Cottrell and J. B. Speed, "Separating and Collecting Particles of One Liquid Suspended in Another Liquid," U.S. Patent No. 987,115 (filed May 20, 1909); F. G. Cottrell and J. B. Speed, "Apparatus for Separating and Collecting Particles of One Liquid Suspended in Another Liquid," U.S. Patent No. 987,116 (filed May 20, 1909); and F. G. Cottrell and A. C. Wright, "Separating and Collecting Particles of One Liquid Suspended in Another Liquid," U.S. Patent No. 987,117 (filed Dec. 1, 1910). On Cottrell's work with Speed, see Buckner Speed, "An Appreciation of Dr. Cottrell," *JIEC*, 11 (Feb. 1919), 153–154; Cameron, *Samaritan of Science*, pp. 140–144; and White, "Centenary of Frederick Gardner Cottrell" (1978), pp. 23–24. Speed himself led the early efforts to develop the process.

36. After Speed's departure, Schmidt was asked to join the project, and Wright assumed the leadership role – see Cameron, *Samaritan of Science*, pp. 144–145. Wright's buyout is mentioned in ibid., pp. 151–152; and "Random Notes by Walter A. Schmidt" (1945). The Petroleum Rectifying Company was a commercial success – see Cameron, *Samaritan of Science*, p. 272. But as Schmidt observed in his 1945 memo: "This enterprise was entirely independent of Research [Corporation] and Western [Precipitation]. . . ."

37. Robert W. Lesley, *History of the Portland Cement Industry in the United States* (1924; rpt. New York: Arno Press, 1972), pp. 168–170 and p. 297; Cameron, *Samari-*

tan of Science, pp. 146–147; and White, "Centenary of Frederick Gardner Cottrell" (1978), p. 12. Lesley noted (op. cit., p. 1) that "portland cement is a scientifically controlled product" in which the raw materials are mixed in definite proportions and heated. At the Riverside plant, crushed limestone and shale were heated in 8 by 125-foot rotary kilns. In New Jersey, at about the same time, Thomas Edison was increasing the length of cement kilns to 260 feet — see ibid., pp. 110–111; and Michael Peterson, "Thomas Edison's Concrete Houses," *American Heritage of Invention and Technology*, 11 (Winter 1996), 50–56.

38. Regarding the latter, he noted: "At Riverside, after one year's development work, and numerous controversies with Cottrell and Burns, I found that neither the pubescent electrode nor the mica electrode were necessary, but that a fine wire electrode would do a much better job," (Schmidt to Barker, Mar. 21, 1949). Elsewhere — see W. A. Schmidt, "Electrical Precipitation in Retrospect," *Industrial and Engineering Chemistry*," 16 (Oct. 1924), 1039 — he described in more detail how he arrived at the new technique:

> About this time Whitehead, Ryan, and Peek were carrying on their researches on corona losses, and the phenomenon of gaseous ionization was commencing to be well understood through the researches of J. J. Thompson [*sic*] and others. It was a relatively simple matter to apply this new knowledge to the precipitation art, and by running up the impressed voltage to approximately 50,000 it was found that a bare, smooth conductor served admirably well as an ionizing electrode, although it took a long time to definitely prove this.

On yet another occasion Schmidt called the new technique "perhaps the greatest improvement in the art since Cottrell's pioneering work" — see Schmidt and Anderson, "Electrical Precipitation" (1938), p. 333. For an early general account of his work at Riverside, see W. A. Schmidt, "The Control of Dust in Portland Cement Manufacture by the Cottrell Precipitation Processes," in *Original Communications, Eighth International Congress of Applied Chemistry*, Vol. 5, pp. 117–124; also published in *JIEC*, 4 (Oct. 1912), 719–723.

39. Schmidt to Barker, Mar. 21, 1949; and Cameron, *Samaritan of Science*, pp. 147–148. Developed first at Selby, the technique that Cottrell used involved serrated mica strips — see F. G. Cottrell and H. A. Burns, "Apparatus for Separating Suspended Particles from Gaseous Bodies," U.S. Patent No. 1,035,422, issued Aug. 13, 1912 (filed Sept. 9, 1909). Also at Garfield, W. H. Howard discovered that electrostatic precipitation of some substances was enhanced if the fumes were injected with fine sprays of water — see White, "Centenary of Frederick Gardner Cottrell" (1978), p. 15.

40. Schmidt to Barker, Mar. 21, 1949. In his 1937 article "The Social Responsibility of the Engineer-II" (p. 554), Cottrell offered another reason for the transfer: "Some of our clientele . . . were somewhat perturbed at the prospect of becoming guinea pigs in the Research Corporation experiment. . . ." The transfer of rights to Schmidt,

was also discussed in International Precipitation Company to the Board of Regents of the Smithsonian Institution, May 28, 1912, RU 45, Box 47, SI Archives; "Random Notes by Walter A. Schmidt" (1945); "Western Precipitation Corporation," in Haynes, *American Chemical Industry: The Chemical Companies*, p. 477; and Cameron, *Samaritan of Science*, pp. 151–152.

41. International Precipitation Company to the Board of Regents of the Smithsonian Institution, May 28, 1912, RU 45, Box 47, SI Archives.

42. F. G. Cottrell to C. D. Walcott, Mar. 6, 1912, RU 45, Box 47, SI Archives.

43. Quoted in Linn Bradley to F. A. Goetze, Mar. 27, 1912, Box A14, RC Archives.

44. Linn Bradley to F. A. Goetze, Mar. 27, 1912, Box A14, RC Archives.

45. Ibid. "As Dr. Cottrell is to reach the Coast very early next month," Bradley continued, "the delay will be but short any way. . . . There is absolutely no doubt that Mr. Schmidt considers this the best thing to do and personally, I see no objection to his proposal." "In the meantime," he added, "I would suggest that we proceed with our business negotiations in the same manner as though the assignments had already been executed but not sign any contracts in which we claim to be the actual owner of any particular patents until after same have been definitely assigned."

46. International Precipitation Company to the Board of Regents of the Smithsonian Institution, May 28, 1912, RU 45, Box 47, SI Archives.

47. Letter from W. A. Schmidt dated Oct. 15, 1912, quoted in Meeting of the Executive Committee, Dec. 16, 1912, RC Minutes, RU 51, Box 3, SI Archives. In his letter, Schmidt left no doubt about his ambitions. He wanted nothing less than "the most rapid development, commercially and technically, of the electrical precipitation process."

48. W. A. Schmidt to C. D. Walcott, May 9, 1916, RU 51, Box 2, SI Archives. On Western Precipitation's laboratory, see also "Glimpses of New Pacific Coast Industries in the Making," *MCE*, 15 (Nov. 1, 1916), 511–512; and Alfred D. Flinn, "Research Laboratories in Industrial Establishments of the United States of America," *Bulletin of the National Research Council*, No. 2 (Mar. 1920), 103.

49. For Schmidt's own assessment of Wolcott's research and that of Anderson and Horne, see W. A. Schmidt, "Recent Conclusions Pertaining to Electrical Precipitation," *Trans. AIEE*, 41 (1922), 804–806; and Schmidt, "Electrical Precipitation in Retrospect" (1924), p. 1041. For a similar assessment, see White, "Centenary of Frederick Gardner Cottrell" (1978), pp. 15–16. For Wolcott's article, see E. R. Wolcott, "Effects of Dielectrics on the Sparking Voltage," *Physical Review*, 12 (Oct. 1918), 284–292. On Wolcott, see *WWE*, 3rd Ed. (1931), p. 1455; and *AMS*, 10th Ed. (1961), Vol. 4, p. 4481. On Anderson – who studied chemistry at Berkeley, received his B.S. degree in 1913, and joined Western Precipitation that same year – see Schmidt and Anderson, "Electrical Precipitation" (1938), p. 332; *AMS*, 6th Ed. (1938), p. 28; and "Western Precipitation Corporation," in Haynes, *American Chemical Industry: The Chemical Companies*, p. 477.

50. "Random Notes by Walter A. Schmidt" (1945). For brief accounts of the elder

Möller's work, see Cottrell, "Problems in Smoke, Fume, and Dust Abatement" (1913), p. 665; and R. Durrer, "Elektrische Ausscheidung von festen and flüssigen Teilchen aus Gasen," *Stahl und Eisen*, 39 (Nov. 13, 1919), 1379.

51. International Precipitation Company to the Board of Regents of the Smithsonian Institution, Oct. 18, 1911, RU 45, Box 47, SI Archives. "Closed up Contract with Schmidt and Moller about 9:30 AM . . . ," Cottrell noted in his diary entry for August 2, 1911 (Cottrell Papers, Box 1). On the agreement with Möller, see also Cameron, *Samaritan of Science*, p. 166. Likely another motive here was Cottrell's commitment to the ideal of international cooperation – see ibid., pp. 166–167. Long important in the ideology of Western science, this ideal would be significantly undercut by the national allegiances of researchers during World War I – see Lawrence Badash, "British and American Views of the German Menace in World War I," *Notes and Records of the Royal Society of London*, 34 (July 1979), 91–121. Yet Cottrell remained committed to the ideal – see F. G. Cottrell, "Medal Address: International Scientific Relations," *JIEC*, 12 (July 1920), 697–700.

52. International Precipitation Company to the Board of Regents of the Smithsonian Institution, Oct. 18, 1911, RU 45, Box 47, SI Archives.

53. "Outline of arrangements for the segregation of the rights under the Cottrell Precipitation Patents . . . ," n.d. (probably fall 1911), RU 45, Box 17, SI Archives.

54. Ibid. Each party was also required to "maintain the patents and apply for new patents in his own 'operating territory'. . . ."

55. In addition to the biographical sources cited in an earlier chapter, see Eric W. Vincent and Percival Hinton, *The University of Birmingham: Its History and Significance* (Birmingham, England: Cornish Brothers, 1947), especially pp. 72–78.

56. Oliver Lodge, "Conference on Smoke Abatement: Presidential Address," *Journal of the Royal Sanitary Institute*, 27 (1907), 42.

57. Oliver Lodge to F. G. Cottrell, Dec. 6, 1911, RU 45, Box 47, SI Archives. In a letter to Lodge dated June 13, 1912 (RU 45, Box 47, SI Archives), Möller referred to Lodge's invention as "a high voltage mercury rectifier of a high tension valve for electrical precipitation of dust, which takes less space than a mechanical rectifier." In a reply to Möller (June 18, 1912, RU 45, Box 47, SI Archives), Lionel Lodge noted:

> The type of apparatus that we have arrived at is not very different from that used by Dr. Cottrell, except in the method of generating the high tension current. . . . The mercury valves which we employed at first, we found were not suitable for regular running and continual use; our present type are the outcome of several years experimental work, and they have worked very satisfactorily in practical use
>
> From particulars supplied by Dr. Cottrell, our transforming apparatus takes up considerably less room than the arrangement he uses, and the first cost must also be less, at any rate for a small or moderate sized plant.

A company brochure, *Lodge-Cottrell Limited: Pioneers of Electrical Precipitation* – enclosed in J. E. Schork (president of Research-Cottrell) to Richard Hodgson, June 5,

1972, Publication Archive, RC Archives — noted that in 1905 Lodge had taken out "British Patent No. 25047 for mercury arc rectifiers" and that in 1909 Lodge had formed the Agricultural Electric Discharge Company "to apply precipitation to agricultural purposes, e.g. the production of rain, improvement of crops, etc." The American patent was O. J. Lodge, "Means for Producing High-Potential Electrical Discharges," U.S. Patent No. 803,180, issued Oct. 31, 1905 (filed Oct. 10, 1904). For a brief account of Lodge's revived commercial efforts, see also Cottrell, "Problems in Smoke, Fume, and Dust Abatement" (1913), p. 685.

58. Oliver Lodge to F. G. Cottrell, June 19, 1912, RU 45, Box 47, SI Archives.

59. Lionel Lodge to Erwin Möller, June 18, 1912, RU 45, Box 47, SI Archives. In both a commercial sense and an experimental sense, Lionel had taken the lead from his father — see Lodge, *Electrical Precipitation: A Lecture Delivered before the Institute of Physics* p. 25; and Lodge, *Advancing Science*, pp. 65–66.

60. F. G. Cottrell to Oliver Lodge, July 5, 1912, RU 45, Box 47, SI Archives.

61. *The Electrician*, 71 (May 9, 1913), 202. A third director was William F. Newman. The brochure *Lodge-Cottrell Limited: Pioneers of Electrical Precipitation* noted that the "[f]irst discussions . . . with a view to forming a company to apply precipitation to the deposition of dust, fume and mist" had taken place "in Sir Oliver Lodge's laboratory at Birmingham University" in 1912.

62. Erwin Möller to C. D. Walcott, June 15, 1912, RU 45, Box 47, SI Archives. "The matter itself," Möller continued, "appeared to be a new form of the so-called 'Göttinger Bestrebungen,' the originator of which is Professor Dr. Felix Klein, Göttingen, Germany. . . ." On Klein's efforts to bring academic mathematics into closer relationship with industrial needs, see David E. Rowe, "Klein, Hilbert, and the Göttingen Mathematical Tradition," *Osiris*, 2nd Ser., Vol. 5 (1989), 202–204.

63. Erwin Möller to C. D. Walcott, June 15, 1912, RU 45, Box 47, SI Archives.

64. Research Corporation to Erwin Möller, n.d. (probably mid-1912), Box A14, RC Archives.

65. F. G. Cottrell to C. D. Walcott, Oct. 11, 1912, RU 45, Box 47, SI Archives (emphasis added).

66. Ibid.

67. "The Congress," Cottrell wrote Lodge on July 5, 1912 (RU 45, Box 47, SI Archives), "promises on the whole to be one of the most interesting gatherings of its kind for years." Later A. D. Little would write of the event — see his article "Chemical Engineering Research: Lifeblood of American Industry," in Sidney D. Kirkpatrick, ed., *Twenty-Five Years of Chemical Engineering Progress* (New York: D. Van Nostrand, 1933), p. 4: "The impression derived from its proceedings as published in twenty-four volumes is that of an airplane survey of the status of applied chemistry throughout the world. The mass effect of its papers and demonstrations upon our own industrialists was in a sense not unlike that of the Centennial on the thought of American manufacturers."

68. Although Möller sent Research Corporation a new draft agreement in early

1913, Cottrell's reply (Mar. 7, 1913, RU 45, Box 47, SI Archives) revealed his frustration with the slow progress of their negotiations: "It seems to me that the repeated and partly unexplained delays in your assignments culminating now in the present proposed further agreement indicate a certain blinding by over-anxiety for detail, suggesting lack of confidence in the point of view and sense of justice of the directorate of the Research Corporation which is entirely incompatible with intelligent, helpful cooperation with the movement in the broad, altruistic lines along which it is already so successfully developing."

69. Specifically, Schmidt recalled — (Schmidt to Barker, 21 Mar. 1949):

> Starting in 1913, I undertook the job of putting the overall business into shape, and this was quite a mess, because Cottrell had made loose commitments to [J. G.] Davidson for Canada, Möller for the Continent of Europe, and Lodge for England. He also had made some loose commitments to L. L. Johnson of Indianapolis for the blast furnace industry in the East, and to Robert Kennedy Duncan of Pittsburgh for coal smoke. The latter two were ironed out by Cottrell, Bradley, and me, while I ironed out the former three alone. All of this took an enormous amount of time and effort and the expenditure of considerable money as well as the relinquishment of the European territory.

On Schmidt's 1913 trip, see also "Western Precipitation Corporation," in Haynes, *American Chemical Industry: The Chemical Companies*, p. 477.

70. "Random Notes by Walter A. Schmidt" (1945). For similar assessments, see H. J. Bush, "Electrical Precipitation," *JSCI*, 41 (Feb. 15, 1922), 28T; and Harry J. White, "The Art and the Science of Electrostatic Precipitation," *Journal of the Air Pollution Control Association*, 34 (Nov. 1984), 1163–1167. Schmidt's understanding of the complexity of the installations led him to emphasize the need to rely on highly trained engineers for their design. For example, in his 1922 article, "Recent Conclusions Pertaining to Electrical Precipitation," he commented (p. 806) that "the choice of precipitator types and the analysis of the factors entering into the phenomenon of precipitation, can be properly accomplished only by the experienced specialized engineer. . . ." Similarly, in his 1924 article, "Electrical Precipitation in Retrospect," he noted (p. 1041): "It is not the purpose of this discussion . . . to lay down rules for the design of precipitators. This is a matter which should be entrusted to the engineers trained and experienced in the art."

71. In Schmidt's words ("Random Notes by Walter A. Schmidt," 1945): "Long distance engineering was impractical and the process had to be developed and commercialized by local engineering concerns."

72. Ibid. Electrostatic precipitation was probably a more attractive method than Schmidt's remarks would indicate. For example, the standard practice in the copper smelting industry before the advent of electrostatic precipitation was the use of long settling-chambers between the furnaces and the chimneys. "Although quite expensive," wrote one engineer, "when constructed of steel pipes with hoppers and header

flues, the Cottrell plant proved to be a very good investment on account of the large amount of solids recovered which would not settle out by gravity" — see Ross B. Rathbun, "Electrical Precipitation of Solids from Smelter Gases," *Trans. AIEE*, 41 (1922), 816. As a result, Rathbun continued (p. 817), "smelter construction has been revolutionized by the Cottrell process . . . and long settling chambers are no longer necessary." For Cottrell's own assessment of the alternatives ("washing methods . . . filtration methods . . . settling chambers and baffles . . . [and] application of centrifugal force"), see his 1913 article, "Problems in Smoke, Fume, and Dust Abatement," pp. 661–663.

73. "Random Notes by Walter A. Schmidt" (1945).

74. Ibid. In reply to an inquiry from the assistant editor, F. E. Wormser — see "The Work of the Research Corporation" (1923), p. 1073 — A. A. Hamerschlag commented: "The funds which have been expended [by Research Corporation for salaries] have been based upon a salary scale so low that the devoted staff who have worked so enthusiastically to introduce electrical precipitation into modern industry have had scarcely more than the prevailing living wage."

75. "Random Notes by Walter A. Schmidt" (1945).

76. Ibid.

77. At the meeting of Research Corporation's executive committee on January 22, 1914 (RC Minutes, RU 51, Box 3, SI Archives), John B. Pine reported that Schmidt "had concluded negotiations with Erwin Möller in respect to the application of the Cottrell Processes in Europe and that Möller had formally agreed to transfer to the Research Corporation three United States Patent Applications, [Serial] Nos. 512142 — filed August 10, 1909; 643568 — filed August 11, 1911; and 682331 — filed March 7, 1912."

78. The minutes for the meeting of the executive committee on December 22, 1917 (RC Minutes, RU 51, Box 4, SI Archives) noted: "The attorney of the Research Corporation having called to the attention of the Executive Committee an Act of Congress entitled 'Trading with the Enemy Act,' we find ourselves in a position where we must advise the Western Precipitation Company and the International Precipitation Company, if they have not already done so, to abrogate their contract for the exchange of information with the Metallbank of Germany, and notify us that this has been done. . . ."

79. On the creation of Lodge-Cottrell I consulted the brochure *Lodge-Cottrell Limited: Pioneers of Electrical Precipitation*. As part of the postwar negotiations, Schmidt arranged for Cottrell to receive 1,500 shares of stock in Lodge-Cottrell — see Cameron, *Samaritan of Science*, pp. 218–219. In 1916 International Precipitation licensed the Huntington–Heberlein Company of England (a competitor of Lodge's firm) to build electrostatic precipitators — see Jewkes, Sawers, and Stillerman, *The Sources of Invention*, p. 297. After the war Western Precipitation purchased Huntington-Heberlein — as reported in "Random Notes by Walter A. Schmidt" (1945); and H. J. Bush, "Electrostatic-Separation," *The Electrician*, 85 (Nov. 5, 1920), 533. But it did not

retain ownership long. Thus Schmidt commented in "Random Notes by Walter A. Schmidt" (1945) that "as soon as the opportunity presented itself, Western disposed of Huntington-Heberlein Company. . . ."

80. "Western Precipitation Corporation," in Haynes, *American Chemical Industry: The Chemical Companies*, p. 477. See also "Electrostatic Dust Separation," *JSCI*, 52 (Sept. 1, 1933), 709.

81. "Random Notes by Walter A. Schmidt" (1945).

82. Ibid.

83. Floyd L. Vaughan, *The United States Patent System: Legal and Economic Conflicts in American Patent History* (Norman: University of Oklahoma Press, 1956), pp. 160–161. Lodge-Cottrell, Metallgesellschaft, and two other German firms were listed as "co-conspirators" in the "Final Judgment" — see *CCH Trade Cases, 1946–1947* (Chicago: Commerce Clearing House, 1948), Decision No. 57,458. According to the provisions of the consent decree, the defendants were required to file a bibliography of technical publications in the libraries at Columbia University, the University of Chicago, and the University of California, Berkeley. I consulted the one at Columbia — see the online catalog listing for Research Corporation, "Bibliography of Published Articles on Electrical Precipitation."

84. Western Precipitation Company to Research Corporation, Jan. 10, 1914, Box A13, RC Archives. The agreement had other distinctive features, as well. Schmidt formally transferred to Western Precipitation his rights to use the Cottrell process in the Portland cement industry, and in place of receiving 10 percent of Western Precipitation's net profits, Research Corporation accepted $7,500 (par value) in Western Precipitation stock (copy of the agreement, Feb. 4, 1914, Box A13, RC Archives; and Research Corporation to Western Precipitation Company, Feb. 2, 1914, Box A14, RC Archives). In the overall arrangement that Schmidt had in mind, International Precipitation would function as the clearing house for technical information regarding the Cottrell process — "Random Notes by Walter A. Schmidt," 1945; and Schmidt to Barker, Mar. 21, 1949. Thus the new agreement would enable International Precipitation to promote the Cottrell process worldwide without compromising the proprietary interests that any one firm (including Research Corporation) might acquire in different processes.

85. Schmidt judged that by the time of the agreement, "Cottrell's contributions to the art had become obsolete, except for two things; namely, the use of rectified alternating current, and the use of negative polarity," (Schmidt to Barker, Mar. 21, 1949).

86. Western Precipitation Company to Research Corporation, Jan. 10, 1914, Box A13, RC Archives.

87. Although Duncan did not receive a Ph.D. degree, he pursued graduate studies at Clark University, Columbia, and universities in Europe. On his career, see John W. Servos, "Robert Kennedy Duncan," *ANB*, Vol. 7 (1999), pp. 76–77. "One of the most notable and persuasive of the exponents of industrial research," Little once noted,

"was Robert Kennedy Duncan" — see Little, "Chemical Engineering Research: Life-blood of American Industry" (1933), p. 3. On the fellowship programs see Robert Kennedy Duncan, "Temporary Industrial Fellowships, *North American Review*, 185 (May 3, 1907), 54–62; and Robert Kennedy Duncan, "Industrial Fellowships of the Mellon Institute," *Science*, 39 (May 8, 1914), 672–678. On Duncan and the fellow-ships, see also Noble, *America by Design*, pp. 122–123. On Andrew Mellon — who later served as secretary of the treasury under Presidents Harding, Coolidge, and Hoover — see Allan Nevins, "Andrew William Mellon," *DAB*, Supp. 2 (1958), pp. 446–452; on R. B. Mellon, see *NCAB*, Vol. 24 (1935), pp. 56–57. The Mellons learned of the Kansas program by reading the concluding chapter in Duncan's book, *The Chem-istry of Commerce: A Simple Interpretation of Some New Chemistry in Its Relation to Modern Industry* (New York: Harper, 1907) — see Andrew W. Mellon, "The Dedica-tion of Mellon Institute," in Mellon Institute of Industrial Research, *Addresses at the Exercises and Science Symposium during the Dedication of the New Building of Mellon Institute . . .* (Pittsburgh: Mellon Institute, 1937), pp. 7–8.

88. For a list of the Pittsburgh fellowships see Robert Kennedy Duncan, "Indus-trial Fellowships: Five Years of an Educational Industrial Experiment," *Journal of the Franklin Institute*, 175 (Jan. 1913), 53–56. For an historical assessment of the Mellon Institute (which in 1967 was merged with the Carnegie Institute of Technology to form Carnegie Mellon University), see John W. Servos, "Changing Partners: The Mellon Institute, Private Industry, and the Federal Patron," *Technology and Culture*, 35 (Apr. 1994), 221–257. For discussions of the Mellon Institute's early work, see also Philip H. Love, *Andrew W. Mellon: The Man and His Work* (Baltimore: F. Heath Coggins and Co., 1929), pp. 30–33; Harvey O'Connor, *Mellon's Millions, the Biogra-phy of a Fortune: The Life and Times of Andrew W. Mellon* (New York: The John Day Company, 1933), pp. 247–250; "Mellon Institute," in Haynes, *American Chemical Industry: The Chemical Companies* (1949), pp. 268–270; Edward R. Weidlein, "A Thumb-nail History of Mellon Institute," in Harold P. Klug, ed., *Science and Human Progress: Addresses at the Celebration of the Fiftieth Anniversary of Mellon Institute* (Pittsburgh: Mellon Institute of Industrial Research, 1964), pp. 19–25; and David E. Koskoff, *The Mellons: The Chronicle of America's Richest Family* (New York: Thomas Y. Crowell, 1978), pp. 155–157. For the merger with the Carnegie Institute of Technology, see also Harold Orlans, *The Nonprofit Research Institute: Its Origin, Operation, Problems, and Prospects* (New York: McGraw-Hill, 1972), pp. 32–33, p. 131, and pp. 153–154.

89. "Quart of Soot in Lungs," *NYT*, May 16, 1912, p. 1, col. 6. (The headline re-ferred to the soot reportedly removed "from the lungs of a man who had lived fifty years" in Pittsburgh.) Bituminous coal, Benner noted on another occasion, "is the smoke producing fuel par excellence — see R. C. Benner, "Why Smoke Is an Indus-trial Nuisance," *Iron Age*, 91 (Jan. 9, 1913), 135. "The nature and composition of soot," he wrote elsewhere, "make it the worst possible kind of dirt" — see R. C. Benner, "How and Why Smoke Is Injurious," *MCE*, 10 (Nov. 1912), 736. On Benner,

who served as the chief fellow of the smoke program during its first two years, see *NCAB*, Vol. 39 (1954), pp. 436–437. On the city's air-pollution problems, see J. T. Holdsworth, *Report of the Economic Survey of Pittsburgh* (Pittsburgh, 1912), pp. 31–45; and Tarr, *The Search for the Ultimate Sink*, pp. 87–90. On the different forms taken by the smoke problem nationally, see R. Dale Grinder, "The Battle for Clean Air: The Smoke Problem in Post-Civil War America," in Martin V. Melosi, ed., *Pollution and Reform in American Cities, 1870–1930* (Austin: University of Texas Press, 1980), especially pp. 83–85. On all these topics, see also Stradling, *Smokestacks and Progressives*.

90. R. K. Duncan to F. G. Cottrell, Apr. 27, 1911, USBM Records, 1910–1911. In his initial letter (Apr. 12, 1911, USBM Records, 1910–1911) Duncan explained that he had learned of Cottrell's work from Arthur W. Gray, a physicist who was then at the Bureau of Standards but had served on the faculty at Berkeley from 1905 to 1909. On Gray, see *NCAB*, Vol. E (1938), p. 27. On Duncan's offer, see also Cameron, *Samaritan of Science*, p. 155.

91. R. K. Duncan to F. G. Cottrell, Apr. 27, 1911, USBM Records, 1910–1911. Mellon viewed the smoke program as more public-service oriented than the other Mellon Institute programs. Thus in 1922 the institute's new director would note: "It was intended by its donor . . . rather as a benevolence than for purposes of personal profit. . . ." — see Edward R. Weidlein, "Introduction" to Robert James McKay, *Recent Progress in Smoke Abatement and Fuel Technology in England*, Mellon Institute of Industrial Research, Smoke Investigation Bulletin (hereafter MI Smoke Investigation Bull.), No. 10 (1922), p. iii. Mellon's role in the new program also illustrated Duncan's general view of how innovation actually worked. "We often hear it stated that some man, eminent in science, has 'given' his results to the people. This is utter nonsense. No man can 'give' his results to the people" (R. K. Duncan, "Speech at Residence of Dr. McCormick," Oct. 17, 1910, Box 205, Mellon Institute Papers, Carnegie Mellon University Archives — hereafter MI Papers). Instead, "the results of scientific investigation can go to the people only through the industrialists" — a process that he intended the program of Industrial Fellowships to facilitate.

92. F. G. Cottrell to J. A. Holmes, May 4, 1911, USBM Records, 1910–1911. Perhaps Cottrell's concern with "sensationalism" reflected the declining status of popular-science writing at the turn of the century — see Ronald C. Tobey, *The American Ideology of National Science, 1919–1930* (Pittsburgh: University of Pittsburgh Press, 1971), especially pp. 8–12.

93. Robert Kennedy Duncan, "Industrial Research," *Harper's Monthly Magazine*, 126 (Feb. 1913), 385. In that same article Duncan also applied his writing talents to Cottrell's precipitator (p. 390): "One has but to 'put in his thumb' anywhere to produce the fruit of some noble thought embodied in accurate experimentation and presented for the use of mankind. To demonstrate this, one finds Cottrell's beautiful development of a process for precipitating the noxious smelter-smoke of the ore-

smelters of the West...." Interestingly, Duncan's younger brother Norman was a professional writer – see Edward R. Weidlein and William A. Hamor, *Glances at Industrial Research during Walks and Talks in Mellon Institute* (New York: Reinhold Publishing Corp., 1936), 21; *WWWA*, Vol. 1 (1942), p. 346; and Janet Giltrow, "Norman Duncan," in W. H. New, ed., *Canadian Writers, 1890–1920*, Vol. 92 of *Dictionary of Literary Biography* (Detroit, Mich.: Gale Research Inc., 1990), pp. 94–96.

94. F. G. Cottrell to C. D. Walcott, Feb. 28, 1912, RU 45, Box 47, SI Archives. Cottrell had met with Duncan on February 24, 1912 – see his diary entry for that date (Cottrell Papers, Box 1).

95. For early mention of the Mellon Institute's smoke program, see Robert Kennedy Duncan, "On Certain Problems Connected with the Present-Day Relation between Chemistry and Manufacture in America," *JIEC*, 3 (Mar. 1911), 182. For an early list of the staff, see Ellwood H. McClelland, *Bibliography of Smoke and Smoke Prevention*, MI Smoke Investigation Bull., No. 2 (1913); for a revised list, see Robert Kennedy Duncan, "Industrial Fellowships of the Mellon Institute" (1914), pp. 672–673. Annual funding for the smoke program, during the three years of its existence, was as follows: $12,000 for the first year; $15,000 for the second; and $12,000 for the third (ibid., p. 672). For the overall scope of the program, see the report of the group's economist (and the group's chief fellow during the smoke program's third year), John O'Connor, Jr., "Four Points in the Indictment of the Smoke Nuisance," *Popular Science Monthly*, 87 (1915), 244–249. For contemporary assessments of the program, see Robert Hessler, "The Smoke Investigations of Mellon Institute: A Review," *Survey*, 33 (Mar. 13, 1915), 648–650; and C. H. Benjamin, "Pittsburgh Smoke Investigation," *National Municipal Review*, 6 (Sept. 1917), 591–598. For later assessments, see H. B. Meller, "Smoke Abatement, Its Effects and Its Limitations," *Mechanical Engineering*, 48 (Nov. 1926), 1275–1283; and Stradling, *Smokestacks and Progressives*, pp. 98–100. For brief accounts of the Smoke and Dust Abatement League, see Roy Lubove, *Twentieth-Century Pittsburgh: Government, Business, and Environmental Change* (New York: John Wiley, 1969), p. 48; Robert Dale Grinder, "From Insurgency to Efficiency: The Smoke Abatement Campaign in Pittsburgh before World War I," *Western Pennsylvania Historical Magazine*, 61 (July 1978), 200–201; and Stradling, op. cit., pp. 76–77.

96. In his article, "Research on the Smoke Problem at the Department of Industrial Research of the University of Pittsburgh," *Science*, 35 (June 28, 1912), 977, R. C. Benner wrote: "We have an unpretentious laboratory, designated as the 'smoke house,' a small, fireproof building, 18 feet wide and 30 feet long, which is situated at a sufficient distance from the main laboratory, so that the smoke in quantities as great as we may need in our work can be made without interfering with the other researches being carried on. In this building there is a furnace, so constructed that it is possible, by varying conditions, to get any kind of coal smoke." On Strong, see *NCAB*, Vol. E (1938), p. 382; and *AMS*, 9th Ed. (1955), p. 1883. On Nesbit, see ibid., 2nd Ed. (1910), p. 343; and the "Class of 1895" listing in Massachusetts Institute of Technol-

ogy, *Register of Former Students* (Cambridge, Mass.: MIT Press, 1930), p. 43. For published accounts of their technical work, see W. W. Strong, "The Electrical Precipitation of Suspended Matter in Gases," *Journal of the Franklin Institute*, 174 (Sept. 1912), 239–263; and W. W. Strong, "The Positive and Negative Corona and Electrical Precipitation," *Trans. AIEE*, 32 (1913), 1755–1765. For a list of their patents, see Lois Heaton, *A List of the Books, Bulletins, Journal Contributions, and Patents by Members of Mellon Institute, 1911–1927*, Mellon Institute of Industrial Research, Bibliographic Series Bulletin, No. 2 (1927), pp. 54–55.

97. R. K. Duncan to F. G. Cottrell, Apr. 12, 1911, USBM Records, 1910–1911.

98. F. G. Cottrell to R. K. Duncan, Apr. 22, 1911, USBM Records, 1910–1911.

99. R. K. Duncan to F. G. Cottrell, Apr. 27, 1911, USBM Records, 1910–1911.

100. Specifically, he noted (ibid.): "If you will come to me here and will join with others whom I shall choose for the prosecution of this work, I shall see to it that you are provided with an ample stipend to live on and with every possible incentive to success, relative to apparatus, helpers, sympathetic cooperation, etc."

101. F. G. Cottrell to R. K. Duncan, Apr. 22, 1911, USBM Records, 1910–1911.

102. F. G. Cottrell to R. K. Duncan, May 3, 1911, USBM Records, 1910–1911.

103. F. G. Cottrell to J. A. Holmes, June 28, 1911, USBM Records, 1910–1911.

104. "Arrived Pittsburg[h] 9 AM," Cottrell noted in his diary entry for June 28, 1911 (Cottrell Papers, Box 1), "and went to Duncan's lab & spent A.M. with him taking lunch together. . . . He wrote Dr. Strong to be ready to leave for Calif. July 7/ 11." At the time Strong was only just taking up his duties as a smoke fellow. His card in the Personnel Card File (MI Papers) gave the date he began work as July 1, 1911. In his diary entry for July 13, 1911 (Cottrell Papers, Box 1), Cottrell explicitly mentioned meeting Strong at the Balaklala smelter, and on September 11, 1913, Strong submitted to Linn Bradley a "Tentative Plan of Precipitation Work" (Box A19, RC Archives) that summarized the accomplishments of the Pittsburgh program and noted (in reference to himself): "In the beginning of the work, Dr. F. G. Cottrell gave one of the members of the staff of this Investigation all the privileges of visiting his own laboratory at the University of California, and of studying several plants then in the process of precipitating copper smelter fumes and cement dust."

105. F. G. Cottrell to C. D. Walcott, Oct. 27, 1911, RU 45, Box 47, SI Archives. "If you should have an opportunity to talk with Professor Duncan . . . on the matter of the possible applications of this work to the smoke situation," Cottrell reminded Walcott in a letter dated November 3, 1911 (RU 45, Box 47, SI Archives), "I think it would be highly desirable, as he is actively taking up this side of the problem. . . ." This bifurcation of the smoke problem would continue. Thus Cottrell began his remarks on "The Problem of Smelter Smoke," *Transactions of the Commonwealth Club of California*, 8 (Sept. 1913), 487: "The problem of smelter smoke is entirely distinct from that of ordinary city smoke." The bifurcation even shows up in Stradling's book, *Smokestacks and Progressives*, which includes little discussion of smelter smoke and no mention of Cottrell or electrostatic precipitation.

106. For example, R. F. Bacon wrote Duncan on March 19, 1912: "Dr. Cottrell was with us yesterday afternoon and gave us an illustrated lecture on his precipitation process" (Box 199, MI Papers).

107. Meeting of the Executive Committee, May 2, 1912, RC Minutes, RU 51, Box 3, SI Archives. Along with Duncan's work at Pittsburgh, Bradley also mentioned the work of A. H. White at the University of Michigan. On White — who founded Michigan's chemical engineering department in 1914 (and headed it until 1938) — see *NCAB*, 49 (1966), pp. 33–34. On White's use of electrostatic precipitation for cleaning tar from illuminating gas, see Bradley, "Electrical Precipitation of Suspended Particles" (1912), pp. 494–495; and Bradley, "Practical Applications of Electrical Precipitation and Progress of the Research Corporation" (1915), p. 431.

108. Diary of F. G. Cottrell, Sept. 20, 1912, Cottrell Papers, Box 1. For their first conference, see Cottrell's diary entry for Sept. 19, 1912. Bacon was a chemical engineer who received his doctorate from the University of Chicago in 1904 and then joined the Pittsburgh program in 1911 as a fellow for the petroleum fellowship. In 1912 he became associate director (which meant that he was in charge when Duncan was out of town); and following Duncan's death in 1914 he became director, serving in that capacity until 1922. On his career, see *WWWA*, Vol. 3 (1960), p. 40; and *NCAB*, Vol. 46 (1963), p. 574.

109. Diary of F. G. Cottrell, Dec. 9, 1912, Cottrell Papers, Box 1. Other than Bureau of Mines personnel, Cottrell's main interactions were with Arthur A. Hamerschlag, who headed the Carnegie Institute of Technology (and about whom the final chapter will have more to say). It was Hamerschlag who took Cottrell to the Smoke Exposition on the 9th (after which they dined together at Hamerschlag's home). In addition, Cottrell noted in his diary entry for the 11th (Cottrell Papers, Box 1): "Went over to Carnegie lab about 5 & ran over lantern slides & and rigged up apparatus with electrostatic machine to show [precipitation] work." At 8:30 that evening he gave his lecture to the students' engineering club and then caught the 11:55 train back to Washington. "While spending an evening with Dr. Hammerschlagg [*sic*] in Pittsburgh," Cottrell wrote Walcott on February 3, 1913 (RU 51, Box 1, SI Archives), "we discussed Research Corporation's aims and objects at considerable length...." On Cottrell's early contact with Hamerschlag, see also Cameron, *Samaritan of Science*, p. 284.

110. According to his card in the Personnel Card File (MI Papers), Nesbit began work as one of the Smoke Fellows on July 17, 1912. To my knowledge, the fullest treatment of Strong and Nesbit's system is found in their "Tentative Plan of Precipitation Work," [1913], Box A19, RC Archives. "During the course of the work," the document noted, "nine patent applications have been filed with the United States Commissioner of Patents through Messrs. Hodges and Hodges of Washington, D.C." Although no patent application numbers were given, the document included a brief description of each. Some focused on electrode design (both the discharge electrodes and the collecting electrodes), while others focused on the electrical circuit, the

rectifier, a "regulating apparatus," and a smoke detector.

111. W. W. Strong and A. F. Nesbit, "Tentative Plan of Precipitation Work," [1913], Box A19, RC Archives. These remarks also serve to remind us that economic assessments of electrostatic precipitation had to take into consideration the character of local air-pollution laws.

112. L. N. Scott to C. D. Walcott, Jan. 9, 1913, RU 51, Box 1, SI Archives.

113. Meeting of the Executive Committee, Jan. 17, 1913, RC Minutes, RU 51, Box 3, SI Archives. The upshot was a decision to write R. B. Mellon and S. B. McCormick, "setting forth the attitude of the Corporation toward the activities of Mr. Duncan." On McCormick — who since 1904 had been chancellor of the University of Pittsburgh — see Elizabeth Zoe Vicary, "Samuel Black McCormick," *ANB*, Vol. 14 (1999), p. 925.

114. F. A. Goetze to C. D. Walcott, Feb. 26, 1913, RU 51, Box 1, SI Archives. In his letter, however, Goetze also noted that "we have been letting the matter lie dormant," while Lawrence traveled to Cuba. "Mr. Gibbs" was probably George Gibbs, an electrical engineer with an impressive record of service with the Pennsylvania Railroad in New York City — see *NCAB*, Vol. E (1938), pp. 120–121; and William E. Worthington, Jr., "George Gibbs," *ANB*, Vol. 8 (1999), pp. 917–918.

115. Linn Bradley to C. D. Walcott, Feb. 26, 1913, RU 51, Box 1, SI Archives. On Lyon, see *WWE*, 3rd Ed. (1931), pp. 816–817. On his selection as Research Corporation's representative, see Meeting of the Executive Committee, Oct. 30, 1912, RC Minutes, RU 51, Box 3, SI Archives. On Meston, see *NYT*, Sept. 29, 1948, p. 29, col. 3.

116. Diary of F. G. Cottrell, Jan. 3, 1913, Cottrell Papers, Box 1. Cottrell arrived in Pittsburgh the day before and first consulted with Lyon at that time — see Cottrell's diary entry for January 2, 1913. At a subsequent meeting, Research Corporation's executive committee authorized $500 for constructing a demonstration precipitator at the Bureau of Mines laboratory — see Meeting of the Executive Committee, Jan. 17, 1913, RC Minutes, RU 51, Box 3, SI Archives. For a public announcement of the Bureau of Mines' project, see "Takes Up Smoke Problem," *NYT*, Jan. 19, 1913, sec. 3, p. 6, col. 4. On Searle as the city's chief smoke inspector, see *Some Engineering Phases of Pittsburgh's Smoke Problem*, MI Smoke Investigation Bull., No. 8 (1914), p. 18. In his diary, Cottrell identified the railroad official he spoke with only as "Cooke." In all likelihood "Cooke" was Thomas R. Cook, a mechanical engineer working under the general supervision of D. F. Crawford — see American Society of Mechanical Engineers, *Yearbook* (1913), p. 43; and *WWE*, 7th Ed. (1954), p. 488. Writing to Walcott on April 16, 1913 (RU 51, Box 1, SI Archives), Bradley noted: "Dr. Strong stated that Mr. Cook, Assistant Mechanical Engineer of the Pennsylvania at Pittsburgh, told him that the question of the validity of our Patents had been submitted to a legal board which looks into such matters for a number of railroads."

117. Telegram from Linn Bradley to W. A. Schmidt dated Feb. 11, 1913, quoted in F. G. Cottrell to C. D. Walcott, Feb. 17, 1913, RU 45, Box 47, SI Archives.

118. *Electrical World*, 61 (May 10, 1913), 1015. This notice came to the attention of Bradley, Cottrell, and Walcott via Schmidt. Specifically, Bradley enclosed in a letter to Walcott dated May 29, 1913 (RU 51, Box 1, SI Archives), extracts from a letter from Schmidt. "Upon my return to the office this morning," Schmidt wrote Bradley on May 22, 1913:

> I found a clipping regarding the electrical Precipitation Company at Pittsburg[h] and immediately wrote to Cottrell regarding same. . . . It seems to me that these people cannot operate without infringing upon at least two of our patents, no matter what patents they may possess. These are the Rectifier combination and the polarity patent. I personally feel that the proper time to talk matters over with them is before they have had an opportunity of doing any commercial work. Once having started with commercial installations they cannot easily retract their steps and it then will almost of necessity become a subject of patent litigation to drive them from the field of competition. If, on the other hand you are able to present the subject in the proper light to them and they are led to believe that they are merely inviting themselves into serious complications by starting off in a field in which they have no ligitimate [*sic*] rights, that they will think twice before proceeding further with their work.

119. R. F. Bacon to R. K. Duncan, Mar. 4, 1913, MI Papers, Box 199.

120. Ibid. The amount that Bacon mentioned was $5,000.

121. Some of the urgency that Bacon felt may have arisen from the prospects of yet another company taking shape. Thus Strong reported to Bradley on March 31, 1913 (Box A19, RC Archives): "Certain incidents have recently occurred that indicate the entrance of the field by an outside company should the proposed 'Electrical Precipitation Company of Pittsburgh' and the Research Corporation not come to an agreement. If this happens, I take it that the whole method will be thrown open to the public."

122. "Plan for Company to Put Upon Market Smoke and Dust Prevention Apparatus," n.d., Archives of Industrial Society, 83:7, Mellon Institute of Industrial Research, Smoke Investigation Activities 1911–1957, Ser. I, University of Pittsburgh Archives (hereafter Smoke Investigation Papers). Although the "Plan" exists in three drafts (each with the same title) I have drawn exclusively from the third.

123. Ibid. Despite an overall capitalization of $100,000, the plan anticipated "that between $15,000 and $20,000 will be necessary for carrying on the work for the next year."

124. Ibid.

125. "It is evident," the document explained (ibid.), "that the possibility of experiments in this field have not been exhausted, and if it should develop that the present inventions are incomplete or constitute an infringement upon other patents, there is a sufficiently wide field for their carrying on the work in the effort of making further inventions with respect to apparatus of this nature."

126. F. G. Cottrell to C. D. Walcott, Feb. 17, 1913, RU 45, Box 47, SI Archives.

127. Ibid.

128. Ibid.

129. Ibid.

130. F. G. Cottrell to C. D. Walcott, Mar. 5, 1913, RU 45, Box 47, SI Archives.

131. Another factor was the distinctive character of the Eastern U.S. market. "While the middle and western states are mainly producers of primary metals," noted Harry V. Welch, in his article "Collection of Lead and Zinc Dusts and Fumes by the Cottrell Process," *Transactions of the American Institute of Mining and Metallurgical Engineers*, 121 (1936), 333, "the eastern states do the major portion of the refining and secondary metal recovery. Primary production is in relatively few large plants.... The great number and variety of operations and the general small volume of individual secondary plants make description of individual plants out of the question...." Welch joined the Western Precipitation staff as a research chemist in 1915 and became chief chemist the following year – see *AMS*, 9th Ed. (1955), p. 2062.

132. R. K. Duncan to R. F. Bacon, July 16, 1913, MI Papers, Box 199. To this, Bacon replied (July 20, 1913, MI Papers, Box 199): "in view of the very doubtful status of the Research Corporation I felt it was just as well to wait until fall to see whether they were going to the wall or not." Since 1912, William Horace Ross (a chemist who had received his Ph.D. from the University of Chicago in 1907) had been a scientist on the staff at the Bureau of Soils – see *WWWA*, Vol. 2 (1950), p. 460. For his interest in electrostatic precipitation, see "New York Meeting of American Chemical Society," *MCE*, 15 (Oct. 1, 1916), 380–381; W. H. Ross, J. N. Carothers, and A. R. Merz, "The Use of the Cottrell Precipitator in Recovering the Phosphoric Acid Evolved in the Volatilization Method of Treating Phosphate Rock," *JIEC*, 9 (Jan. 1917), 26–31; and A. F. Meston, "Electrical Precipitation in the Chemical Industries," *Electric Journal*, 14 (June 1917), 251.

133. Linn Bradley, "Electrical Precipitation of Suspended Particles," *Proceedings of the Engineers' Society of Western Pennsylvania*, 29 (Apr. 1913), 124. By mid-June 1913 the experimental electrostatic precipitator at the Bureau of Mines was completed – see Meeting of the Executive Committee, June 20, 1913, RC Minutes, RU 51, Box 3, SI Archives. On the experimental unit, which was installed under Meston's direction, see also A. F. Meston, "Application of Electrostatic Precipitation to the Cleaning of Coal Smoke," Jan. 8, 1914, RU 51, Box 1, SI Archives; and Bradley, "Practical Applications of Electrical Precipitation and Progress of the Research Corporation" (1915), p. 429.

134. Linn Bradley to C. D. Walcott, Mar. 25, 1913, RU 51, Box 1. Regarding the main commercial initiative of Duncan's group, Bradley noted: "The Pennsylvania Railroad people are doing nothing at the present time with the University of Pittsburgh people." Finally, he offered a brief review of the patent situation and concluded, opti-

mistically, "that the situation is advancing nicely in our favor, and that in due time everything will be quite satisfactory in this connection."

135. Ibid.

136. Meeting of the Executive Committee, Apr. 2, 1913, RC Minutes, RU 51, Box 3, SI Archives. At the same time, Hooker was asked to extend a similar invitation to L. H. Baekeland. For Mellon's refusal, see Meeting of the Executive Committee, June 20, 1913, RC Minutes, RU 51, Box 3, SI Archives. Likewise, Goetze reported for Hooker "that it would be impossible to get Mr. Baekeland to become director . . . owing to his many other interests." For more on Baekeland and Research Corporation, see Chapter 5.

137. Diary of F. G. Cottrell, June 12, 1913, Cottrell Papers, Box 1.

138. Ibid. Cottrell also described Bacon's proposal: "He stated they were ready to turn over their patents to Research Corporation but wanted vindication of their attitude & particularly of Prof. Duncan's part in it. He first suggested that Allegheny County be give a free license but later said he did not believe even this necessary."

139. Meeting of the Executive Committee, June 20, 1913, RC Minutes, RU 51, Box 3, SI Archives. For the lunch with Goetze, see Diary of F. G. Cottrell, June 14, 1913, Cottrell Papers, Box 1. The Engineers' Club represented yet another example of the rich organizational environment that New York City offered Research Corporation. Emerging in the late 19th century, the Engineers' Club acquired a new building in 1907 as part of Andrew Carnegie's gift of $1,500,000 — see Thomas Commerford Martin [president of the Engineers' Club], "Mr. Carnegie's Noteworthy Endowment for Engineering," *Harpers Weekly*, 51 (Apr. 13, 1907), 546; and "Engineers' New Home," *NYT*, Apr. 26, 1907, p. 2, col. 3.

140. "We all know it is quite impossible to build a fresh fire in the house grate or stove without smoke, and that quite dense smoke will continue until a considerable portion of fuel is fully ignited," Crawford once wrote, appealing to the everyday experiences of his readers — see D. F. Crawford, "The Abatement of Locomotive Smoke," *Scientific American Supplement*, 76 (Dec. 6, 1913), 355. Starting fires in locomotives while they sat in roundhouses or terminals gave rise to similar problems on a much larger scale. On Crawford, see American Society of Mechanical Engineers, *Yearbook* (1913), p. 46; and *AMS*, 5th Ed. (1933), p. 241. On the air-pollution concerns of the Pennsylvania Railroad, see Stradling, *Smokestacks and Progressives*, pp. 91–95. On the air pollution concerns of railroads generally, see also Harold C. Livesay and Glenn Porter, "William Savery and the Wonderful Parsons Smoke-Eating Machine," *Delaware History*, 14 (Apr. 1971), 161–176; and Tarr, *The Search for the Ultimate Sink*, Chap. 9, "Railroad Smoke Control: The Regulation of a Mobile Pollution Source," pp. 262–283.

141. D. F. Crawford, "The Elimination of Smoke," *Scientific American Supplement*, 75 (June 14, 1913), 384.

142. Ibid.

143. Linn Bradley to C. D. Walcott, Apr. 16, 1913, RU 51, Box 1, SI Archives. Interest on the part of the Pennsylvania Railroad remained strong. Thus at a meeting on February 25, 1915 (RC Minutes, RU 51, Box 3, SI Archives), Research Corporation's executive committee noted that "the situation in Pittsburgh warranted the making of favorable terms" and then approved an agreement with the Pennsylvania Railroad, "allowing them to use the precipitation patents for the nominal sum of $100. for the Allegheny Enginehouse and $100. per stall for other roundhouses." For his part, Nesbit saw the railroad project as directly related to his own earlier efforts: "The Electrical Precipitation apparatus, which is to be installed at an early date at the roundhouse is the outgrowth of research work done by the undersigned at the University of Pittsburgh" — see A. F. Nesbit to W. K. Brown, Jan. 28, 1915, Smoke Investigation Papers.

144. Diary of F. G. Cottrell, July 19–23, 1913, Cottrell Papers, Box 1. During the period of their earliest contact, Cottrell consistently misspelled Hamerschlag's name (as did Cameron throughout *Samaritan of Science*). There are several features of these entries that I still do not fully understand. What did Scott and Lyon say that so upset Duncan? What was McCormick's role in these proceedings? Hamerschlag's? What did Duncan mean by "relations with Ba[e]keland"? What did Cottrell mean by "the Parsons and Sir Thomas Oliver incident"?

145. R. K. Duncan to R. F. Bacon, July 25, 1913, MI Papers, Box 199. As mentioned in the previous note, I do not fully understand the circumstances that so upset Duncan.

146. W. W. Strong and A. F. Nesbit, "Tentative Plan of Precipitation Work," [1913], Box A19, RC Archives.

147. Ibid.

148. A. F. Nesbit, "Diary of Work on the R. B. Mellon Smoke Fellowship," enclosed in A. F. Nesbit to R. B. Mellon, June 18, 1914, MI Papers, Box 140. Permission to reproduce this document has been granted by The Carnegie Mellon University Archives, at Hunt Library, Carnegie Mellon University, Pittsburgh, Pa.

149. Arthur Benjamin Bellows was identified as a mechanical engineer on the list of "Staff of the Smoke Investigation" in *Some Engineering Phases of Pittsburgh's Smoke Problem*, MI Smoke Investigation Bull., No. 8 (1914). He received his B.S. degree from MIT in 1889 — see Massachusetts Institute of Technology, *Register of Former Students*, p. 23.

150. O. R. McBride and A. A. Straub were identified as mechanical engineers on the list of "Staff of the Smoke Investigation" in the published report, *Some Engineering Phases of Pittsburgh's Smoke Problem*, MI Smoke Investigation Bull., No. 8 (1914). In his introductory note, John O'Connor, Jr., acknowledged the contributions of Bellows, Straub, McBride, Nesbit, and others.

151. "Mr. Phillips" was probably Henry A. Phillips, who has been described as "a behind-the-scenes power in the Mellon financial empire" — see *NYT*, Jan. 16, 1950, p. 26, col. 2 — and as "[a] trusted employee" and one of "the most important personal

assistants to A[ndrew] W. [Mellon] and R[ichard] B. [Mellon] — see Koskoff, *The Mellons: The Chronicle of America's Richest Family*, p. 69 and p. 124.

152. R. F. Bacon to A. F. Nesbit, May 19, 1914, MI Papers, Box 140. For Nesbit's inquiry, see A. F. Nesbit to R. F. Bacon, May 1, 1914, MI Papers, Box 140. Earlier he had approached Bacon informally. "During this last April," he wrote in his "Diary of Work on the R. B. Mellon Smoke Fellowship" (enclosed in A. F. Nesbit to R. B. Mellon, June 18, 1914, MI Papers, Box 140), "I asked Dr. Bacon as to what was to be his action in regard to my vacation allowance, as specified at frequent intervals by Dr. Duncan."

153. F. G. Cottrell, "Electrical Precipitation: Historical Sketch," *Trans. AIEE*, 34 (1915), 387–396; W. W. Strong, "Electrical Precipitation: Theory of the Removal of Suspended Matter from Fluids," ibid., 397–404; A. F. Nesbit, "The Theoretical and Experimental Consideration of Electrical Precipitation," ibid., 405–420; and Linn Bradley, "Practical Applications of Electrical Precipitation and Progress of the Research Corporation," ibid., 421–457.

154. "Electric Smoke and Fume Precipitation before the American Institute of Electrical Engineers," *MCE*, 13 (Mar. 1915), 160. On the Engineering Societies Building, which housed the American Society of Mechanical Engineers and (after 1916) the American Society of Civil Engineers, as well as the American Institute of Electrical Engineers and the American Institute of Mining Engineers, see C. W. Hunt, "The Activities of the American Society of Civil Engineers during the Past Twenty-Five Years," *Transactions of the American Society of Civil Engineers*, 82 (1918), 1582–1589; Robert M. Lester, *Forty Years of Carnegie Giving: A Summary of the Benefactions of Andrew Carnegie . . .* (New York: Scribners, 1941), p. 88; and Edwin T. Layton, Jr., *The Revolt of the Engineers: Social Responsibility and the American Engineering Profession* (Cleveland: Case Western Reserve University Press, 1971), pp. 82–84. On the participation of the mining engineers, see also "Proceedings of the One Hundred and Tenth Meeting, New York City, February, 1915," *Trans. AIME*, 51 (1916), xxii. On Paul Martyn Lincoln, who was then a senior engineer at Westinghouse and professor of electrical engineering at the University of Pittsburgh, see *NCAB*, Vol. B (1927), pp. 280–281.

155. "The demonstration," noted the report "Electric Smoke and Fume Precipitation before the American Institute of Electrical Engineers" (1915), p. 160 — "was very successful, the smoke being instantaneously stopped by closing the circuit of the Cottrell apparatus, and appearing again quickly when the circuit was opened." On January 26, 1917, Bradley and Strong again gave paired papers, this time at a joint meeting of the New York sections of the American Electrochemical Society and the American Institute of Mining Engineers — see "Symposium on the Smelter Smoke and Fume Problem," *MCE,* 16 (Feb. 1, 1917), 128; Linn Bradley, "The Cottrell Process in Practice," ibid., (Mar. 15, 1917), 336–340; and W. W. Strong, "Some Theoretical Aspects of Electrical Fume Precipitation," ibid., (June 1, 1917), 648–652.

156. "Electric Smoke and Fume Precipitation before the American Institute of

Electrical Engineers" (1915), p. 160.

157. Linn Bradley, "Solution of Smoke, Fume and Dust Problems by Electrical Precipitation," *MCE*, 13 (Dec. 1, 1915), 913. For mention of Bradley's remarks, see "First National Exposition of Chemical Industries," ibid., (Oct. 1, 1915), 697. Bradley also helped with Research Corporation's booth at the exposition – see ibid., pp. 693–695. "Among the exhibits of machinery and equipment for manufacturing chemists," noted another account of the exposition, "was a most interesting installation of smoke precipitation apparatus" – see "America As Her Own Chemist . . . ," *Scientific American*, 113 (Oct. 2, 1915), 302.

158. Agreement enclosed in W. W. Strong to Research Corporation, Mar. 30, 1915, Box A19, RC Archives. This time the agreement listed the patents in question: U.S. Patent No. 1,117,531, issued Nov. 19, 1914; U.S. Patent No. 1,119,469, issued Dec. 1, 1914; U.S. Patent No. 1,120,560, issued Dec. 8, 1914; and U.S. Patent No. 1,120,561, issued Dec. 8, 1914. Also listed were several U.S. Patent Applications still pending: Serial No. 747,782; Serial No. 747,786; and Serial No. 747,788.

159. The patent involved was probably W. A. Schmidt and G. C. Roberts, "Apparatus for Separating Suspended Particles from Gases," U.S. Patent No. 1,132,124, issued Mar. 16, 1915 (filed Apr. 6, 1914).

160. Linn Bradley to W. W. Strong, May 13, 1915, Box A19, RC Archives.

161. W. W. Strong to Linn Bradley, May 19, 1915, Box A19, RC Archives.

162. In a letter to Strong dated June 25, 1915 (Box A19, RC Archives), Bradley mentioned "interference No. 38,558" and commented that the interference would now "be adjusted." Writing to Hooker on March 22, 1916 (RU 51, Box 2, SI Archives), Bradley explained: "Dr. Strong has filed a concession of priority, but Nesbit refused to do so." Writing to Strong on May 25, 1916 (Box A19, RC Archives), Bradley blamed one of the attorneys whom Nesbit had consulted for building up "false hopes" on Nesbit's part and causing him "to forget his fundamental ideas of justice and the ethics in the case." R. B. Mellon also played a role, but mainly by letting events take their course – see R. F. Bacon to W. A. Schmidt, Mar. 1, 1916, RU 51, Box 2, SI Archives; and W. A. Schmidt to C. D. Walcott, May 9, 1916, RU 51, Box 2, SI Archives.

163. Even Cottrell participated. "10-11 at Walter Allens [*sic*] office gave testimony on Schmidt Nesbit interference &c.," he noted in his diary entry for April 3, 1916 (Cottrell Papers, Box 1). For Townsend's services, see Meeting of the Executive Committee, Oct. 10, 1916, RC Minutes, RU 51, Box 4, SI Archives. On Townsend – who had worked as a patent examiner and who had developed (in cooperation with Elmer Sperry) the process that Hooker had adopted as the basis for his company's work – see Hughes, *Elmer Sperry*, pp. 90–96; and Thomas, *Salt & Water, Power & People*, p. 12.

164. Stockholders Meeting, Feb. 16, 1917, RC Minutes, RU 51, Box 4, SI Archives. On Eugene A. Byrnes, see *WWWA*, Vol. 4 (1968), p. 144.

165. Meeting of the Executive Committee, June 22, 1917, RC Minutes, RU 51,

Box 4, SI Archives.

166. John J. O'Connor, Jr., to S. B. Linhart, Jan. 26, 1915, Smoke Investigation Papers; Robert James McKay, *Recent Progress in Smoke Abatement and Fuel Technology in England*, MI Smoke Investigation Bull., No. 10 (1922); Meller, "Smoke Abatement, Its Effects and Its Limitations" (1926), p. 1280; Agnes Lynch Starrett, *Through One Hundred and Fifty Years: The University of Pittsburgh* (Pittsburgh: University of Pittsburgh Press, 1937), p. 321; "Dr. Meller Dead; Expert on Smoke," *NYT*, June 29, 1943, p. 20, col. 3; and the Meller entry in *WWWA*, Vol. 2 (1950), p. 368.

167. Meeting of the Board of Directors, Jan. 17, 1919, RC Minutes, RU 51, Box 4, SI Archives. Steere had pursued research on electrostatic precipitation at the University of Michigan – see F. W. Steere, "An Electrical Process for Detarring Gas," *MCE*, 12 (Dec. 1914), 775–778.

168. Meeting of the Board of Directors, Jan. 16, 1920, RC Minutes, RU 51, Box 4, SI Archives. Although Dillon also noted that "the Steere Company continues action," he did not consider it to be a serious competitor.

169. Meeting of the Executive Committee, Nov. 18, 1915; and Meeting of the Board of Directors, Jan. 21, 1916, RC Minutes, RU 51, Box 3, SI Archives. At the same time, plans were also made for a branch office in Chicago. Later a branch office was opened in Salt Lake City – see Meeting of the Board of Directors, Jan. 18, 1918, RC Minutes, RU 51, Box 4, SI Archives.

170. For Strong's work for Research Corporation, see Chapter 5. For an early version of the employees' contract, see L. N. Scott to C. D. Walcott, Dec. 10, 1913, RU 51, Box 1, SI Archives. A later version appeared in the RC Archives (Research Corporation to Western Precipitation Company, Feb 2, 1914, Box A14; and the agreement among Research Corporation, Western Precipitation, and International Precipitation, Feb. 4, 1914, Box A14).

171. Meeting of the Board of Directors, Jan. 21, 1916, RC Minutes, RU 51, Box 3, SI Archives. Bradley wrote in his "Proposed Organization for Development of Activities of Research Corporation" (Apr. 6, 1916, RU 51, Box 2, SI Archives):

> We are planning to rent space in a factory building in Brooklyn whereby we can have a suitable Field Laboratory of our own, and thus be able to carry on certain investigations by ourselves and without in any manner being a burden to our clients. This Field Laboratory can be made quite valuable for such work as opportunity is available for actual furnace fumes. This Laboratory should serve nicely as a training school for new Field Engineers and Assistants, and should also give us our own Demonstration Plant for prospective customers.

172. Meeting of the Executive Committee, Sept. 27, 1917, RC Minutes, RU 51, Box 4, SI Archives.

173. Agreement involving Research Corporation, International Precipitation, and Western Precipitation, Jan. 28, 1919, Box A13, RC Archives.

174. On the general tendency toward vertical expansion in the case of the techno-

logically complex goods produced by the electrical industry, see Glen Porter, *The Rise of Big Business, 1860–1910* (Arlington Heights, Ill.: Harlan Davidson, 1973), pp. 51–53. On the general importance of industrial research in the electrical industry with emphasis on GE and AT&T, see Leonard S. Reich, *The Making of American Industrial Research: Science and Business at GE and Bell,* 1876–1926 (Cambridge, England: Cambridge University Press, 1985).

175. Linn Bradley, "Proposed Organization for Development of Activities of Research Corporation," Apr. 6 1916, RU 51, Box 2, SI Archives.

176. Ibid.

177. Meeting of the Executive Committee, Jan. 16, 1917, RC Minutes, RU 51, Box 4, SI Archives.

178. On Hooker's work for Roosevelt and the Progressive Party, see Theodore Roosevelt, *Theodore Roosevelt: An Autobiography* (New York: Macmillan, 1913), pp. 309–310; and John Allen Gable, *The Bull Moose Years: Theodore Roosevelt and the Progressive Party* (Port Washington, N.Y.: Kennikat Press, 1978), p. 37 and p. 118. Although Hooker's serving as president in 1912 was out of the question, Pine hoped that he would at least be willing to serve as treasurer (J. B. Pine to E. H. Hooker, Feb. 17, 1912, Box A14, RC Archives). Nevertheless, Hooker resisted. "...I still must beg off from your proposal that I become treasurer...," he wrote Pine (Feb. 20, 1912, Box A14, RC Archives). "The demands upon my time in a number of directions are constant, and I scarcely feel that it would be right...for me to give...any large portion of my energy to the new corporation." Hooker did agree to serve on the executive committee, but at the first official board of directors meeting (Feb. 27, 1912, RC Minutes, RU 51, Box 3, SI Archives) B. B. Lawrence was elected treasurer. In 1913 Hooker was serving as chairman of the Progressive Party's finance committee — see Morison, *The Letters of Theodore Roosevelt,* Vol. 7, p. 543, n. 1; and Gable, op. cit., pp. 163–165. Accordingly, he again resisted efforts to elect him president — see Meeting of the Board of Directors, Jan. 17, 1913, RC Minutes, RU 51, Box 3, SI Archives. Instead, the directors tried electing William H. Nichols, the industrial chemist who took Thomson's place as director. But Nichols declined to serve (see C. D. Walcott to F. G. Cottrell, Jan. 27, 1913, RU 45, Box 47, SI Archives), and a year later the Thomson-Nichols directorship was given to George F. Kunz, a mineralogist and gem expert — see Meeting of the Stockholders, Jan. 16, 1914, RC Minutes, RU 51, Box 3, SI Archives. On Nichols, see Daniel P. Jones and Robert F. Gould, "William Henry Nichols, 1852–1930," in Miles, *American Chemists and Chemical Engineers,* pp. 363–365. On Kunz, see Lawrence H. Conklin, "George Frederick Kunz," *ANB,* Vol. 12 (1999), pp. 952–953.

179. Meeting of the Board of Directors, Jan. 15, 1915, RC Minutes, RU 51, Box 3, SI Archives.

180. E. H. Hooker to T. E. Knowlton, Mar. 10, 1917, RU 51, Box 2, SI Archives. On Knowlton, see *NCAB,* Vol. 48 (1965), pp. 333–334. Subsequently, Knowlton became a Research Corporation director (replacing Storrow) and was also elected a member

of the executive committee — see Meeting of the Board of Directors, Jan. 18, 1918, RC Minutes, RU 51, Box 4, SI Archives.

181. T. E. Knowlton to E. H. Hooker, May 26, 1917, RU 51, Box 4, SI Archives. "Got report on Res. Corp. from Knowlton & wired that it was OK," Cottrell noted in his diary entry for May 28, 1917 (Cottrell Papers, Box 1).

182. For Bradley's appointment as manager, see Meeting of the Executive Committee, Dec. 28, 1917, RC Minutes, RU 51, Box 4, SI Archives. For the board's action, and Whitaker's election as a director (replacing Baekeland), see Meeting of the Board of Directors, Jan. 18, 1918, RC Minutes, RU 51, Box 4, SI Archives. For Dillon's appointment (at an annual salary of $7,500), see Meeting of the Executive Committee, May 20, 1918, RC Minutes, RU 51, Box 4, SI Archives. (Bradley's salary had just been increased to $6,500 — see Meeting of the Executive Committee, Feb. 7, 1918, RC Minutes, RU 51, Box 4, SI Archives.) On July 18, 1918, Hooker reported to Walcott (RU 51, Box 2, SI Archives) that Dillon's acceptance had been secured "through the kind offices of Dr Whitaker." On Whitaker — a chemical engineer who had recently returned to industry after heading Columbia's chemical engineering department (as Charles F. Chandler's successor) from 1910 to 1916 — see "Perkin Medal Award," *Industrial and Engineering Chemistry*, 15 (Feb. 1923), 195–203; and *NCAB*, Vol. 50 (1968), p. 314. For Dillon's organizational changes, see "General Letter No. 1," June 29, 1918, RU 51, Box 2, SI Archives. Although nothing untoward came of it, Bradley's departure was a source of concern — see Meeting of the Board of Directors, Jan. 16, 1920, RC Minutes, RU 51, Box 4, SI Archives.

183. A. D. Little to the Executive Committee, Jan. 15, 1918, RU 51, Box 2, SI Archives. Although he mentioned "a site containing three to five acres" somewhere other than Manhattan, Little did not specify the exact location. But he did offer two examples of what he had in mind. One was his own firm's new building at Cambridge, near MIT. The other was in Washington, D.C.: "Those of you who are familiar with the location of the United States Bureau of Standards will appreciate the great advantages of a suburban site...." On those new facilities, see Rexmond C. Cochrane, *Measures for Progress: A History of the National Bureau of Standards* (Washington, D.C.: National Bureau of Standards, U.S. Department of Commerce, 1966), pp. 68–73. Also relevant here are Little's general views on industrial research laboratories — see Little, "Organization of Industrial Research" (1918), pp. 22–31.

184. Linn Bradley to C. D. Walcott, Apr. 10, 1916, RU 51, Box 2, SI Archives.

185. A. D. Little to E. H. Hooker, Jan. 26, 1918, RU 51, Box 2, SI Archives. Two other factors at work here were the decision of the board of directors not to accept Bradley as the new general manager and the decision to remove Goetze from the executive committee.

186. Toward the end of January, Walcott wrote "to express the hope that you will continue to serve as a member of the executive committee ..." (C. D. Walcott to A. D. Little, Jan. 28, 1918, RU 51, Box, 2, SI Archives). In early February, Hooker made his views clear: "Dr Whitaker, Mr Lawrence, Mr Knowlton and I [the other members

of the newly reformed Executive Committee] felt that it was altogether impossible for us to accept your resignation . . ." (E. H. Hooker to A. D. Little, Feb. 7, 1918, RU 51, Box 2, SI Archives).

187. Alfred D. Chandler, Jr., *Scale and Scope: The Dynamics of Industrial Capitalism* (Cambridge, Mass.: Belknap Press of Harvard University Press, 1990), especially Chap. 2, "Scale, Scope, and Organizational Capabilities," pp. 14–46. A firm's organizational capabilities can be analyzed on the basis of its functional activities: production, distribution, purchasing, research, and finance (p. 35). Another approach is examining its hierarchy of responsibility: upper management, middle management, lower management, and the work force (p. 36). I thank W. Bernard Carlson for suggesting that I refer to Chandler's work here.

188. E. H. Hooker to C. D. Walcott, Dec. 16, 1918, RU 51, Box 2, SI Archives.

CHAPTER FIVE—AN ASPIRING PHILANTHROPIC ORGANIZATION
PAGES 116–156

1. Thus Cottrell wrote Walcott (Dec. 4, 1914, RU 45, Box 47, SI Archives): "An important difference which I see between its proper policy and that of one of the great commercial companies of the day is that it can legitimately use its efforts and resources to forwarding matters of general interest and benefit even where there is no likelyhood [*sic*] that it as an organization will ever profit thereby even indirectly."

2. Meeting of the Executive Committee, May 2, 1912, RC Minutes, RU 51, Box 3, SI Archives. The invention in question was a knitting machine.

3. "Report of [the] Executive Committee of the Research Corporation for the Year 1913," RU 51, Box 1, SI Archives.

4. The term "altruism" was a recent coinage by the nineteenth-century French philosopher, Auguste Comte. For glosses on its usage at the turn of the century, see "Altruism," *Encyclopaedia Britannica*, 11th Ed. (Cambridge, England: Cambridge University Press, 1910), Vol. 1, p. 766; and *The Oxford English Dictionary*, 2nd Ed. (Oxford, England: Clarendon Press, 1989), Vol. 1, p. 371.

5. M. Grier Kidder, "Altruism," *Overland Monthly*, 61 (Feb. 1913), 186.

6. C. D. Walcott to C. F. Choate, Jr., Mar. 28, 1912, RU 45, Box 47, SI Archives (emphasis added). Similar letters went out to the other regents. For the conditions Walcott described, see *Research Corporation: Certificate of Incorporation, By-Laws and Stockholders' Agreement* (1912). Walcott's notion of altruism had been central to his earliest contact with Cottrell. Thus he noted in a personal memo ("Memorandum: Remarks by Mr. Walcott on the Origin of the Research Corporation," [1915], RU 51, Box 1, SI Archives — emphasis added):

> I was deeply impressed with the blending of the highest idealism with
> keen business sagacity in Dr. Cottrell. This, united with the transparent
> honesty of purpose and enthusiasm, convinced all whom he approached

that he was not seeking any personal business or financial advantage, and that the work was of a purely *altruistic* nature.

7. For biographical sources on Goetze, see Chapter 3.

8. F. A. Goetze to F. G. Cottrell, Apr. 9, 1914, RU 51, Box 1, SI Archives. The problem was compounded by Goetze's sense that his background was not what Research Corporation really needed. Thus he added in his letter: "If I had had the requisite technical training along the lines of applied chemistry and metallurgy I should like nothing better than to take over the active administration of the work of the Research Corporation myself. . . ."

9. F. A. Goetze to C. D. Walcott, Apr. 11, 1914, RU 51, Box 1, SI Archives.

10. C. D. Walcott to F. G. Cottrell, Jan. 27, 1913, RU 45, Box 47, SI Archives. Regarding the title Walcott used in referring to Goetze, in 1905 Columbia had awarded Goetze an honorary M.S. degree, but not until 1929 did it award him an honorary Doctor of Science degree — see the entry on Goetze in *WWE*, 6th Ed. (1948), p. 744. Regarding the choice of a president, even as late as the fall of 1914 Hooker was still resisting. "While the Research Corporation is now in admirable shape and the Electrochemical Company has been restored to its full output [after a major fire]," he wrote Walcott (Oct., 30, 1914, RU 51, Box 1, SI Archives), "yet other duties of mine which have been neglected in the meantime . . . are not yet properly taken care of, and I am definitely opposed therefore to taking on any more responsibility at the present time."

11. C. D. Walcott to B. B. Lawrence, Nov. 6, 1914, RU 51, Box 1, SI Archives. When consulted by Walcott, Cottrell expressed opposition to the honorarium idea. Instead, his preference was to have the firm hire a general manager, thereby maintaining "a sharp separation between the Board of Directors and the employees of the Corporation" (F. G. Cottrell to C. D. Walcott, Dec. 4, 1914, RU 45, Box 47, SI Archives).

12. B. B. Lawrence to C. D. Walcott, Dec. 9, 1914, RU 51, Box 1, SI Archives. Social status was probably a factor here. "The engineering professions should be followed by gentlemen," Lawrence had written — see his article, "Engineering Professions," in *The School of Mines Quarterly*, 31 (Apr. 1910), 207. Presumably, by refusing compensation Goetze maintained his status as a gentleman engineer.

13. Meeting of the Board of Directors, Nov. 19, 1914, RC Minutes, RU 51, Box 3, SI Archives. It was not hard for those associated with Research Corporation to draw a clear distinction between Scott's case and Goetze's. Thus Cottrell wrote Walcott afterwards (Dec. 4, 1914, RU 45, Box 47, SI Archives):

> I do not consider the cases of Mr. Pine and Mr. Scott as in any sense precidents [*sic*] in this matter [of Goetze's honorarium] as from the very outset both Mr. Pine and Mr. Lawrence took pains to clearly point out that both these gentlemen were taking up the work primarily as employees and only incidentally and temporarily as Directors in order to assure against difficulties in getting a quorum and other technicalities during

the early stages of the development of the Corporation.

14. Meeting of the Executive Committee, Jan. 16, 1917, and Meeting of the Board of Directors, Jan. 18, 1918, RC Minutes, RU 51, Box 4, SI Archives. To put the amount of Goetze's honorarium in context, at the board of directors meeting on January 15, 1915 (RC Minutes, RU 51, Box 3, SI Archives) Hooker praised Goetze as being "a $25,000 a year man, whose services the Research Corporation received for nothing."

15. C. D. Walcott to C. F. Choate, Jr., Nov. 20, 1911, RU 45, Box 47, SI Archives (emphasis added).

16. C. D. Walcott to L. F. Spear, Jan. 27, 1915, RU 51, Box 1, SI Archives (emphasis added). In a letter to New York State Senator Samuel H. Hofstadter on January 29, 1930 (Box A27, RC Archives), Research Corporation explained:

> During the first years of the Corporation's existence its income was entirely devoted to the development of the patent and the matter of taxes was not of importance. However, in 1915 the question of Federal Income Taxes was taken up with the Department in Washington, and on February first of that year, the Corporation was given exemption on the basis that it was "an institution maintained exclusively for educational and scientific purposes, no part of whose income inures to the profit of any private stockholder or individual" and "Therefore so long as the purposes and manner of distributing the revenue of the Research Corporation remain as stated by its Secretary, the Corporation will not be required to make an annual return of net income."

17. J. B. Pine to Charles J. Tobin, May 24, 1916, Box A14, RC Archives. Tobin was a partner in the partnership of Stanley and Tobin, whose offices were located in Albany. Official notice of the rejection had come from John J. Merrill, the state's Deputy Tax Commissioner.

18. J. B. Pine to Charles J. Tobin, May 29, 1916, Box A14, RC Archives.

19. Charles J. Tobin to J. B. Pine, July 3, 1917, Box A14, RC Archives. As the dates suggest, these negotiations were pursued over an extended period.

20. L. N. Scott to [Charles J. Tobin], Aug. 13, 1917, Box A14, RC Archives.

21. Charles J. Tobin to L. N. Scott, Aug. 23, 1917, Box A14, RC Archives.

22. Research Corporation to New York State Senator Samuel H. Hofstadter, Jan. 29, 1930, Box A27, RC Archives. The letter went on to note that in 1922 such a bill was indeed prepared. It was never presented, however, and no further action was taken until 1930 (which was the occasion for the letter to Hofstadter).

23. J. B. Pine to [Charles J. Tobin], July 27, 1917, Box A14, RC Archives. For legal purposes, however, the tax lawyer did not find the comparison useful (Charles J. Tobin to J. B. Pine, July 30, 1917, Box A14, RC Archives). Christian A. Herter established the *Journal of Biological Chemistry* in 1905 in order to consolidate biochemistry as a distinctive professional discipline, and after Herter's death in 1910 his former assistant, Henry D. Dakin, and three other scientists continued to edit it — see Rob-

ert E. Kohler, *From Medical Chemistry to Biochemistry: The Making of a Biomedical Discipline* (Cambridge, England: Cambridge University Press, 1982), pp. 197–199 and p. 213; and Percival Hartley, "Henry Drysdale Dakin, 1880–1952," *Obituary Notices of Fellows of the Royal Society*, 8 (Nov. 1952), 139.

24. Cottrell wrote Linn Bradley on July 3, 1912 (RU 45, Box 47, SI Archives): "Speaking of Prof. Lodge, if you have time, look up a volume of the tracts of the Fabian Society of London, entitled 'Socialism and Individualism'[,] the last of the articles in this little volume being a reprint of a paper by Prof. Lodge. . . ." The specific version Cottrell read was probably Oliver Lodge, "Public Service versus Private Expenditure," in Sidney Webb, Bernard Shaw, Sidney Ball, and Oliver Lodge, *Socialism and Individualism* (New York: John Lane, 1911), pp. 92–102. Lodge's remarks were originally published as Fabian Tract No. 121 (London: The Fabian Society, 1905). The latter publication classified Lodge's tract under the heading "General Socialism in its various aspects."

25. F. G. Cottrell to Linn Bradley, July 3, 1912, RU 45, Box 47, SI Archives. On July 5, 1912, Cottrell sent a similar message to Lodge himself (RU 45, Box 47, SI Archives): "It so chanced that shortly before the receipt of your letter there came into my hands a copy of your address on 'Public Service vs Private Expenditure'. . . and it has greatly encouraged me to believe that you would be in general accord with the underlying spirit of the Research Corporation movement. . . ." Cottrell often used the word "movement" when talking about the firm's founding. For examples in print, see Cottrell, "The Research Corporation, an Experiment in Public Administration of Patent Rights" (1912), p. 867; and Cottrell, "Discussion," at the end of Bradley, "Electrical Precipitation of Suspended Particles" (1912), p. 497.

26. Lodge, "Public Service versus Private Expenditure" (1911), p. 92.

27. Ibid., p. 96.

28. Ibid., pp. 95–96 (emphasis added).

29. F. G. Cottrell to S. C. Clark, Oct. 8, 1912, RU 45, Box 47, SI Archives.

30. F. G. Cottrell to C. D. Walcott, Nov. 3, 1911, RU 45, Box 47, SI Archives. On April 10, 1912, Malm wrote Cottrell, returning the material on Cottrell's arrangement with the Smithsonian and noting (RU 45, Box 47, SI Archives): "I have discussed this matter with our Board of Directors [of the Western Metals Company] and they are willing that our patents, outside of a very limited territory, should be disposed of in this way. . . ." Although the patents themselves were not listed, they likely included: J. L. Malm, "Process of Treating Metal and Mineral Bearing Materials," U.S. Patent No. 1,049,746, issued Jan. 7, 1913 (filed Aug. 9, 1909); and J. L. Malm, "Process of Treating Metal and Mineral Bearing Materials," U.S. Patent No. 1,185,817, issued June 6, 1916 (filed Feb. 21, 1911). On Malm, a metallurgical engineer who had studied at Case School of Applied Science, see *WWE*, 2nd Ed. (1925), p. 1373.

31. F. G. Cottrell to C. D. Walcott, Apr. 17, 1912, RU 45, Box 47, SI Archives.

32. C. D. Walcott to F. G. Cottrell, Apr. 23, 1912, RU 45, Box 47, SI Archives. To

this Cottrell responded on April 28, 1912 (RU 45, Box 47, SI Archives): "I thoroughly agree with you in what you say in connection with the Malm patents about the necessity of extreme care where any outside financial interests are concerned."

33. Diary of F. G. Cottrell, June 14, 1913, Cottrell Papers, Box 1.

34. F. A. Goetze to F. G. Cottrell, Apr. 9, 1914, RU 51, Box 1, SI Archives; F. A. Goetze to C. D. Walcott, Apr. 11, 1914, RU 51, Box 1, SI Archives; and Meeting of the Executive Committee, Apr. 28, 1914, RC Minutes, RU 51, Box 3, SI Archives. On Easton — a mining engineer who received his B.S. degree from the University of California in 1894 and who since 1903 had been manager of the Bunker Hill and Sullivan Mining and Concentrating Company — see *AMS*, 3rd Ed. (1921), p. 195; and *WWWA*, Vol. 4 (1968), p. 275.

35. F. G. Cottrell to F. A. Goetze, June 25, 1914, RU 45, Box 17, SI Archives.

36. Ibid.

37. Ibid.

38. Ibid.

39. Ibid.

40. Ibid.

41. Meeting of the Executive Committee, Nov. 19, 1914, RC Minutes, RU 51, Box 3, SI Archives.

42. F. G. Cottrell to C. D. Walcott, Dec. 4, 1914, RU 45, Box 47, SI Archives. Cottrell recognized that assistance from the Bureau of Mines would likely be restricted to laboratory work, which would do little to help Malm introduce his new process on a commercial scale — hence his hopes for the role that Research Corporation might play. The idea was one he had expressed previously. "In our Bureau of Mines relationships," he wrote Walcott on April 17, 1912 (RU 45, Box 47, SI Archives), "we are extremely limited in this direction, but the Research Corporation could in an informal way do much to encourage this work."

43. F. G. Cottrell to C. D. Walcott, Dec. 4, 1914, RU 45, Box 47, SI Archives.

44. Meeting of the Executive Committee, Jan. 15, 1915, RC Minutes, RU 15, Box 3, SI Archives. At the meeting on February 25, 1915 (RC Minutes, RU 15, Box 3, SI Archives) Lawrence made the favorable comment "that the dry chlorinization patents were directly in the line of the work of the Research Corporation and should be give serious consideration."

45. Several years later Dorsey A. Lyon and Oliver C. Ralston noted in *Innovations in the Metallurgy of Lead*, USBM Bull., No. 157 (Washington, D.C.: GPO, 1918), p. 123: "The Bunker Hill & Sullivan Mining & Concentrating Co., of Kellogg, Idaho, two or three years ago started an experimental plant. . . . The Malm process of dry chloridizing was tried and failed. . . ." For another mention of the process see Charles G. Maier, "Possibilities of Dry Chlorination of Oxidized Zinc Materials," *Engineering and Mining Journal-Press*, 115 (Jan. 13, 1923), 51.

46. Regis Chauvenet, "Hydrometallurgy: Joys of Its Theory, Woes of Its Practice," *MCE*, 11 (Sept. 1913), 486–491. On Chauvenet, see *NCAB*, Vol. 7 (1897), p.

446; *WWW*, Vol. 1 (1942), p. 214; and Spence, *Mining Engineers and the American West*, p. 249.

47. Chauvenet, "Hydrometallurgy: Joys of Its Theory, Woes of Its Practice" (1913), p. 486.

48. Ibid., p. 491.

49. Warren F. Bleecker, "Hydrometallurgy – Joys of Its Theory, Woes of Its Practice," Letter to the Editor, *MCE*, 11 (Oct. 1913), 538.

50. Ibid., p. 539. Bleecker emphasized: "there are certain standard operations, the practice of which the metallurgist may correctly assume to fit into his proposed process without difficulty. Among these may be included crushing, screening, roasting, pulverizing, heating, agitation, decantation, filtration, absorption, drying, sampling, the application of power and electricity, and classes of materials. These things have all been studied and standardized." For historical treatments of the concept of "unit operations" – a term that A. D. Little coined in 1915 – see Martha M. Trescott, "Unit Operations in the Chemical Industry: An American Innovation in Modern Chemical Engineering," in William F. Furter, ed., *A Century of Chemical Engineering* (New York: Plenum Press, 1982), pp. 1–18; Jean-Claude Guédon, "From Unit Operations to Unit Processes: Ambiguities of Success and Failure in Chemical Engineering," in John Parascandola and James C. Whorton, Eds., *Chemistry and Modern Society: Historical Essays in Honor of Aaron J. Ihde* (Washington, D.C.: American Chemical Society, 1983), pp. 43–60; and Clive Cohen, "The Early History of Chemical Engineering: A Reassessment," *British Journal for the History of Science*, 29 (1996), 171–194.

51. Regis Chauvenet, "Hydrometallurgy – Joys of Its Theory, Woes of Its Practice," Letter to the Editor, *MCE*, 11 (Nov. 1913), 602.

52. John L. Malm, "Hydrometallurgy: Joys of Its Theory, Woes of Its Practice," Letter to the Editor, *MCE*, 11 (Dec. 1913), 669.

53. Ibid.

54. Warren F. Bleecker, "Hydrometallurgy – Joys of Its Theory, Woes of Its Practice," Letter to the Editor, *MCE*, 12 (Jan. 1914), 8–10.

55. John L. Malm, "Hydrometallurgy – Joys of Its Practice, Woes of Its Theory," Letter to the Editor, *MCE*, 12 (Feb. 1914), 75. He noted that in 1911 Bleecker had refused his invitation "to accompany a party of engineers ... to inspect the plant under construction. . . ."

56. John L. Malm, "Dry Chloridization of Ores," ibid., pp. 128–129.

57. Forbes Rickard, "Malm Process in Colorado," *Mining and Scientific Press*, 99 (Nov. 13, 1909), 662–663; and brief notices, ibid., 108 (Apr. 4, 1914), 589; and 109 (Dec. 12, 1914), 903.

58. "The Malm Process," *EMJ*, 101 (Apr. 15, 1916), 679. For the earlier report, see W. R. Ingalls, "Metallurgy of Zinc in 1914," ibid., 99 (Jan. 9, 1915), 96.

59. John L. Malm, "The Malm Process," ibid., 101 (May 13, 1916), 864.

60. S. A. Ionides, "The Malm Process," ibid., 865. At about the same time, Ionides

published an article on the process – see S. A. Ionides, "The Dry Chlorination of Complex Ores," *Mining and Scientific Press*, 112 (May 27, 1916), 781–787. In it he described the project's origin (p. 781): "The main development took place in Montana some seven or eight years ago, the experiments carried on by John L. Malm for the late F. Augustus Heinze reaching a stage where the latter was preparing for the erection of a $2,000,000 plant, when the crisis in his affairs caused the project to be dropped." On Ionides, see *WWE*, 5th Ed. (1941), p. 896.

61. Malm, "The Malm Process" (1916), 864.

62. Kathleen H. Ochs, "The Rise of American Mining Engineers: A Case Study of the Colorado School of Mines," *Technology and Culture*, 33 (Apr. 1992), 279–280. More recently, Logan Hovis and Jeremy Mouat have confirmed: "The new emphasis on the expertise of university-trained engineers reflected the transformation of the mining industry, a process that devalued the traditional work practices of the skilled miner" – see their article, "Miners, Engineers, and the Transformation of Work in the Western Mining Industry, 1880–1930," ibid., 37 (July 1996), 429.

63. "Tells of Phthisis Cure," *NYT*, Nov. 7, 1912, p. 1, col. 6. For mention of Friedmann's work, see J. Arthur Myers, *Invited and Conquered: Historical Sketch of Tuberculosis in Minnesota* (St. Paul: Minnesota Public Health Association, 1949), pp. 157–160; and Selman A. Waksman, *The Conquest of Tuberculosis* (Berkeley: University of California Press, 1964), p. 99. On Friedmann, see I. Fischer, ed., *Biographisches Lexikon der hervorragenden Ärzte der letzen fünfzig Jahre*, Vol. 1 (Berlin: Urban and Schwarzenberg, 1932), p. 452.

64. "Dr. Friedmann Here, Bringing His 'Cure,' " *NYT*, Feb. 26, 1913, p. 1, col. 1.

65. "Forbids Friedmann to Treat in Clinics," ibid., Mar. 5, 1913, p. 14, col. 1. For the two possibilities, see "Warn Dr. Friedmann to Observe the Law," ibid., Mar. 4, 1913, p. 1, col. 1.

66. F. G. Cottrell to C. D. Walcott, Mar. 6, 1913, RU 45, Box 47, SI Archives.

67. L. N. Scott to C. D. Walcott, Mar. 7, 1913, RU 51, Box 1, SI Archives.

68. F. G. Cottrell to C. D. Walcott, Mar. 24, 1913, RU 51, Box 1, SI Archives.

69. F. G. Cottrell to Linn Bradley, Mar. 31, 1913, RU 51, Box 1, SI Archives. I have seen nothing to indicate that Friedmann ever replied to Cottrell.

70. F. G. Cottrell to Linn Bradley, Apr. 15, 1913, RU 51, Box 1, SI Archives.

71. "Friedmann Sells for $1,925,000," *NYT*, Apr. 27, 1913, sec. 2, p. 1, col. 1; "Friedmann to Open First Branch Here," ibid., Apr. 28, 1913, p. 4, col. 4; "Friedmann Cure Placed Under Ban," ibid., May 30, 1913, p. 7, col. 1; and "Friedmann Sails Away," ibid., June 18, 1913, p. 9, col. 2.

72. Cameron, *Samaritan of Science*, p. 44 and p. 140. Along these same lines, Buckner Speed recalled from the time when Cottrell was a member of the Berkeley faculty – see his 1919 remarks, "An Appreciation of Dr. Cottrell," pp. 153–154:

> It was a familiar phrase to be heard in the University of California
> anywhere from the botany to the physiology departments when any question of any description came up: "Oh, go over and talk to Cott about it –

he doesn't know anything about the subject but he will put some idea in your head before you have talked with him ten minutes," and this he invariably did.

73. Charles Marchand to C. D. Walcott, Apr. 30, 1912, RU 45, Box 47, SI Archives. On Forwood, see Mary C. Gillett, "William Henry Forwood," *ANB*, Vol. 8 (1999), pp. 281–283.

74. This problem first came to his attention when he was a college student in Paris, attending the lectures of the chemist Berthelot. The patent was Charles Marchand, "Process of Making Sterilized Granulated Meat Fiber," U.S. Patent No. 1,167,193, issued Jan. 4, 1916 (filed Mar. 14, 1907). For a brief description of Marchand's process, see also Charles Marchand to F. G. Cottrell, Nov. 15, 1912, RU 45, Box 47, SI Archives. For a general history of hydrogen peroxide in the nineteenth century, see the introductory chapter of Walter C. Schumb, Charles N. Satterfield, and Ralph L. Wentworth, *Hydrogen Peroxide* (New York: Reinhold Publishing Corp., 1955), pp. 1– 32. For Marchand's career, see the death notice in *NYT*, Jan. 18, 1917, p. 11, col. 3; as well as a more extensive obituary by Charles A. Doremus, "Charles Marchand," *JIEC*, 9 (Mar. 1917), 321; and "Article Appearing in 'San Francisco News Letter & California Advertiser': 'A Genius in Chemical Engineering,' " TS copy, [1917], RU 51, Box 2, SI Archives.

75. C. D. Walcott to Charles Marchand, May 8, 1912, RU 45, Box 47, SI Archives.

76. Linn Bradley to C. D. Walcott, May 12, 1912, RU 51, Box 1, SI Archives.

77. Charles Marchand to Linn Bradley, June 14, 1912, RU 51, Box 1, SI Archives. "The mere fact that the enterprise should be backed by the Smithsonian Institution, through the Research Corporation," Marchand added, "should give the preparation a good send-off, which would induce the most skeptical doctors to investigate it. *Investigation means Endorsement. . . .*"

78. Meeting of the Board of Directors, May 22, 1912, RC Minutes, RU 51, Box 3, SI Archives.

79. For the distribution and evaluation of the samples, see from RU 45, Box 47, SI Archives: C. D. Walcott to Charles Marchand, Dec. 26, 1912; and Charles Marchand to C. D. Walcott, Dec. 28, 1912. See from RU 51, Box 1, SI Archives: A. D. Holmes and C. F. Langworthy, "The Coefficient of Digestibility of a Diet with Meat Powder as the Principle Protein Constituent," n.d. (the cover letter from Langworthy to Walcott is dated May 13, 1913); D. L. Edsall to A. D. Little, May 6, 1913; A. D. Little to C. D. Walcott, Jan. 13, 1913; and N. B. Foster to Linn Bradley, Oct. 31, 1912. For Langworthy's evaluation, see also *Annual Reports of the Department of Agriculture for the Year Ended June 30, 1913*, p. 283. On Langworthy, see *WWWA*, Vol. 1 (1942), p. 704. On Edsall, see Joseph C. Aub, "David Linn Edsall," *DAB*, Supp. 3 (1973), pp. 243–244. On Foster, see *WWWA*, Vol. 1 (1942), p. 417. Walcott's son, Charles Doolittle Walcott, Jr., died on April 7, 1913 — see *Washington Post*, Apr. 8, 1913, p. 3, col. 1.

80. Diary of F. G. Cottrell, Aug. 23, 1912, and Oct. 16, 1912, Cottrell Papers; and F. G. Cottrell to C. D. Walcott, Oct. 17, 1912, RU 45, Box 47, SI Archives. On Sollmann,

see G. P. Jenkins, "Torald Hermann Sollmann," *Dictionary of American Medical Biography* (Westport, Conn.: Greenwood Press, 1984), Vol. 2, p. 705. On O'Hara — the newly appointed administrative secretary to the lab's director, Francis G. Benedict (who was absent at the time of Cottrell's visit) — see Carnegie Institution of Washington, *Yearbook* for 1912, pp. 219–220.

81. F. G. Cottrell to C. D. Walcott, Mar. 5, 1913, RU 45, Box 47, SI Archives; F. G. Cottrell to Linn Bradley, Apr. 15, 1913, RU 51, Box 1, SI Archives; and Diary of F. G. Cottrell, Aug. 6, 1913, Cottrell Papers. On Biddle, see *WWWA*, Vol. 1 (1942), p. 92. On Jaffa, see ibid., p. 627. On Alvarez, see Clark W. Nelson, "Walter Clement Alvarez," *ANB*, Vol 1 (1999), pp. 395–397; and Walter C. Alvarez, *Incurable Physician: An Autobiography* (Englewood Cliffs, N.J.: Prentice-Hall, 1963), especially Chap. 5, "I Get My Special Training as an Internist," pp. 50–77.

82. Charles Marchand to F. G. Cottrell, Nov. 15, 1912, RU 45, Box 47, SI Archives. Much of the existing literature regarding turn-of-the-century food production focuses on the Pure Food and Drug Act of 1906, as well as the role played by Harvey Wiley, the chief chemist for the U.S. Department of Agriculture. See, for example, Jack High and Clayton A. Coppin, "Wiley and the Whiskey Industry: Strategic Behavior in the Passage of the Pure Food Act," *Business History Review*, 62 (Summer 1988), 286–309; and James Harvey Young, *Pure Food: Securing the Federal Food and Drugs Act of 1906* (Princeton: Princeton University Press, 1989).

83. D. L. Edsall to A. D. Little, May 6, 1913, RU 51, Box 1, SI Archives.

84. "Dr. Cottrell, Smoke Wizard, Makes Rich Gift to Nation," *The New York Sun*, Sept. 2, 1917, p. 8. For Edison's reputation, see Wachhorst, *Thomas Alva Edison*, especially Chap. 2, "The Wizard of Menlo Park," pp. 17–46.

85. F. G. Cottrell to C. D. Walcott, Feb. 3, 1913, RU 51, Box 1, SI Archives. Cottrell went on to liken Baekeland to Theodore Roosevelt: "He is a man a good deal of the Roosevelt type and in a general way would have some of the same advantages and possibly be open to some of the same criticisms. In this, I am referring more, perhaps, to slightly ancient history rather than Roosevelt up to date."

86. Ibid. For early references to Baekeland, see the entries for Dec. 10, 1911, and Feb. 1, 1912, Diary of F. G. Cottrell, Cottrell Papers, Box 1. Apparently, some consideration was given to asking Baekeland to serve as president of Research Corporation — see A. D. Little to C. D. Walcott, Mar. 5, 1913, RU 51, Box 1, SI Archives. Equally unsuccessful were the early efforts to make him a director. Finally, he accepted the directorship vacated by Philipp's resignation — see Meeting of the Board of Directors, Jan. 21, 1916, RC Minutes, RU 51, Box 3, SI Archives.

87. "You all know his multifarious activities," he said: "a helping hand here, a word of inspiration there, a cheery hand grasp, with wisdom dissolving away technical difficulties, speech clean, from a heart that thinks no ill of others, the standard of professional ethics carried high where all can approve, and a breadth of scientific grasp and knowledge which illumines whatever his swift mind plays upon" — see E. H. Hooker, "An Appreciation of Dr. Baekeland," *JIEC*, 8 (Feb. 1916), 183. For

Baekeland's work as Hooker's consultant, see Hughes, *Elmer Sperry*, p. 93. On Baekeland, see also Charles F. Kettering, "Leo Hendrik Baekeland: 1863–1944," *Biog. Mem. NAS*, 24 (1947), 281–302; and Anthony N. Stranges and Richard C. Jones, "Leo Hendrik Baekeland," *ANB*, Vol. 1 (1999), pp. 861–864.

88. "Article Appearing in 'San Francisco News Letter & California Advertiser': 'A Genius in Chemical Engineering,' " TS copy, n.d. [1917], RU 51, Box 2, SI Archives.

89. C. D. Walcott to F. G. Cottrell, Oct. 21, 1912, RU 45, Box 47, SI Archives.

90. C. D. Walcott to F. G. Cottrell, Jan. 27, 1913, RU 51, Box 1, SI Archives.

91. F. G. Cottrell to Charles Marchand, Feb. 7, 1913, RU 51, Box 1, SI Archives.

92. F. G. Cottrell to C. D. Walcott, Feb. 3, 1913, RU 51, Box 1, SI Archives. Marchand raised the salary question in a conversation with Cottrell – see Charles Marchand to F. G. Cottrell, Nov. 15, 1912, RU 45, Box 47, SI Archives. "Arrangements on this basis are in existence in France . . . ," he later explained to Walcott – see Charles Marchand to C. D. Walcott, Nov. 26, 1912, RU 45, Box 47, SI Archives.

93. A. D. Little to C. D. Walcott, Dec. 10, 1912, RU 45, Box 47, SI Archives.

94. L. N. Scott to C. D. Walcott, Jan. 24, 1913, RU 51, Box 1, SI Archives.

95. F. G. Cottrell to Linn Bradley, June 20, 1912, RU 51, Box 1, SI Archives; and F. G. Cottrell to C. D. Walcott, Oct. 21, 1912, RU 45, Box 47, SI Archives.

96. C. D. Walcott to F. A Goetze, Apr. 17, 1914, RU 51, Box 1, SI Archives.

97. A. D. Little to C. D. Walcott, Apr. 21, 1914, RU 51, Box 1, SI Archives.

98. Meeting of the Executive Committee, Apr. 28, 1914, RC Minutes, RU 51, Box 3, SI Archives. See also C. D. Walcott to Charles Marchand, May 11, 1914, RU 51, Box 1, SI Archives.

99. C. D. Walcott to F. G. Cottrell, Oct. 21, 1912, RU 45, Box 47, SI Archives.

100. C. D. Walcott to Julius Kruttschnitt, Dec. 21, 1914, RU 51, Box 1, SI Archives.

101. F. G. Cottrell to C. D. Walcott, Apr. 28, 1912, RU 45, Box 47, SI Archives. Regarding Wolf, Cottrell noted: "He was one of the constructing engineers for the U.S. fortifications on the north heads of S[an] F[rancisco] Bay from 1898–1904 and since then has been in private practice in this state." Earlier Wolf had pursued civil engineering studies at MIT – see the "Class of 1895" listing in MIT, *Register of Former Students*, p. 44. On his career, see also *WWE*, 2nd Ed. (1925), p. 2313. The patent involved was probably J. H. G. Wolf, "Concrete Railroad Cross-Tie," U.S. Patent No. 1,195,634, issued Aug. 22, 1916 (filed Sept. 5, 1911). Walcott viewed the project favorably. "Your tie is one of the most promising [ideas] that I have known of . . . ," he wrote Wolf on March 15, 1915 (RU 51, Box 1, SI Archives). If nothing else, Walcott and the others associated with Research Corporation had personal, firsthand knowledge of railroads, because railroads constituted the nation's primary transportation system. Not all such experiences were positive, however. In 1911 Walcott's wife Helen had been killed in a dramatic accident – see "12 Dead and 48 Hurt in Rail Disaster," *Washington Post*, July 12, 1911, p. 1, col. 7. Writing to Research Corporation's tax lawyer, C. J.

Tobin, on August 13, 1917 (Box A14, RC Archives), L. N. Scott noted yet another railroad connection. "The capital of the [Research] Corporation," he commented, "is invested largely in Railroad bonds. . . ."

102. Meeting of the Executive Committee, June 20, 1913, RC Minutes, RU 51, Box 3, SI Archives. For the earlier meetings, see Meetings of the Executive Committee, May 2, 1912, and Dec. 16, 1912, RC Minutes, RU 51, Box 3, SI Archives.

103. "Agreement for Special Research upon the Problem of Concrete Ties," June 9, 1913, Box A14, RC Archives.

104. Meeting of the Executive Committee, Nov. 19, 1914, RC Minutes, RU 51, Box 3, SI Archives. On the work at Riverside, see F. G. Cottrell to F. A. Goetze, June 25, 1914, RU 45, Box 17, SI Archives; and F. A. Goetze to C. D. Walcott, Dec. 14, 1914, RU 51, Box 1, SI Archives.

105. Meetings of the Executive Committee and the Board of Directors, Nov. 19, 1914, RU 51, Box 3, SI Archives. On Parsons, see James Kip Finch, "William Barclay Parsons," *DAB*, Vol. 14 (1934), pp. 276–278. Parsons replaced Kirchhoff, who had resigned due to ill health, see Meeting of the Stockholders, Jan. 16, 1914, RC Minutes, RU 51, Box 3, SI Archives. Parsons himself resigned in early 1917, at which time he was replaced by J. J. Carty – see Meeting of the Board of Directors, Feb. 16, 1917, RC Minutes, RU 51, Box 4, SI Archives. On Carty – an electrical engineer and an early leader of organized research at AT&T– see Robert G. Ferguson, "John Joseph Carty," *ANB*, Vol. 4 (1999), pp. 505–507; and Patrick J. McGrath, *Scientists, Business, and the State, 1890–1960* (Chapel Hill: University of North Carolina, 2002), pp. 19–21.

106. W. B. Parsons to C. D. Walcott, Mar. 9, 1915, RU 51, Box 1, SI Archives.

107. C. D. Walcott to W. B. Parsons, Mar. 11, 1915, RU 51, Box 1, SI Archives.

108. Julius Kruttschnitt to C. D. Walcott, May 14, 1915, RU 51, Box 1, SI Archives. "If the other replies are not more favorable," Hooker wrote Walcott (May 17, 1915, RU 51, Box 1, SI Archives), "I think we had better let the tie business die a natural death." For the early interest of the New Haven Railroad, see Linn Bradley to C. D. Walcott, Dec. 4, 1912, RU 51, Box 1, SI Archives. Research Corporation also approached representatives of the Pennsylvania and Sante Fe Railroads – see E. H. Hooker to Apr. 20, 1915, RU 51, Box 1, SI Archives; and E. H. Hooker to C. D. Walcott, Apr. 29, 1915, RU 51, Box 1, SI Archives. For the altered consensus in the east, see C. D. Walcott to Julius Kruttschnitt, May 21, 1915, RU 51, Box 1, SI Archives.

109. Sherry H. Olson, *The Depletion Myth: A History of Railroad Use of Timber* (Cambridge, Mass.: Harvard University Press, 1971).

110. William H. Sellew, *Railway Maintenance Engineering with Notes on Construction* (New York: D. Van Nostrand, 1915), p. iii. Aggregate railroad mileage in the United States peaked in 1916 at 254,037 miles, and the total number of railroad workers peaked in 1920 at "just over two million" – see John F. Stover, *American Railroads* (Chicago: University of Chicago Press, 1961), p. 146 and p. 176.

111. Sellew, *Railway Maintenance Engineering with Notes on Construction*, p. iv.

112. C. D. Walcott to L. N. Scott, Dec. 12, 1914, RU 51, Box 1, SI Archives. The specific directorship that Walcott had in mind was the one that Meadows had held. In 1915 Meadows's place was filled by George W. Perkins — see Meeting of the Stockholders, Jan. 15, 1915, RC Minutes, RU 51, Box 3, SI Archives. On Perkins — a financier, a Morgan partner, and in 1912 the chairman of the national executive committee of the Progressive Party — see John A. Garraty, "George Walbridge Perkins," *ANB*, Vol. 17 (1999), pp. 343–345; and Roland Marchand, *Creating the Corporate Soul: The Rise of Public Relations and Corporate Imagery in American Big Business* (Berkeley: University of California Press, 1998), pp. 22–24.

113. C. D. Walcott to Julius Kruttschnitt, Dec. 21, 1914, RU 51, Box 1, SI Archives. On Kruttschnitt, see *NCAB*, Vol. 25 (1936), p. 196.

114. O. H. Kahn to C. D. Walcott, Dec. 31, 1914, RU 51, Box 1, SI Archives. For Kahn's formal election — which was made possible by L. N. Scott's resignation — see Meeting of the Board of Directors, Mar. 3, 1915, RC Minutes, RU 51, Box 3, SI Archives. On Kahn, see William Weisberger, "Otto Herman Kahn," *ANB*, Vol. 12 (1999), pp. 342–344. It was Hooker who had first approached both Kahn and Perkins — see E. H. Hooker to C. D. Walcott, Dec. 21, 1914, RU 51, Box 1, SI Archives.

115. Meeting of the Board of Directors, Mar. 3, 1915, RC Minutes, RU 51, Box 3, SI Archives. Hooker's perception was not unique. At the annual meetings of the American Railway Engineering Association, for example, a special committee on ties regularly reported various efforts to study the matter — see "Index to Proceedings, American Railway Engineering Association, Showing History of Metal, Composite, and Concrete Ties," *Proceedings of the Sixteenth Annual Convention of the American Railway Engineering Association . . . 1915* (Chicago: American Railway Engineering Association, 1915), pp. 536–537.

116. F. G. Cottrell to C. D. Walcott, Feb. 3, 1913, RU 51, Box 1, SI Archives.

117. F. G. Cottrell to C. D. Walcott, Dec. 4, 1914, RU 45, Box 47, SI Archives.

118. F. G. Cottrell to C. D. Walcott, Feb. 17, 1913, RU 45, Box 47, SI Archives.

119. C. D. Walcott to Charles Marchand, Oct. 24, 1916, RU 51, Box 2, SI Archives.

120. Charles Marchand to C. D. Walcott, Apr. 10, 1915, RU 51, Box 1, SI Archives. In his letter Marchand explained his motives and elaborated his plans:

> As I strongly believe that the accumulation of great wealth in the hands of the few is a menace to the social and economic well-being of mankind, it has been agreed between me and my friends Drs. [Emile F.] Pernot and [Leroy] Huntley, that should the net income from my discovery exceed the average sum of $1,000,000.00 per year for each one of us, that three-fourths (3/4) of the annual surplus shall be spent and employed in various ways conducive to the relief of the deserving, needy, and unfortunate, the plans and details for the distribution of said funds to be worked out and applied by us and under my supervision.

At the time, Marchand resided in Portland, Oregon, and his letter bore the letterhead of the Pernot Laboratories which listed him as a member of the staff. On Emile Francis Pernot, the lab's director, see *NCAB*, Vol. 21 (1931), p. 322. For a preliminary installation of Marchand's new process by the Kimberly-Clark Paper Company in Wisconsin, see "Alcohol from Waste Sulphite Liquor," *MCE*, 14 (June 1, 1916), 669.

121. Meeting of the Executive Committee, Nov. 18, 1915, RC Minutes, RU 51, Box 3, SI Archives.

122. Ibid.

123. Meeting of the Board of Directors, Feb. 16, 1917, RC Minutes, RU 51, Box 4, SI Archives.

124. On November 4, 1914, Lawrence wrote Walcott (RU 45, Box 47, SI Archives): "Personally, I am of the opinion that any income which we may derive from these patents of Dr. Cottrell's should be devoted in large part — if not altogether — to research work along metallurgical lines in co-operation with the smelting works to which we have sold our rights."

125. F. G. Cottrell to C. D. Walcott, Dec. 4, 1914, RU 45, Box 47, SI Archives.

126. O. P. Hood, "Discussion," at the end of Bradley, "Electrical Precipitation of Suspended Particles" (1913), p. 128. On Hood, see *WWWA*, Vol. 1 (1942), p. 584.

127. Little, "Industrial Research in America" (1913), p. 800. "Of all that has been said about the founding of the Research Corporation, I may truthfully say that your expression in regard to it in this paper has pleased and touched me most of all," Cottrell wrote Little on January 7, 1914 (RU 51, Box 1, SI Archives).

128. "Dinner to Frederick G. Cottrell," *MCE*, 13 (Feb. 1915), 82. A copy of the banquet program was found in Box A14, RC Archives. On Jennings — who was a mining engineer, vice-president of United States Smelting, Refining, and Mining Co., and Hennen Jennings's brother — see *NCAB*, Vol. 26 (1937), p. 326. On Saunders — an engineer who joined Ingersoll Rock Drill Co. in 1882 and who presided over its expansion into Ingersoll-Rand — see *NCAB*, Vol. 26 (1937), p. 81. Besides Walcott, other speakers that evening were F. Austin Lidbury, who represented the American Electrochemical Society, and Walter Renton Ingalls, who represented the Mining and Metallurgical Society of America.

129. Meeting of the Board of Directors, Jan. 15, 1915, RC Minutes, RU 51, Box 3, SI Archives; also quoted in "Dinner to Frederick G. Cottrell" (1915), p. 81; and in "The Cottrell Dinner," *EMJ*, 99 (Jan. 23, 1915), 199.

130. Meeting of the Executive Committee, Nov. 18, 1915, RC Minutes, RU 51, Box 3, SI Archives.

131. Meeting of the Board of Directors, Mar. 3, 1915, and Meeting of the Executive Committee, Nov. 18, 1915, RC Minutes, RU 51, Box 3, SI Archives. As an example of Cottrell's earlier interest, see F. G. Cottrell to C. D. Walcott, Feb. 28, 1912, RU 45, Box 47, SI Archives.

132. For Cottrell's activities in this period, see Cameron, *Samaritan of Science*, pp. 177–182 and pp. 184–186. On the Anaconda Smelter Commission, see also "Ana-

conda Co. Gives In," *NYT*, May 2, 1911, p. 6, col. 4; Linn Bradley, "Memorandum," Sept. 1–3, 1914, RU 51, Box 1, SI Archives; John Hays Hammond, *The Autobiography of John Hays Hammond* (New York: Farrar & Rinehart, 1935), Vol. 2, pp. 562–563; and LeCain, "The Limits of 'Eco-Efficiency' " (2000), pp. 341–343.

133. On the Panama-Pacific International Exposition, generally, see Robert W. Rydell, *All the World's a Fair: Visions of Empire at American International Expositions, 1876–1916* (Chicago: University of Chicago Press, 1984), pp. 208–233. For the Bureau of Mines exhibits, see Frank Morton Todd, *The Story of the Exposition, Being the Official History of the International Celebration Held at San Francisco in 1915 . . .* (New York: G. P. Putnam's Sons, 1921), Vol. 4, pp. 193–204. That same volume included a description of C. H. Thordarson's efforts to install the millon-volt transformer (pp. 184–187). For details of the technical work, see F. G. Cottrell to C. D. Walcott, June 27, 1914, RU 45, Box 17, SI Archives; Cottrell, "Electrostatic Precipitation: Historical Sketch" (1915), pp. 394–395; F. G. Cottrell to Linn Bradley, Oct. 23, 1915, USBM Records, 1915; and F. G. Cottrell, "Discussion," at the end of Aldrich, "Treatment of Silver Fume by the Cottrell Process," (1916), pp. 128–135. For reference to the final report, see F. G. Cottrell to C. D. Walcott, May 17, 1916, RU 45, Box 47, SI Archives. In addition to support from Research Corporation, the Smithsonian provided $2,000 (from the Hodgkins Fund) — see "Proceedings of the Board of Regents of the Smithsonian Institution," Dec. 9, 1915, and Dec. 14, 1916, RU 1, SI Archives.

134. H. R. Carveth to A. D. Little, Nov. 14, 1914, RU 51, Box 1, SI Archives. On Carveth, see *WWWA*, Vol. 2 (1950), p. 106. Bancroft's journal was important outlet for research in the new field of physical chemistry. Articles by Cottrell, for example, had appeared in the volumes for 1898, 1900, 1906, and 1914.

135. H. R. Carveth to A. D. Little, Nov. 14, 1914, RU 51, Box 1, SI Archives.

136. An article on "Scientific Journals and the Public" in *Popular Science Monthly*, 87 (Sept. 1915), noted (p. 310): "There are over a hundred journals and proceedings devoted to the publication of research work in America, not one of which pays its expenses on a regular basis."

137. Meeting of the Board of Directors, Nov. 19, 1914, RC Minutes, RU 51, Box 3, SI Archives.

138. J. B. Pine to A. D. Little, Nov. 20, 1914, Box A14, RC Archives. On the publishing activities of the Wistar Institute, see Margaret P. O'Neill Davis, "The Wistar Institute of Anatomy and Biology," in Joseph C. Kiger, ed., *Research Institutions and Learned Societies*, Greenwood Encyclopedia of American Institutions, Vol. 5 (Westport, Conn.: Greenwood Press, 1982), p. 484.

139. C. D. Walcott to A. D. Little, Nov. 23, 1914, RU 51, Box 1, SI Archives. Several days later Little responded (Nov. 28, 1914, RU 51, Box 1, SI Archives):

> I can, of course, readily understand the reasons which led the Board
> to its decision regarding the Journal of Physical Chemistry, and, in view
> of the outline of the arguments which Mr. Pine sent me and the ques-

tions of general policy involved, I am inclined to think that had I been present I would have been persuaded to vote with the Board. If, however, the Corporation had been in position and inclined to make the grant it would undoubtedly have been a worthy and useful one.

140. C. D. Walcott to C. L. Parsons, Nov. 23, 1914, RU 51, Box 1, SI Archives. On Parsons, see *NCAB*, Vol. 47 (1965), pp. 49–50.

141. C. L. Parsons to C. D. Walcott, Nov. 24, 1914, RU 51, Box 1, SI Archives.

142. Ibid.

143. "By articulating and promoting an agenda for physical chemistry that was at odds with the dominant tradition in the discipline," Servos wrote (*Physical Chemistry from Ostwald to Pauling*, p. 201), "Bancroft imposed upon himself the burden of maintaining the *Journal of Physical Chemistry*. It was the one forum in which he, and other physical chemists who dissented from orthodoxy, could freely argue their case."

144. Ibid., pp. 315–321. See also S. C. Lind, "*The Journal of Physical and Colloid Chemistry*," in Browne and Weeks, *A History of the American Chemical Society*, pp. 420–421. Lind succeeded Bancroft's as the journal's editor.

145. L. N. Scott to F. G. Cottrell, Jan. 11, 1916, USBM Records, 1916. Hooker too encouraged Cottrell to think more concretely about how they should proceed. From Hooker's point of view, what was needed was not a general statement of purpose (which already appeared in the firm's certificate of incorporation) but specific "policy . . . for the coming year" (E. H. Hooker to F. G. Cottrell, Jan. 18, 1916, USBM Records, 1916).

146. F. G. Cottrell to L. N. Scott, Jan. 19, 1916, USBM Records, 1916.

147. J. B. Pine to E. H. Hooker, Dec. 15, 1916, RU 51, Box 2, SI Archives. The American Academy in Rome, which Charles F. McKim established in 1894, offered several fellowships — see Lucia Valentine and Alan Valentine, *The American Academy in Rome, 1894–1969* (Charlottesville: University Press of Virginia, 1973); and American Academy in Rome, *Annual Report*, 1916–1917. These fellowships amounted to $1,000 a year for three years. In addition, fellows received accommodations in Rome.

148. Meeting of the Board of Directors, Feb. 16, 1917, RC Minutes, RU 51, Box 4, SI Archives. Earlier Walcott explained to Pine (Jan. 8, 1917, Box A14, RC Archives):

> Frankly, I do not think much of fellowships, as from the results of many years' experience in connection with research work I have found that when you find a man who has something worth doing it is better to assist him directly than to offer a fellowship open to all. It might be well for you to correspond with Dr. R. S. Woodward, President of the Carnegie Institution of Washington, who has had wide experience at Columbia University and in the Carnegie Institution in connection with fellowships and grants for research.

For a discussion of Woodward's experiences at the Carnegie Institution of Washington, see Reingold, "National Science Policy in a Private Foundation: The Carnegie Institution of Washington" (1979), especially pp. 318–324.

149. The fellowship idea figured into the ongoing efforts to exempt Research Corporation from payment of state taxes. "When you were last in Albany you spoke to me about sending me some data as to scholarships given by the Research Corporation . . . ," Charles J. Tobin wrote Pine on March 26, 1917 (Box A14, RC Archives). The next day Scott replied (Mar. 27, 1917, Box A14, RC Archives): "We herewith enclose a copy of resolution adopted by the Executive Committee for the creation of this fellowship and trust that it is what you need."

150. F. G. Cottrell to E. H. Hooker, Apr. 10, 1917, RU 45, Box 47, SI Archives. In his letter, Cottrell noted that he had not yet consulted Walcott on the matter.

151. "The Research Corporation," *Science*, 46 (Aug. 10, 1917), 132. The wording of the fellowship's purpose had been left deliberately broad. Thus Hooker wrote Pine on June 30, 1917 (Box A14, RC Archives):

> I am entirely in accord with the idea of using the Fellowship in something dealing with military efficiency of the United States. . . . I think, however, with Dr. Cottrell, that it is unnecessary and probably more desirable not to so state in these permanent documents, but to leave the description general and simply act in that direction in making the award.
>
> This I think . . . meets Dr. Cottrell's objection by not committing us away from the arts of peace or narrowing the field under consideration.

152. C. D. Walcott to L. N. Scott, Nov. 2, 1917, RU 51, Box 8, SI Archives. Walcott served as president of the National Academy of Sciences from 1917 to 1923. On Bartsch, see *WWWA*, Vol. 4 (1968), p. 62.

153. From RU 51, Box 8, SI Archives, see L. N. Scott to C. D. Walcott, Nov. 12, 1917; C. D. Walcott to L. N. Scott, Nov. 16, 1917; Julius Stieglitz to L. N. Scott, Dec. 3, 1917; and E. H. Hooker to L. N. Scott, Dec. 11, 1917. In the same location are 23 completed applications. The original total was probably higher, for I have come across at least one case where the application materials were afterward returned to the applicant (A. F. Meston to W. W. Strong, Mar. 30, 1918, Box A19, RC Archives). Walcott's other recommendation was Archer Bell Stuart, who had worked in H. J. Ryan's electrical engineering laboratory at Stanford and who proposed a study of high-frequency electrical arcs. On Stieglitz, see Albert B. Costa, "Julius Stieglitz," *ANB*, Vol. 20 (1999), pp. 767–768. One of the names Hooker added was Monroe Work, an African-American educator who proposed to study the role of African-Americans in industrial development. On Monroe Nathan Work, see Joseph J. Boris, ed., *Who's Who in Colored America* (New York: Who's Who in Colored America Corp., 1927), Vol. 1, p. 229.

154. Undated TS note attached to P. E. Edelman, "Application for a Fellowship," Oct. 10, 1917, RU 51, Box 8, SI Archives. On Stratton, who had become the first director of the National Bureau of Standards in 1901, see Nelson R. Kellogg, "Samuel

Wesley Stratton," *ANB*, Vol. 21 (1999), pp. 2–3. On Austin – who joined the National Bureau of Standards in 1904 and headed the navy's radio research lab there since 1908 – see Lyman J. Briggs, "Louis Winslow Austin," *Science*, 76 (Aug. 12, 1932), 137. Although I have been unable to locate the documents that Edelman submitted to support his application, they apparently included a list of his publications and patents and a letter of recommendation from H. A. Erikson, the head of Minnesota's physics department. For the action of the jury, see C. D. Walcott to L. N. Scott, Dec. 14, 1917, RU 51, Box 8, SI Archives; and L. N. Scott to C. D. Walcott, Jan. 2, 1918, RU 51, Box 8, SI Archives. On Edelman, see also *AMS*, 4th ed. (1927), p. 276.

155. L. N. Scott to C. D. Walcott, Jan. 2, 1918, RU 51, Box 8, SI Archives. On Pupin, see Alois F. Kovarik, "Michael Idvorsky Pupin," *DAB*, Supp. 1 (1944), pp. 611–615. As Pupin himself explained in his autobiography – see Michael I. Pupin, *From Immigrant to Inventor* (New York: Scribners, 1924), pp. 363–369 – the Engineering Foundation was the result of a gift of $200,000 in 1914 (later increased) from Ambrose Swasey, a manufacturer of high-quality machine tools and large telescopes. Based on Swasey's gift, the United Engineering Society created the Engineering Foundation in New York to promote the United Engineering Society's mandate of "advancing the engineering arts and science in all their branches" (ibid., p. 364). In Pupin's eyes, Andrew Carnegie's support of the United Engineering Society and Swasey's gift both illustrated "the same motives of idealism which had guided the great men of revolutionary times when they organized the United States" (ibid., pp. 365–366). On the origins and early history of the Engineering Foundation (which supported the National Research Council during the first year of its existence), see also "The Engineering Foundation," *Journal of the American Society of Mechanical Engineers*, 37 (Feb. 1915), III–X; and Lance E. Metz and Ivan M. Viest, *The First 75 Years: A History of the Engineering Foundation* (New York: Engineering Foundation, 1991), pp. 1–44.

156. C. D. Walcott to L. N. Scott, Jan. 7, 1918, RU 51, Box 8, SI Archives.

157. P. E. Edelman, "Memorandum," Jan. 8, 1918, RU 51, Box 8, SI Archives. Shortly after the U.S. entered World War I, Harvard offered to let the navy use its recently created electrical laboratory – the Cruft Laboratory – for a radio training school, and the program very quickly expanded to more than a thousand trainees; see G. W. Pierce, "The Cruft Laboratory," in *Annual Report of the President of Harvard University, 1916–1917*, pp. 213–214; Julian Lowell Coolidge, "Naval Training at Harvard," *Harvard Graduates' Magazine*, 26 (Dec. 1917), 202–204; and Samuel Eliot Morison, *Three Centuries of Harvard, 1636–1936* (Cambridge, Mass.: Harvard University Press, 1936), p. 458. For overviews of the wartime radio work at the Bureau of Standards, see National Bureau of Standards, *War Work of the Bureau of Standards*, Miscellaneous Publication No. 46 (Washington, D.C.: GPO, 1921), pp. 222–245; and Cochrane, *Measures for Progress*, pp. 191–199.

158. P. E. Edelman to C. D. Walcott, Jan. 29, 1918, RU 51, Box 8, SI Archives. For

Walcott's suggestion of Minnesota, see C. D. Walcott to E. H. Hooker, Jan. 24, 1918, RU 51, Box 8, SI Archives; and C. D. Walcott to P. E. Edelman, Jan. 29, 1918, RU 51, Box 8, SI Archives. Along the way, Hooker informed Edelman that Walcott would serve as his official advisor — see E. H. Hooker to P. E. Edelman, Jan. 24, 1918, RU 51, Box 8, SI Archives. For the general disruption at the Minnesota campus caused by the country's entry into the war, see James Gray, *The University of Minnesota, 1851–1951* (Minneapolis: University of Minnesota Press, 1951), pp. 244–245.

159. C. D. Walcott to E. H. Hooker, Feb. 28, 1918, RU 51, Box 8, SI Archives. Thus we are reminded that Walcott tended to view true research as inherently altruistic.

160. B. B. Lawrence to C. D. Walcott, Apr. 1, 1918, RU 51, Box 8, SI Archives. Regarding Edelman, Lawrence noted: "I saw Prof. Pupin, and he told me confidentially that the man had made a very bad impression at Columbia, and that they would not have him up there under any circumstances."

161. C. D. Walcott to B. B. Lawrence, Apr. 3, 1918, RU 51, Box 8, SI Archives. Writing to Hooker (Feb. 28, 1918, RU 51, Box 8, SI Archives), Walcott was even more succinct: "[Edelman's] case is an illustration of the difficulty of sizing up a man from papers and recommendations."

162. For assessments of the NRC fellowship program, see Daniel J. Kevles, *The Physicists: The History of a Scientific Community in Modern America* (New York: Knopf, 1978), pp. 197–199; and Robert E. Kohler, "Science, Foundations, and American Universities in the 1920s," *Osiris*, 2nd Ser., Vol. 3 (1987), 135–164.

163. C. D. Walcott to R. S. Griffin, Apr. 2, 1918, RU 51, Box 8, SI Archives; P. E. Edelman to C. D. Walcott, Apr. 15, 1918, RU 51, Box 8, SI Archives; and Meeting of the Executive Committee, Dec. 3, 1918, RC Minutes, RU 51, Box 4, SI Archives. On Griffin, see Allan Westcott, "Robert Stanislaus Griffin," *DAB*, Supp. 1 (1944), p. 361. For brief mention of the Bureau of Steam Engineering's radio work, see Susan J. Douglas, "Technological Innovation and Organizational Change: The Navy's Adoption of Radio, 1899–1919," in Merritt Roe Smith, ed., *Military Enterprise and Technological Change: Perspectives on the American Experience* (Cambridge, Mass.: MIT Press, 1985), p. 152 and pp. 164–165.

164. L. N. Scott to C. D. Walcott, Oct. 17, 1917, RU 51, Box 2, SI Archives. For Goetze's report, see Meeting of the Executive Committee, Sept. 27, 1917, RC Minutes, RU 51, Box 4, SI Archives.

165. L. N. Scott to C. D. Walcott, Oct. 17, 1917, RU 51, Box 2, SI Archives.

166. After the war, Scott prepared the official report of the Naval Consulting Board's work — see Lloyd N. Scott, *Naval Consulting Board of the United States* (Washington, D. C.: GPO, 1920). For NACA's wartime efforts, see Alex Roland, *Model Research: The National Advisory Committee for Aeronautics, 1915–1958* (Washington, D.C.: National Aeronautics and Space Administration, 1985), Vol. 1, pp. 27–49. For Cottrell's wartime work, see Cameron, *Samaritan of Science*, pp. 186–195.

167. W. W. Strong to Linn Bradley, Mar. 31, 1913, Box A19, RC Archives.

168. W. W. Strong to "Pres. Research Corporation," Apr. 9, 1914, Box A19, RC Archives.

169. On Ames, a physicist and later president of the Johns Hopkins University, see Daniel J. Kevles, "Joseph Sweetman Ames," *DSB*, Vol. 1 (1970), pp. 132–133. On Jones, see J. Sam Guy, "Harry Clary Jones," ibid., Vol. 10 (1933), pp. 173–174; and Servos, *Physical Chemistry from Ostwald to Pauling*, pp. 75–78. For explicit mention of Strong in connection with a grant from the Carnegie Institution of Washington (which was one in a series to Jones), see Carnegie Institution of Washington *Yearbook* for 1911, p. 16 and p. 217. The spectroscopic studies were conducted in the university's Physical Laboratory – see Harry C. Jones and W. W. Strong, *The Absorption Spectra of Solutions of Comparatively Rare Salts* . . . (Washington, D.C.: Carnegie Institution of Washington, 1911), p. vi.

170. For the end date of Strong's service at the Mellon Institute, see Personnel Card File, MI Papers. His personnel card also gave his address as the Institute of Agricultural Research, in Mechanicsburg. For Strong's position with the new company, see "William Walker Strong," *NCAB*, Vol. E (1938), p. 382. The earliest letter on company letterhead that I have seen was W. W. Strong to "Pres. Research Corporation," Apr. 9, 1914, Box A19, RC Archives. Listed on the letterhead were products the company offered to make: "Transformers, motors, generators, high voltage apparatus, farm electrical apparatus, precipitation apparatus, smoke indicators, smoke monitors, smoke recorders, electric bells, electric clocks, radiomicrometers, electrostatic machines, electroscopes, etc., etc." The company was a small outfit. Thus the entry in Alfred D. Flinn and Ruth Cobb, "Research Laboratories in Industrial Research Establishments of the United States," *Bulletin of the National Research Council*, No. 16 (Dec. 1921), p. 70, characterized the staff as "W. W. Strong and 1 or 2 skilled men." That same source listed the company's areas of research as "ionization of gases, precipitation of fumes, deblooming oil, nitrogen fixation, diamond surfaced glass, smoke and fume recorders and masks, etc." (p. 71).

171. W. W. Strong to Linn Bradley, Apr. 27, 1915, Box A19, RC Archives. "I was very much interested to learn that the Institute is putting in a new 200,000 volt 100 K.W. transformer," Bradley replied on May 13, 1915 (Box A19, RC Archives). "As you say, this certainly will give exceptional advantages for high tension experiments." On Leete, who served as dean of the College of Engineering from 1909 to 1917, see Arthur Wilson Tarbell, *The Story of Carnegie Tech, Being a History of Carnegie Institute of Technology from 1900 to 1935* (Pittsburgh: Carnegie Institute of Technology, 1937), pp. 54–55.

172. W. W. Strong to Research Corporation, Feb. 14, 1916, Box A19, RC Archives. Because the new generator had not yet arrived, Strong wrote, "I am limited to the 26,000 volt transformer here. . . ." The health problems of Strong's parents were mentioned in W. W. Strong to Linn Bradley, Sept. 9 and Nov. 8, 1915, Box A19, RC Archives. On April 26, 1916, Linn Bradley informed W. A. Schmidt (Box A19, RC Archives) "that Dr. Strong has found it necessary to remain in Mechanicsburg for

some time yet on account of his father and that we are paying him a salary to conduct certain investigations for us. . . ." The *NCAB* entry on Strong listed the period of his formal association with Research Corporation as 1915–1919. The "General Salaries Account [for the] Year Ending December 31, 1915" appended to the minutes of the Stockholders Meeting on Jan. 21, 1916 (RC Minutes, RU 51, Box 3, SI Archives) listed Strong's salary as $304.15, while the "Salaries [for the] Year Ending December 31, 1916" appended to the minutes of the Stockholders Meeting on Feb. 16, 1917 (RC Minutes, RU 51, Box 4, SI Archives) listed his salary as $1,550. The difference in these two figures suggests that Strong began working for Research Corporation late in 1915.

173. W. W. Strong to Research Corporation, Feb. 14, 1916, Box A19, RC Archives. For Strong's plans, see also his 10-page typescript attached to a cover letter to Linn Bradley, dated March 30, 1916 (RU 51, Box 2, SI Archives).

174. W. W. Strong to Research Corporation, Feb. 14, 1916, Box A19, RC Archives. "The problem is not as big as it looks," he added, by way of reassurance, "and once the experimental equipment is gotten much of this data can be taken very quickly."

175. Ibid.

176. W. A. Schmidt to Linn Bradley, Apr. 20, 1916, Box A19, RC Archives.

177. Ibid. The paper in question was entitled "The Space Charge Effect." Schmidt noted that he would also be discussing it with his Western Precipitation colleague, E. R. Wolcott, and on April 25, 1916, Wolcott submitted his assessment (E. R. Wolcott to Research Corporation, Box A19, RC Archives). Echoing Schmidt's views, he wrote: "The difficulty of making calculations that apply to actual treater conditions is greatly enhanced by the large number of variables to be considered."

178. Linn Bradley to W. A. Schmidt, Apr. 26, 1916, Box A19, RC Archives.

179. Ibid.

180. Ibid.

181. Ibid. Although Bradley favored Schmidt's approach, in a letter to Strong (Nov. 22, 1916, Box A19, RC Archives), he also indicated that supporting *two* programs was likely to work to Research Corporation's advantage: "It will be interesting to learn the results that both of you obtain independently. In some ways this is very desirable on research work of this kind as one or the other may develop important things which have escaped the attention of the other party."

182. Evald Anderson, "Recent Progress in Electrical Precipitation," *Chemical and Metallurgical Engineering*, 26 (Jan. 25, 1922), 151.

183. Ibid. Although both approaches continued to be important, the engineering side tended to dominate. Thus H. J. White noted in his 1984 article, "The Art and the Science of Electrostatic Precipitation" (p. 1163): "a common saying in vogue when I first started precipitation work [was] that 'precipitation is more of an art than a science.' "

184. Linn Bradley to W. A. Schmidt, Apr. 26, 1916, Box A19, RC Archives (emphasis added).

185. Thus he wrote Bradley (Apr. 1, 1916, Box A16, RC Archives): ". . . with the present organization and with the equipment gradually becoming available I believe the Research Corporation could do for $2,000 per annum what it would require the War Department to spend say $10,000 per annum."

186. Linn Bradley to W. W. Strong, April 18, 1916, Box A19, RC Archives.

187. C. D. Walcott to Linn Bradley, Apr. 27, 1916, Box A19, RC Archives. "I thoroughly agree with the thoughts expressed . . . in your letter . . . ," Bradley replied (Apr. 29, 1916, RU 51, Box 2, SI Archives). He then summarized what had emerged as the consensus view: "Dr. Strong has a very fertile imagination and one of the major problems in connection with our present research work and facilities is to properly direct those working along academic lines so as to avoid suppressing ideas which may be found of practical value to the corporation and thus to the public."

188. Specifically, he noted (C. D. Walcott to Linn Bradley, Apr. 27, 1916, Box A19, RC Archives): "It does not seem to us that the data thus far furnished by Dr. Strong justifies taking up the question with any of the Government Departments."

189. On May 25, 1916, Bradley wrote Strong (Box A19, RC Archives): "Prof. [H. F.] Fischer soon expects to have his work far enough along that he can run down to Mechanicsburg sometime either alone or with me and we can then get together and make more thorough plans for the advancement of the Research work."

190. Linn Bradley to W. W. Strong, July 19, 1916, Box A19, RC Archives.

191. A. F. Meston to W. W. Strong, May 15, 1917, Box A19, RC Archives.

192. Ibid.

193. For Sperry's work, as well as an account of how the Naval Consulting Board was formed, see Hughes, *Elmer Sperry*, pp. 244–258.

194. W. W. Strong to A. F. Meston, n.d. (received by Research Corporation, May 18, 1917), Box A19, RC Archives.

195. A. F. Meston to W. W. Strong, June 2, 1917, Box A19, RC Archives.

196. On Durand's career, see Frederick E. Terman, "William Frederick Durand: March 5, 1859–August 9, 1958," *Biog. Mem. NAS*, 48 (1976), 153–193. For Durand's NRC position and the formation of the group at Nahant, see Robert A. Millikan, *The Autobiography of Robert A. Millikan* (New York: Prentice-Hall, 1950), pp. 137–145. On the Nahant group and the NRC work at New London, see also Dupree, *Science in the Federal Goverment*, pp. 318–319; Kevles, *The Physicists*, pp. 118–126; and Wise, *Willis R. Whitney*, p. 187–194.

197. A. F. Meston to W. W. Strong, June 2, 1917, Box A19, RC Archives.

198. Ibid.

199. W. W. Strong to A. F. Meston, June 8, 1917, Box A19, RC Archives.

200. In the preface to his book, *The New Science of the Fundamental Physics* (Mechanicsburg, Pa.: Scientific Instrument and Electrical Machine Co., 1918), Strong noted (p. vii): "The author wishes to record that the formation of the Research Corporation by Dr. F. G. Cottrell appears as an important step toward the time when the

ambitions and dreams of our youth will be for knowledge and truth and the employment of wealth will be for the realization of all those visions that experience inti-
mates will be for the uplift of all." The preface was dated "March 8–June 7, 1918."

201. A. F. Meston to E. P. Dillon, July 1, 1918, Box A19, RC Archives.

202. Linn Bradley to W. W. Strong, July 5, 1918, Box A19, RC Archives.

203. Ibid. At the board of directors meeting on January 17, 1919 (RC Minutes, RU
51, Box 4, SI Archives), Dillon justified the move: "This gives us a modest machine
shop for a limited amount of manufacture, as well as maintaining our test equipment." On the facilities at St. Pauls Ave., see also the entry for Research Corporation
in Flinn and Cobb, "Research Laboratories in Industrial Establishments of the United
States" (1921), p. 68.

204. W. W. Strong, *The New Philosophy of Modern Science* (York, Pa.: Kyle Publishing Co., 1920), p. 181.

205. Ibid., p. 185.

206. Ibid., p. 184.

207. Ibid., p. 185. In 1913 Johannes Stark discovered that spectral lines can be
split by an electric field, which won him a Nobel Prize for physics in 1919 – see
Armin Hermann, "Johannes Stark," *DSB*, Vol. 12 (1975), pp. 614–615; and Alan D.
Beyerchen, *Scientists under Hitler: Politics and the Physics Community in the Third
Reich* (New Haven: Yale University Press, 1977), pp. 103–106.

208. Strong, *The New Philosophy of Modern Science*, p. 186.

209. Ibid., pp. 182–186.

210. Ibid., p. 186. For example, he pursued his doctoral research at his
Mechanicsburg home as well as at Johns Hopkins – see W. W. Strong, "Ionization in
Closed Vessels," *Physical Review*, 27 (July 1908), 46 and passim.

Chapter Six—Conclusion
PAGES 157–190

1. Francis Bacon, *New Atlantis*, Great Books of the Western World, Vol. 30 (Chicago: Encyclopedia Britannica, 1952), pp. 199–214.

2. As Joseph Ben-David has suggested in *The Scientist's Role in Society: A Comparative Study* (Englewood Cliffs, N.J.: Prentice-Hall, 1971), what Bacon offered was less
an organizational model, as such, and more "a valid strategy of conduct for scientists"
(p. 73). "By sticking to empirically verified facts...," Ben-David explained, "the
[Baconian] method enabled its practitioners to feel like members of the same 'community,' even in the absence of a commonly accepted theory" (p. 74).

3. Jonathan Swift, *Gulliver's Travels*, Great Books of the Western World, Vol. 36
(Chicago: Encyclopaedia Britannica, 1952), pp. 1–184.

4. Ibid., p. 107. For an assessment of this portion of *Gulliver's Travels*, see Marjorie

Nicolson and Nora M. Mohler, "The Scientific Background of Swift's 'Voyage to Laputa,'" *Annals of Science*, 2 (July 15, 1937), 299–334, especially 319–332.

5. David C. Mowery and Nathan Rosenberg, "The U.S. National Innovation System," in Richard R. Nelson, ed., *National Innovation Systems: A Comparative Analysis* (New York: Oxford University Press, 1993), pp. 29–75.

6. See, for example, Thomas P. Hughes, *Rescuing Prometheus* (New York: Pantheon Books, 1998).

7. See, for example, Peter Galison and Bruce Hevly, eds., *Big Science: The Growth of Large-Scale Research* (Stanford: Stanford University Press, 1992).

8. David H. Guston and Kenneth Keniston, "Introduction: The Social Contract for Science," in David H. Guston and Kenneth Keniston, eds., *The Fragile Contract: University Science and the Federal Government* (Cambridge, Mass.: MIT Press, 1994), p. 1.

9. "The Treasures: America's Scientific Institutions Are the Envy of the World," *Time*, 127 (June 16, 1986), 34.

10. Roger L. Geiger, *To Advance Knowledge: The Growth of American Research Universities, 1900–1940* (New York: Oxford University Press, 1986), pp. 1–93. For the funding needs of academic researchers at the turn of the century, see also Howard Plotkin, "Edward C. Pickering and the Endowment of Scientific Research in America, 1877–1918, *Isis*, 69 (Mar. 1978), 44–57.

11. A. O. Leuschner, "The Organization and Budget of the Graduate School and Its Relation to the Other Schools of the University," *Journal of Proceedings and Addresses . . .* (of the Association of American Universities), 17 (1915), 41. On Leuschner, an astronomer on the faculty at Berkeley who had known Cottrell when Cottrell was an undergraduate, see Donald E. Osterbrock, "Armin Otto Leuschner," *ANB*, Vol. 13 (1999), pp. 531–532; and Cameron, *Samaritan of Science*, pp. 52–53.

12. Leuschner, "The Organization and Budget of the Graduate School and Its Relation to the Other Schools of the University" (1915), pp. 41–42.

13. Ibid., p. 42.

14. For the debate at the turn of the century, see George H. Daniels, "The Pure-Science Ideal and Democratic Culture," *Science*, 156 (June 30, 1967), 1699–1705; Spencer R. Weart, "The Rise of 'Prostituted' Physics," *Nature*, 262 (July 1, 1976), 13–17; Owen Hannaway, "The German Model of Chemical Education in America: Ira Remsen at Johns Hopkins (1876–1913)," *Ambix*, 23 (Nov. 1976), 145–164; David A. Hounshell, "Edison and the Pure Science Ideal in 19th-Century America," *Science*, 207 (Feb. 8, 1980), 612–617; and Robert Rosenberg, "American Physics and the Origins of Electrical Engineering," *Physics Today*, 36 (Oct. 1983), 48–54.

15. James R. Withrow, "Ownership of Intellectual Property in Educational Institutions," *Transactions of the American Institute of Chemical Engineers*, 28 (1932), 208. Withrow made his remarks at a "Symposium on Patents," held in Washington, D.C., on December 7, 1932. Cottrell was also a contributor, and he opened: "The Research Corporation grew out of the problem involved in the university administration of

patents which Dr. Withrow has discussed" — see "Patent Experience of the Research Corporation," ibid., p. 222. On Withrow, a professor of chemical engineering at Ohio State, see *NCAB*, Vol. 42 (1958), pp. 41–42.

16. F. G. Cottrell, "Commercial Production of Helium," *Chemical and Metallurgical Engineering*, 20 (Feb. 1, 1919), 106.

17. University of California, *Annual Report of the President of the University, 1915–1916*, p. 26.

18. John C. Merriam, "Research Board," in University of California, *Annual Report of the President of the University, 1919–1920*, pp. 156–160; and Stadtman, *The University of California, 1868–1968*, pp. 212–213.

19. T. B. Robertson, "Outline of Heads of a Proposed Agreement between the Research Corporation of New York and T. Brailsford Robertson," enclosed in T. B. Robertson to F. G. Cottrell, June 26, 1917, RU 45, Box 47, SI Archives. Robertson's patent was U.S. Patent No. 1,218,472, "Growth-Controlling Substance Derived from the Anterior Lobe of the Pituitary Gland and Process for Producing the Same," issued Mar. 6, 1917 (filed Oct. 8, 1915). See also T. Brailsford Robertson, "Recent Investigations on the Influence of the Anterior Lobe of the Pituitary Body Upon Growth, and on the Properties of the Growth-Controlling Constituent, Tethelin," *Endocrinology*, 1 (Jan. 1917), 24–37; and "Man May Be Self-Made," *NYT*, Jan. 6, 1917, p. 6, col. 3. On Robertson, see Kohler, *From Medical Chemistry to Biochemistry*, pp. 302–305; Philip J. Pauly, *Controlling Life: Jacques Loeb and the Engineering Ideal in Biology* (New York: Oxford University Press, 1987), p. 109; and G. E. Rogers, "Thorburn Brailsford Robertson," *Australian Dictionary of Biography*, Vol. 11 (Melbourne: Melbourne University Press, 1988), pp. 420–421.

20. T. Brailsford Robertson, "The Cash Value of Scientific Research," *Scientific Monthly*, 1 (Nov. 1915), 141.

21. Ibid., 147.

22. T. Brailsford Robertson, "The Strategies of Scientific Investigation," ibid., 3 (Dec. 1916), 552.

23. C. D. Walcott to F. G. Cottrell, Aug. 10, 1917, RU 45, Box 47, SI Archives. "I think I realize and sympathize with your point of view with regard to Professor Robertson's project," Cottrell replied (Sept. 29, 1917, RU 45, Box 47, SI Archives), "and the more I see and think over the workings of the Research Corporation the more I appreciate the force and wisdom of it." For Hooker's views, see F. G. Cottrell to C. D. Walcott, Aug. 4, 1917, RU 45, Box 47, SI Archives.

24. F. G. Cottrell to C. D. Walcott, Sept. 29, 1917, RU 45, Box 47, SI Archives. For the changing situation at Berkeley, see T. B. Robertson to F. G. Cottrell, July 19, 1917, RU 45, Box 47, SI Archives; and T. B. Robertson to F. G. Cottrell, July 27, 1917, RU 45, Box 47, SI Archives. For the resulting agreement with Berkeley, see "Professor Robertson's Gift to the University of California," *Science*, 46 (Oct. 12, 1917), 352–353; T. Brailsford Robertson, "The Utilization of Patents for the Promotion of Research," ibid., 46 (Oct. 19, 1917), 371–379; Charles Weiner, "Science in the

Marketplace: Historical Precedents and Problems," in William J. Whelan and Sandra Black, eds., *From Genetic Experimentation to Biotechnology – The Critical Transition* (New York: Wiley, 1982), pp. 124–126; Charles Weiner, "Universities, Professors, and Patents: A Continuing Controversy," *Technology Review*, 89 (Feb./Mar. 1986), 34–35; and Charles Weiner, "Patenting and Academic Research: Historical Case Studies," *Science, Technology, and Human Values*, 12 (Winter 1987), 51–52. Although an exclusive license was issued to a manufacturing company, tethelin proved far less useful than anticipated and the business was allowed to lapse.

25. Research Corporation, *Research Corporation* (New York: Research Corporation, 1917), p. 7. A copy of this brochure can be found in RU 51, Box 2, SI Archives.

26. Research Corporation, *Research Corporation* (New York: Research Corporation, 1923), p. 10. A copy of this brochure can be found in RU 51, Box 2, SI Archives.

27. "No occurrence since the founding of the [Research] Corporation has touched so deeply its continuity and the inspiration of its inner life as the death a week ago of our Treasurer, Mr. Benjamin B. Lawrence," Hooker noted at the January 28,1921, board of directors meeting (RC Minutes, RC Archives). For Egbert's death, see his entry in *Columbia University Alumni Register.*

28. Little's resignation was announced at the executive committee meeting on January 27, 1922 (RC Minutes, RC Archives). Pine's death was noted at the board of directors meeting on December 19, 1922 (RC Minutes, RC Archives).

29. Biographical sources on Hamerschlag include *NYT*, July 21, 1927, p. 2, col. 5; *NCAB*, Vol. 23 (1933), p. 52; and *WWWA*, Vol. 1 (1942), p. 509. *NYT* and *WWWA* listed Hamerschlag's birth as 1867; *NCAB* gave it as 1872. All listed the years of his engineering field work as 1888–1892 and agreed on the main features of his subsequent career, but none provided details on his previous education. For Hamerschlag at Carnegie Tech, see also Tarbell, *The Story of Carnegie Tech*, pp. 47–84; and Robert H. Kargon and Scott G. Knowles, "Knowledge for Use: Science, Higher Learning, and America's New Industrial Heartland, 1880–1915," *Annals of Science*, 59 (Jan. 2002), 15–18. On Auchmuty and his trade school, see "Richard Tylden Auchmuty," *NCAB*, Vol. 9 (1899), pp. 102–103; and Raymond Garfield Fuller, "Richard Tylden Auchmuty," *DAB*, Vol. 1 (1928), pp. 420–421. On the trade school at St. George's, see Henry Anstice, *History of St. George's Church in the City of New York, 1752–1811–1911* (New York: Harper, 1911), pp. 328–329 and pp. 362–363; W. S. Rainsford, *The Story of a Varied Life: An Autobiography* (Garden City, N.Y.: Doubleday, Page, 1924), pp. 249–252; and Tarbell, op. cit., pp. 28–29. On Rainsford, see also Gardiner H. Shattuck, Jr., "William Stephen Rainsford," *ANB*, Vol. 18 (1999), pp. 83–84. On Morgan's support for the trade schools, see also "John Pierpont Morgan," *NCAB*, Vol. 14 (1917), 68. In his autobiography, Rainsford introduced Hamerschlag as "a graduate of Auchmulty's [*sic*] trade school" (p. 252). Tarbell mentioned the course work at Columbia, but he gave the organization of Hamerschlag's earlier training as the Hebrew Technical Institute (p. 28).

30. Hamerschlag was elected president at the board of directors meeting on December 19, 1922 (RC Minutes, RC Archives), but he did not formally take office until January 26, 1923.

31. Meeting of the Board of Directors, Jan. 28, 1921, RC Archives. I hear in Hooker's remarks something akin to President Calvin Coolidge's 1925 claim that the business of America is business.

32. "Would Reorganize State Government," *NYT*, Apr. 22, 1920, p. 16, col. 3.

33. "Hooker Formally Out For Governor," *NYT*, May 3, 1920, p. 2, col. 5.

34. "Elon Hooker Aims to Reduce Prices," *NYT*, May 22, 1920, p. 3, col. 2. Hooker's campaign was unsuccessful. Nathan L. Miller became the Republican nominee and won the election – see "Miller and Wadsworth Win at Saratoga...," *NYT*, July 29, 1920, p. 1, col. 8; and Oscar Handlin, *Al Smith and His America* (Boston: Little, Brown, 1958), p. 72.

35. Meeting of the Executive Committee, Nov. 30, 1920, RC Minutes, RU 51, Box 4, SI Archives.

36. The fourth member was another newly elected director, Ellwood Hendrick. A chemist by training, Hendrick was also a businessman and a writer – see Daniel D. Jackson, "Ellwood Hendrick," *DAB*, 8 (1932), pp. 533–534. At the time, he worked for Arthur D. Little, Inc., and served as consulting editor for *Chemical and Metallurgical Engineering*. His book, *Everyman's Chemistry: The Chemist's Point of View and His Recent Work Told for the Layman* (New York: Harper, 1917), described Cottrell's early research on electrostatic precipitation and the establishment of Research Corporation (pp. 64–66).

37. Meeting of the Board of Directors, Jan. 28, 1921, RC Minutes, RC Archives. The "clearing house" idea was something that had come up before – see Meeting of the Board of Directors, Dec. 16, 1912; and Meeting of the Executive Committee, Jan. 17, 1913, RC Minutes, RU 51, Box 3, SI Archives.

38. At the board of directors meeting on January 28, 1921 (RC Minutes, RC Archives), three new directors were formally elected. Because Jennings and Perkins had died and Knowlton had resigned, they were replaced by John C. Pennie, Hendrick, and Hamerschlag. On Pennie, a patent lawyer, see *NYT*, Dec. 24, 1921, p. 11, col. 6. Walcott had been Research Corporation's original vice president, but in 1915 Jennings was elected to that position – see Meetings of the Board of Directors, Feb. 27, 1912, and Jan. 15, 1915, RC Minutes, RU 51, Box 3, SI Archives.

39. *Research Corporation* (1923), p. 10.

40. "Algebra Problems Solved By Machine," *NYT*, Apr. 20, 1924, p. 7, col. 1.

41. A. A. Hamerschlag, "Principles of the Research Corporation and Their Application to Industry," *Chemical Age*, 32 (Aug. 1924), 324.

42. Ralph Nicholson, "Clearing House for Inventions," *American Industries*, 25 (Dec. 1924), 27.

43. F. P. Keppel, quoted in Tarbell, *The Story of Carnegie Tech*, p. 83.

44. Ibid., p. 81.

45. Meeting of the Executive Committee, June 24, 1920, RC Minutes, RU 51, Box 4, SI Archives. For the earlier action, see Meeting of the Board of Directors, Jan. 16, 1920, RC Minutes, RU 51, Box 4, SI Archives. On Davis – who in 1928 would become president of the Stevens Institute of Technology – and for a listing of his patents, see *NCAB*, Vol. 40 (1955), pp. 132–133. On his work during World War I, see also Cottrell, "Commercial Production of Helium" (1919), pp. 109–110.

46. "Baly Curve Wrong, Asserts Professor," *NYT*, May 23, 1921, p. 7, col. 2.

47. Dillon reported to the executive committee on May 12, 1921 (RC Minutes, RC Archives): "Considerable progress has resulted on this work, and it is far from finished, but with the present business situation and the financial condition of the [Research] Corporation, we strongly recommend against a renewal of this grant."

48. In his first report to the directors, in 1923 (Box A30, RC Archives), Hamerschlag noted that "the country is on the threshold of tremendous expansion in this direction [i.e., the commercial production of oxygen]," and in his annual report for 1924 (Box A17, RC Archives), he noted that "the production of commercial oxygen is a field which offers perhaps the most promising, even though remote, solution of the problem [of power production]."

49. *Annual Report of the Board of Regents of the Smithsonian Institution... for the Year Ending June 30, 1920*, p. 15.

50. *Annual Report of the Board of Regents of the Smithsonian Institution... for the Year Ending June 30, 1921*, p. 3.

51. Meeting of the Board of Directors, Jan. 18, 1924, RC Minutes, RC Archives. That year the Smithsonian (which had been supporting Goddard's work for several years) granted him $1,000 from the funds supplied by Research Corporation – see *Annual Report of the Board of Regents of the Smithsonian Institution... for the Year Ending June 30, 1924*, p. 125. Apparently the grant was made in two $500 portions – see letters from C. G. Abbot to R. H. Goddard, dated Jan. 21, 1924, and Apr. 26, 1924, in Esther C. Goddard, ed., *The Papers of Robert H. Goddard...*, Vol. 1: *1898–1924* (New York: McGraw-Hill, 1970), pp. 524–525 and p. 543, respectively. Drawing upon the funds from Research Corporation, the Smithsonian gave Goddard a total of $7,500 between 1924 and 1929 – see ibid., Vol. 3: *1938–1945* (New York: McGraw-Hill, 1970), footnote, p. 1557. On the support from Research Corporation, see also Milton Lehman, *This High Man: The Life of Robert H. Goddard* (New York: Farrar, Straus, 1963), p. 148.

52. Meeting of the Board of Directors, Jan. 16, 1925, RC Minutes, RC Archives.

53. *Annual Report of the Board of Regents of the Smithsonian Institution... for the Year Ending June 30, 1928*, p. 151; *Annual Report of the Board of Regents of the Smithsonian Institution... for the Year Ending June 30, 1929*, pp. 102–104; and Paul H. Oehser, *The Smithsonian Institution* (New York: Praeger, 1970), pp. 122–123. Hamerschlag's successor as president of Research Corporation was Howard Andrews Poillon, a mining engineer who first became a Research Corporation director in 1920 (replacing Whitaker) – see B. B. Lawrence to C. D. Walcott, Jan. 2, 1919, RU

51, Box 2, SI Archives; Meeting of the Board of Directors, Jan. 16, 1920, RC Minutes, RU 51, Box 4, SI Archives; *NYT*, Jan. 21, 1954, p. 31, col. 5; and *WWWA*, Vol. 3 (1960), p. 691. Walcott's successor as Secretary of the Smithsonian was Charles G. Abbot, an astronomer — see David DeVorkin, "Charles Greeley Abbot," *ANB*, Vol. 1 (1999), pp. 9–10.

54. Meeting of the Board of Directors, Jan. 16, 1925, RC Minutes, RC Archives.

55. Meeting of the Board of Directors, Nov. 4, 1925, RC Minutes, RC Archives. On Abel, see *NCAB*, Vol. 28 (1940), pp. 23–24; and John Parascandola, "John Jacob Abel," *ANB*, Vol. 1 (1999), pp. 34–35.

56. "Honors in a Democracy," *NYT*, Dec. 26, 1925, p. 14, col. 4. On the award, see also "Abel Wins Research Award," *NYT*, Nov. 26, 1925, p. 39, col. 2; "Wins $2,500 Prize for Promoting Happiness; Did Gland Work with No Hope of Profit," *NYT*., Dec. 25, 1925, p. 1, col. 6; and Carl A. L. Binger, "The Award of the Prize of the Research Corporation to Dr. Abel," *Scientific Monthly*, 22 (Feb. 1926), 183–184.

57. For a complete list of the thirty-eight recipients and the years of their awards, see *Science, Invention, and Society* (1972), p. 26.

58. Discussion of Research Corporation in connection with the work of Lawrence and Van de Graaff may be found in Cameron, *Samaritan of Science*, pp. 288–316. More recent discussions may be found in J. L. Heilbron and Robert W. Seidel, *Lawrence and his Laboratory: A History of the Lawrence Berkeley Laboratory*, Vol. 1 (Berkeley: University of California Press, 1989); and Larry Owens, "MIT and the Federal 'Angel': Academic R&D and Federal-Private Cooperation before World War II," *Isis*, 81 (June 1990), 188–213.

59. "Patenting of Institute Inventions," *Technology Review*, 39 (June 1937), 348; also quoted in Henry Etzkowitz, "Knowledge as Property: The Massachusetts Institute of Technology and the Debate over Academic Patent Policy," *Minerva*, 32 (Winter 1994), 404. Etzkowitz went on to explain that MIT terminated its agreement with Research Corporation in the early 1960s, due to a disagreement involving Jay Forrester's patent rights for magnetic core memories — see pp. 410–412.

60. A. A. Potter, "Research and Invention in Engineering Colleges," *Science*, 91 (Jan. 5, 1940), 1–7. In addition to the thirty-nine institutions he surveyed, Potter mentioned the patent policies of five others from an earlier study — bringing the total discussed in the article to forty-four. On Berkeley's agreement with Research Corporation, see also that earlier study, Archie MacInnes Palmer, "University Patent Policies," *Journal of the Patent Office Society*, 16 (Feb. 1934), 122–123; and Heilbron and Seidel, *Lawrence and His Laboratory*, pp. 106–107.

61. On WARF, see Weiner, "Universities, Professors, and Patents: A Continuing Controversy" (1986), pp. 35–38; Weiner, "Patenting and Academic Research: Historical Case Studies" (1987), pp. 55–57; and Rima D. Apple, "Patenting University Research: Harry Steenbock and the Wisconsin Alumni Research Foundation," *Isis*, 80 (Sept. 1989), 374–394. Also notable in the 1920s were arrangements at the University of Toronto to administer the insulin patent rights — see Michael Bliss,

The Discovery of Insulin (Chicago: University of Chicago Press, 1982).

62. "The Corporation Which Forbids Itself to Pay Dividends," *The New York Sun*, July 24, 1917. The editorial came in response to Research Corporation's announcement of its fellowship program.

63. Boyden Sparkes, "Latter-Day Ben Franklin," *Saturday Review*, 35 (May 3, 1952), 18. On Sparkes – a professional writer and journalist – see *WWWA*, Vol. 3 (1960), p. 806. Other reviews were more positive – see H. A. Spoehr, "The Life and Times of Chemist Frederick Gardner Cottrell," *San Francisco Chronicle*, Mar. 23, 1952, "This World" Sec., p. 20; Forrest F. Cleveland's review in *Science*, 115 (May 23, 1952), 579; Hillier Krieghbaum, " 'Cot' Had the Answers," *New York Times Book Review*, Mar. 30, 1952, p. 7; Farrington Daniels's review in *Chemical and Engineering News*, 30 (June 23, 1952), 2646; and Arthur B. Lamb's review in *JACS*, 74 (Oct. 20, 1952), 5237–5238.

64. Sparkes, "Latter-Day Ben Franklin" (1952), p. 19.

65. Ibid., p. 46. On Hall's gift, see "Bequests for Education of Charles M. Hall," *School and Society*, 1 (Jan. 23, 1915), 127; and Edwards, *The Immortal Woodshed*, pp. 236–240.

66. The exchange was recalled by L. N. Scott in a letter to F. G. Cottrell, Jan. 11, 1916, USBM Records, 1916.

67. Although the historiography of the Progressive Movement is vast, I shall list only a few sources: John C. Burnham, "Essay," in John D. Buenker, John C. Burnham, and Robert M. Crunden, *Progressivism* (Rochester, Vt.: Schenkman Books, 1977), pp. 3–29; Daniel T. Rodgers, "In Search of Progressivism," *Reviews in American History*, 10 (Dec. 1982), 113–132; and Peter G. Filene, "Narrating Progressivism: Unitarians v. Pluralists v. Students," *Journal of American History*, 79 (Mar. 1993), 1546–1562.

68. Jane Addams, "The Subjective Necessity for Social Settlements," in *Philanthropy and Social Progress: Seven Essays* (1893; rpt. Montclair, N.J.: Patterson Smith, 1970), p. 22 (emphasis added).

69. *The Writings of Theodore Roosevelt*, ed. William H. Harbaugh (Indianapolis: Bobbs-Merrill, 1967), p. 110 (emphasis added).

70. Walter Lippmann, *Drift and Mastery: An Attempt to Diagnose the Current Unrest* (1914; rpt. Englewood Cliffs, N.J.: Prentice-Hall, 1961), p. 176 (emphasis added).

71. Cottrell, "The Research Corporation, An Experiment in Public Administration of Patent Rights" (1912), pp. 866–867 (emphasis added).

72. "Dinner to Frederick G. Cottrell" (1915), p. 83 (emphasis added). On Lidbury, see *WWWA*, Vol. 6 (1976), p. 247.

73. *Research Corporation* (1917), p. 4 (emphasis added).

74. Cottrell, "Patent Experience of the Research Corporation" (1932), p. 224 (emphasis added).

75. Clyde Griffen has given the service impulse an explicitly religious meaning.

"Progressivism," he has written, "was the sensitive conscience of American Protestantism during its most expansive and optimistic era..." — see his essay, "The Progressive Ethos," in Stanley Coben and Lorman Ratner, eds., *The Development of an American Culture* (Englewood Cliffs, N.J.: Prentice-Hall, 1970), p. 123.

76. Lippmann, *Drift and Mastery*, p. 36.

77. Ibid.

78. Ibid.

79. Cottrell, "The Research Corporation, An Experiment in Public Administration of Patent Rights" (1912), p. 865. Although he did not elaborate, one of Cottrell's main concerns was that "too direct business relations" would bring to the nation's colleges and universities the undesirable practice of business secrecy. As demonstrated by practices at the Mellon Institute, such concerns were not groundless. For example, Frank Parker Stockbridge noted in his article "Harnessing Science to the Factory," *Popular Mechanics*, 21 (Apr. 1914), 477:

> One of the finest and most inspiring sights at the Mellon Institute is the partition wall in the main office, covered with university pennants. Upon this wall, when he enters the institute to take up research work, each fellow tacks the emblem of his alma mater. It has already become a tradition that in so doing he pledges the honor of his university, not only as to the quality of his work, his enthusiasm and his devotion to it, but by way of an oath to keep his own counsel and never reveal the secrets with which he is intrusted or that he may learn while there.

Similarly, another account reported: "Industrialists are naturally jealous of their trade secrets.... So it is a rigid rule at the [Mellon] [I]nstitute that no fellow shall ever inquire what his associates are doing...." — see Harry Knowles, "Blazing a Trail for the Industries: Contributions of the Mellon Institute...," *Scientific American*, 115 (Sept. 2, 1916), 206.

80. Cottrell, "The Research Corporation, An Experiment in Public Administration of Patent Rights" (1912), p. 865.

81. Quoted in Albert W. Atwood, "For Service Instead of Profit," *The Saturday Evening Post*, 193 (Dec. 4, 1920), 45 (emphasis added). A companion piece, "Does Business Render Service?" followed in the December 18, issue (pp. 11f.). On Atwood, see *NCAB*, Vol. 58 (1979), pp. 394–395. In "For Service Instead of Profit," Atwood explicitly mentioned Henry L. Gantt (p. 42), a mechanical engineer who had also addressed these issues. In his book *Organizing for Work* (New York: Harcourt, Brace, 1919), for example, Gantt noted that the rise of big business had brought in its wake a distressing shift: "the idea that the profits of a business were justified only on account of the service it rendered was rapidly giving way to one in which profits took the first place and service the second" (pp. 4–5). For Gantt the overall lesson was clear (p. v): "In order to resume our advance toward the development of an unconquerable democratic civilization, we must purge our economic system of all autocratic practices of whatever kind, and return to the democratic principle of

rendering service, which was the basis for its wonderful growth."

82. Noble, *America By Design*, p. 6. The book was widely reviewed, notably by W. David Lewis, in *Science*, 198 (Nov. 18, 1977), 722–723; by Merritt Roe Smith, in *American Historical Review*, 83 (June 1978), 817–818; by Alfred D. Chandler, Jr., in *Technology and Culture*, 19 (July 1978), 569–572; and by Nathan Reingold, in *Isis*, 70 (Mar. 1979), 171–173. For later assessments, see Servos, "The Industrial Relations of Science: Chemical Engineering at MIT, 1900–1939" (1980); W. Bernard Carlson, "Academic Entrepreneurship and Engineering Education: Dugald C. Jackson and the MIT–GE Cooperative Engineering Course, 1907–1932," *Technology and Culture*, 29 (July 1988), 536–567; and Christophe Lécuyer, "MIT, Progressive Reform, and 'Industrial Service,' 1890–1920," *Historical Studies in the Physical and Biological Sciences*, 26 (1995), 35–88. Far from being an isolated case, Noble's book can be placed within a much larger corpus of Marxist historiography. For example, Gabriel Kolko's book, *The Triumph of Conservatism: A Reinterpretation of American History, 1900–1916* (New York: Free Press of Glencoe, 1963), treated the Progressive Era as a whole. Where Noble focused on scientists and engineers, E. Richard Brown focused on medical doctors — see his book *Rockefeller Medicine Men: Medicine and Capitalism in America* (Berkeley: University of California Press, 1979); and where Noble focused on events at the turn of the century, David Dickson focused on the post–World War II era — see his book, *The New Politics of Science* (New York: Pantheon Books, 1984).

83. For the discussion of industrial research labs, see Noble, *America By Design*, pp. 110–121. For discussions of Duncan's work and Little's work, see ibid., pp. 122–125.

84. A good example of what I have in mind can be found in Ruth Schwartz Cowan's *More Work for Mother: The Ironies of Household Technology from the Open Hearth to the Microwave* (New York: Basic Books, 1983). At the turn of the century there emerged so many alternatives to housework performed by housewives that the chapter covering them (Chap. 5, "The Roads Not Taken: Alternative Social and Technical Approaches to Housework," pp. 102–150) is the longest in the book. Another source makes a more general point. Speaking of the years prior to World War I, Henry F. May wrote in his book *The End of American Innocence: A Study of the First Years of Our Own Time, 1912–1917* (New York: Knopf, 1959), pp. x–xi:

> On the official surface . . . reigns an intolerable placidity and complacency. Yet if one pokes through the surface almost anywhere, one finds the beginnings of the later [cultural] revolution in nearly all its variety. . . .
> We can see the massive walls of nineteenth-century America still apparently intact, and then turn our spotlight on many different kinds of people cheerfully laying dynamite in the hidden cracks.

85. J. A. Leo Lemay and P. M. Zall, eds., *Benjamin Franklin's Autobiography: An Authoritative Text, Backgrounds, [and] Criticism*, A Norton Critical Edition (New York: Norton, 1986), p. 79.

86. A section heading in Bil Gilbert's article, "'Sand County' Farm Shaped New

Ethic for the Environment," *Smithsonian*, 11 (Oct. 1980), 137. In that section Leopold's daughter, Nina Leopold Bradley, recalled: "Dad always said that land ethic came after breakfast." As for Leopold himself, he wrote at the outset of his environmental classic, *A Sand County Almanac and Sketches Here and There* (New York: Oxford University Press, 1949), p. vii: "These wild things, I admit, had little human value until mechanization assured us of a good breakfast. . . ."

87. Theodore Roosevelt, *Realizable Ideals: Earl Lectures of Pacific Theological Seminary Delivered at Berkeley, California, in 1911* (1911; rpt. Freeport, N.Y.: Books for Libraries Press, 1969), pp. 4–5.

88. Ibid., p. 7.

89. Cottrell, "Patent Experience of the Research Corporation" (1932), p. 224.

90. Ibid., p. 225. In a similar account several years later Cottrell commented: "I mention this to illustrate how inexorably responsibilities grow in the economic field even in an organization which started out with apparently so simple a program" — Cottrell, "The Social Responsibility of the Engineer-II" (1937), p. 555.

91. For an early articulation, see Galambos, "The Emerging Organizational Synthesis in Modern American History" (1970). For assessments, see Wayne K. Hobson, "Professionals, Progressives and Bureaucratization: A Reassessment," *The Historian*, 39 (Aug. 1977), 639–658; and Brian Balogh, *Chain Reaction: Expert Debate and Public Participation in American Commercial Nuclear Power, 1945–1975* (Cambridge, England: Cambridge University Press, 1991), especially Chap.1, "From Fission to Fusion: Professionalization and Politics in Twentieth-Century America," pp. 1–20. I thank Stuart W. Leslie for bringing to my attention Balogh's assessment.

92. E. H. Hooker to C. D. Walcott, Dec. 16, 1918, RU 51, Box 2, SI Archives.

93. Ibid.

94. Ibid. World War I figured prominently in Hooker's thinking. He wished to avoid the "Prussianizing of Science," but he wished to retain the wartime scale of domestic organization and Allied cooperation. Thus he asked Walcott: "Why not then strive in this country for a sympathetic, non-repressive but yet clearly controlled and businesslike management of Science, so as to save the international scientific intercourse developed through the war and go forward as [American] shipbuilding finally went forward under Schwab?" Regarding that last reference, in April 1918 the steel executive Charles M. Schwab agreed to head the nation's Emergency Fleet Corporation, and he quickly increased the production of ships for the war effort — see Robert Hessen, *Steel Titan: The Life of Charles M. Schwab* (New York: Oxford University Press, 1975), pp. 235–244.

95. E. H. Hooker to C. D. Walcott, Dec. 16, 1918, RU 51, Box 2, SI Archives

96. Peter Dobkin Hall, *Inventing the Nonprofit Sector and Other Essays on Philanthropy, Voluntarism, and Nonprofit Organizations* (Baltimore: The Johns Hopkins University Press, 1992), p. 3. For a similar assessment, see Karl and Katz, "The American Private Philanthropic Foundation and the Public Sphere, 1890–1930" (1981), 236–270.

97. Hall, *Inventing the Nonprofit Sector*, p. 5.

98. Ibid.

99. Ibid., p. 43.

100. Louis Galambos (with the assistance of Barbara Barrow Spence), *The Public Image of Big Business in America, 1880–1940: A Quantitative Study in Social Change* (Baltimore: The Johns Hopkins University Press, 1975), pp. 139–140. For Galambos's choice of *Engineering News*, see pp. 30–31.

101. Ibid., p. 151.

102. Richard White, *The Middle Ground: Indians, Empires, and Republics in the Great Lakes Region, 1650–1815* (Cambridge, England: Cambridge University Press, 1991), p. 52.

103. Hall, *Inventing the Nonprofit Sector*, p. 5.

104. David C. Mowery and Bhaven N. Sampat, "Patenting and Licensing University Inventions: Lessons from the History of the Research Corporation," *Industrial and Corporate Change*, 10 (June 1, 2001), 317–355.

105. The earliest of these important moneymakers was the patent for the synthesis of vitamin B1 (Waterman and Williams). The others were for the antifungal agent nystatin (Brown and Hazen), cortisone (Edward C. Kendall), reserpine (Robert B. Woodward), and a process for producing hybrid seed corn (Donald F. Jones and Paul C. Mangelsdorf).

106. David C. Mowery and Bhaven N. Sampat, "University Patents and Patent Policy Debates in the USA, 1925–1980," *Industrial and Corporate Change,* 10 (Aug. 1, 2001), 782–783.

107. Thomas S. Kuhn, *The Structure of Scientific Revolutions*, 2nd Ed. (Chicago: University of Chicago Press, 1970), p. 15, pp. 16–17, and p. 18. Although the "paradigm" concept was central to Kuhn's influential book, it was problematic from the outset and has been widely discussed and evaluated. For an overview, see Paul Hoyningen–Huene, *Reconstructing Scientific Revolutions: Thomas S. Kuhn's Philosophy of Science* (Chicago: University of Chicago Press, 1993), especially Chap. 4, "The Paradigm Concept," pp. 131–162.

108. For Lodge as a Maxwellian, see Hunt, *The Maxwellians*, especially Chap. 2, "FitzGerald, Lodge, and Electromagnetic Waves," pp. 24–47. On the "Ionists," see George Wise, "Ionists in Industry: Physical Chemistry at General Electric, 1900–1915," *Isis,* 74 (Mar. 1983), 6–21; and Servos, *Physical Chemistry from Ostwald to Pauling*, pp. 39–45.

109. Hughes, *Networks of Power*, p. ix. Elsewhere he has written — see Hughes, "The Evolution of Large Technological Systems" (1987), p. 51: "An artifact — either physical or nonphysical — functioning as a component in a system interacts with other artifacts, all of which contribute directly or through other components to the common system goal. If a component is removed from a system or if its characteristics change, the other artifacts in the system will alter characteristics accordingly."

110. Thomas P. Hughes, "The Electrification of America: The Systems Builders," *Technology and Culture*, 20 (Jan. 1979), 126.

111. For a discussion of the process of technological change, see Thomas P. Hughes, "Inventors: The Problems They Choose, the Ideas They Have, and the Inventions They Make," in Patrick Kelly and Melvin Kranzberg, eds., *Technological Innovation: A Critical Review of Current Knowledge* (San Francisco: San Francisco Press, 1978), pp. 166–182.

112. Ruth Schwartz Cowan, *A Social History of American Technology* (New York: Oxford University Press, 1997), p. 171.

113. Paul Greenhalgh, *Ephemeral Vistas: The* Expositions Universelles, *Great Exhibitions and World's Fairs, 1851–1939* (Manchester, England: Manchester University Press, 1988), p. 128. The sculptor was James Earl Fraser. See also Michael L. Smith, *Pacific Visions: California Scientists and the Environment, 1850–1915* (New Haven: Yale University Press, 1987), Chap. 9, "The End of the Trail: Ishi, Science, and the Panama Pacific Exhibition," pp. 186–198.

114. Theodora Kroeber, *Ishi in Two Worlds: A Biography of the Last Wild Indian in North America* (Berkeley: University of California Press, 1961). See also Theodora Kroeber, *Alfred Kroeber: A Personal Configuration* (Berkeley: University of California Press, 1970), pp. 80–85 and pp. 87–93.

115. For the exhibit catalog, see William W. Fitzhugh and Susan A. Kaplan, *Inua: Spirit World of the Bering Sea Eskimo* (Washington, D.C.: Smithsonian Institution Press, 1982). For a brief description of the exhibit, see Michael Olmert, "The True Face of Eskimo Life Stares Out from the Primal Past," *Smithsonian*, 13 (May 1982), 50–59.

116. In his 1915 article, "Cottrell Processes of Electrical Precipitation," p. 37, Schmidt used a similar figure of speech. "The electrical precipitation processes," he wrote, "*give us perhaps the only means for taking hold of the individual particles of suspended matter,* without being directly encumbered with the treatment of the gases themselves" (emphasis added).

117. Olson summarized the "Materials Research" of the railroads in her book *The Depletion Myth*, pp. 45–52. For overviews in the cases of Portland cement and steel, see M. S. J. Gani, *Cement and Concrete* (London: Chapman and Hall, 1997), pp. 6–8; and Thomas J. Misa, *A Nation of Steel: The Making of Modern America, 1865–1925* (Baltimore: The John Hopkins University Press, 1995), pp. 29–39.

118. John Kenneth Galbraith, *The New Industrial State* (Boston: Houghton Mifflin, 1967), especially Chap. 6, "The Technostructure," pp. 60–71.

119. Tracy Kidder, *The Soul of a New Machine* (Boston: Little, Brown, 1981).

120. Michael I. Pupin, "Machine Industry and Idealism," in Charles A. Beard, ed., *Toward Civilization* (London: Longmans, Green, 1930), p. 275.

121. Ibid., p. 275.

122. Ibid., p. 277.

123. Ibid., p. 279.

124. Ibid., p. 280.

125. "Perkin Medal Presented to Frederick G. Cottrell," *Chemical and Metallurgical Engineering*, 20 (Feb. 1, 1919), 102–114; "Perkin Medal Award," *JIEC*, 11 (Feb. 1919), 147–154; and Mary Ellen Bowden and John Kenly Smith, *American Chemical Enterprise: A Perspective on 100 Years of Innovation* ... , Chemical Heritage Foundation Publication, No. 14 (Philadelphia: Chemical Heritage Foundation, 1994), pp. 82–83.

126. A. D. Little, "Chemical Engineering Research: Lifeblood of American Industry" (1933), p. 8.

127. For the creation of the award, see "The Jubilee of the Coal Tar Colour Industry. American Celebrations. New York," *JSCI*, 25 (Dec. 31, 1906), 1207–1208; "Presentation of the Perkin Medal to Mr. J. B. Francis Herreshoff," ibid., 27 (Mar. 31, 1907), 265–266; and "The Perkin Medal Award [to Charles Martin Hall]," in *JIEC*, 3 (Mar. 1911), 143. For a list of the early medalists, see ibid., 9 (Feb. 1917), 192.

128. C. F. Chandler, "Perkin Medal Presentation Address," *Chemical and Metallurgical Engineering*, 20 (Feb. 1, 1919), 102–104. For Chandler's regular presentations of the Perkin Awards, see William H. Nichols, "Presentation Address [for the 1918 Perkin Medal]," *JIEC*, 10 (Feb. 1918), 140–141. On Chandler, see Ellwood Hendrick, "Charles Frederick Chandler," *DAB*, Vol. 3 (1929), pp. 611–613; and Marston Taylor Bogert, "Charles Frederick Chandler, 1836–1925," *Biog. Mem. NAS*, 14 (1931), 127–181.

129. Willis R. Whitney, "Willard Gibbs Medal Award: Presentation Address," *JIEC*, 12 (July 1920), 697. The announcement of the "Award of the Willard Gibbs Medal" in *Science*, 51 (May 28 1920), 536, noted: "This medal was founded by William A. Converse, of Chicago, and is conferred 'In recognition and encouragement of eminent research in theoretical and applied chemistry.' "

130. Whitney, "Willard Gibbs Medal Award: Presentation Address" (1920), p. 697.

131. Meeting of the Board of Directors, Sept. 7, 1927, RC Minutes, RC Archives.

132. Quoted in Cameron, *Samaritan of Science*, pp. 286–287.

133. Interview with Merle A. Tuve, conducted by Thomas D. Cornell, Jan. 13, 1982, tape and transcript deposited at the Center for History of Physics of the American Institute of Physics, College Park, Md. A similar sentiment can be found in W. R. Whitney's response when a Kodak executive asked him about setting up an industrial research lab. After outlining the most important arrangements, Whitney confessed: "I dread organization and system so much that I want to warn others from spending too much time and effort on it" (W. R. Whitney to J. R. Lovejoy, Oct. 24, 1912, quoted in Wise, *Willis R. Whitney*, p. 180).

134. "Long shots" probably became part of Research Corporation's lexicon via Cottrell himself. He told Research Corporation's president, Joseph W. Barker, in 1948, "bet on the youngsters[;] they are long shots, but many will pay off" — see Barker, *Research Corporation (1912–1952)*, p. 17. For other examples, see Research

Corporation's brochure from the mid-1950s, *Long Shots in Science: How Research Corporation, a Non-Profit Foundation, Devotes the Earnings of Inventions to the Further-ance of Scientific Discovery*, a copy of which can be found in the New York Public Library; and "Foundation Head Backs Long Shots," *NYT*, Dec. 5, 1982, p. 63, col. 1.

135. "Dr. Cottrell to Receive Washington Award," *Mechanical Engineering*, 59 (Mar. 1937), 211. The participating societies cooperated in making the award through a seventeen-member Washington Award Commission, which at the time was chaired by Edward J. Mehren. For other notices of the award, see "F. G. Cottrell Given Washing-ton Award," *Industrial and Engineering Chemistry*, News Edition, 15 (Jan. 20, 1937), 35; "Cottrell Receives Washington Award," *Engineering News-Record*, 118 (Jan. 21, 1937), 106; "The Washington Award," *Science*, 85 (Jan. 22, 1937), 95; "Washington Award for 1937 Announced," *Electrical Engineering*, 56 (Feb. 1937), 283; *Fortune*, 15 (Mar. 1937), 216; and H. E. Howe, "Dr. Cottrell, Recipient of the Washington Award," *Scientific Monthly*, 44 (Apr. 1937), 383–385. On the award itself, which was estab-lished in 1916 through a gift from John W. Alvord, see also "Engineers Honor Hoover," *Engineering News-Record*, 82 (Jan. 9, 1919), 114; "Washington Award Conferred on Capt. Robert W. Hunt, ibid., 91 (July 5, 1923), 34; and the entry on Alvord in *NCAB*, Vol. 33 (1947), pp. 14–15. On the four founder societies, see Layton, *The Revolt of the Engineers: Social Responsibility and the American Engineering Profession*, pp. 40–41.

136. F. G. Cottrell, "The Social Responsibility of the Engineer," *Science*, 85 (June 4, 1937), 529–533; and "The Social Responsibility of the Engineer-II," ibid. (June 11, 1937), 553–556. Originally published as a series of essays in *The Dial*, from April to November 1919, *The Engineers and the Price System* was first published as a book in 1921 and was reprinted several times in the early 1930s, when interest in Veblen's writings dramatically increased — see Joseph Dorfman, *Thorstein Veblen and His America* (New York: Viking, 1934), p. 438, p. 460, and p. 517. For an assessment of the book, see also Edwin T. Layton, Jr., "Veblen and the Engineers," *American Quar-terly*, 14 (Spring 1962), 64–72.

137. Cottrell, "The Social Responsibility of the Engineer" (1937), p. 529.

138. Ibid., p. 531.

139. For a brief account of Bush's career, see Larry Owens, "Vannevar Bush," *DSB*, Vol. 17 (1990), pp. 134–139; for a fuller treatment, see G. Pascal Zachary, *Endless Frontier: Vannevar Bush, Engineer of the Century* (New York: Free Press, 1997).

140. Vannevar Bush, "Frederick Gardner Cottrell, 1877–1948," *Biog. Mem. NAS*, 28 (1952), 2.

141. Quoted in ibid.; from Cottrell, "The Social Responsibility of the Engineer" (1937), p. 533.

[BIBLIOGRAPHY]

Selected Cottrell Patents

Patents were a central feature of Research Corporation's early history, and like the individuals mentioned in the text, patents can be seen as comprising extensive networks. Accordingly, just as biographical sources are cited wherever appropriate, so too are patents. Here, however, I list only a selection of Cottrell's:

Cottrell, Frederick G. "Manufacture of Sulfuric Acid U.S. Patent No. 866,843. Issued Sept. 24, 1907 (filed Jan. 4 1906).

———. "Apparatus for Separating Sulfuric Acid." U.S. Patent No. 866,844. Issued Sept. 24, 1907 (filed Jan. 4, 1906).

———. "Art of Separating Suspended Particles from Gaseous Bodies." U.S. Patent No. 895,729. Issued Aug. 11, 1908 (filed July 9, 1907).

———. "Effecting Interchange of Electric Charges between Solid Conductors and Gases." U.S. Patent No. 945,917. Issued Jan. 11, 1910 (filed July 13, 1908).

———. "Process for Separating and Collecting Particles of One Liquid Suspended in Another Liquid." U.S. Patent No. 987,114. Issued Mar. 21, 1911 (filed Oct. 12, 1909).

———, and J. B. Speed. "Separating and Collecting Particles of One Liquid Suspended in Another Liquid." U.S. Patent No. 987,115. Issued Mar. 21, 1911 (filed May 20, 1909).

———, and J. B. Speed. "Apparatus for Separating and Collecting Particles of One Liquid Suspended in Another Liquid." U.S. Patent No. 987,116. Issued Mar. 21, 1911 (filed May 20, 1909).

———, and A. C. Wright. "Separating and Collecting Particles of One Liquid Suspended in Another Liquid." U.S. Patent No. 987,117. Issued Mar. 21, 1911 (filed Dec. 1, 1910).

———. "Purification of Gases." U.S. Patent No. 1,016,476. Issued Feb. 6, 1912 (filed Feb. 26, 1909).

———, and H. A. Burns. "Apparatus for Separating Suspended Particles from Gaseous Bodies." U.S. Patent No. 1,035,422. Issued Aug. 13, 1912 (filed Sept. 9, 1909).

———. "Method of Discharge of Electricity into Gases." U.S. Patent No. 1,067,974. Issued July 22, 1913 (filed Nov. 6, 1911).

Selected Publications to 1940

Ackerman, Carl W. "Recovering Gold from Smoke." *Journal of the American Bankers Association*, 16 (Aug. 1923), 83.

Aldrich, Charles H. "Treatment of Silver Furnace Fume by the Cottrell Process." *Trans. AES*, 28 (1915), 119–137.

"America As Her Own Chemist . . . ." *Scientific American*, 113 (Oct. 2, 1915), 302 and 312.

American Mining Congress. *Joseph Austin Holmes, 1859–1915: A Record of Tributes Paid . . . .* Washington, D.C.: American Mining Congress, 1915.

Anderson, Evald. "Recent Progress in Electrical Precipitation." *Chemical and Metallurgical Engineering*, 26 (Jan. 25, 1922), 151–153.

Atwood, Albert W. "For Service Instead of Profit." *The Saturday Evening Post*, 193 (Dec. 4, 1920), 13, 42, 45–46, and 49.

"Award of the Willard Gibbs Medal." *Science*, 51 (May 28, 1920), 536.

Baekeland, L. H. "The United States Patent System, Its Use and Abuse." *JIEC*, 1 (Mar. 1909), 204–205.

———. "The Incongruities of American Patent Litigation." *JIEC*, 4 (Nov. 1912), 785–789.

Baskerville, Charles, ed. *Municipal Chemistry*. New York: McGraw-Hill, 1910.

Benner, R. C. "Research on the Smoke Problem at the Department of Industrial Research of the University of Pittsburgh." *Science*, 35 (June 28, 1912), 977–979.

———. "How and Why Smoke Is Injurious." *MCE*, 10 (Nov. 1912), 735–737.

———. "Why Smoke Is an Industrial Nuisance." *Iron Age*, 91 (Jan. 9, 1913), 135–138.

Binger, Carl A. L. "The Award of the Prize of the Research Corporation to Dr. Abel." *Scientific Monthly*, 22 (Feb. 1926), 183–184.

Bradley, Linn. "The Electrical Precipitation of Suspended Particles by the Cottrell Process." *JIEC*, 4 (Dec. 1912), 908–910.

———. "Electrical Precipitation of Suspended Particles." *Trans. AES*, 22 (1912), 489–497.

———. "Electrical Precipitation of Suspended Particles." *Proceedings of the Engineers' Society of Western Pennsylvania*, 29 (Apr. 1913), 111–133.

———. "Electric Smoke and Fume Precipitation before the American Institute of Electrical Engineers." *MCE*, 13 (Mar. 1915), 160.

———. "Solution of Smoke, Fume and Dust Problems by Electrical Precipitation." *MCE*, 13 (Dec. 1, 1915), 911–914.

———. "Practical Applications of Electrical Precipitation and Progress of the Research Corporation." *Trans. AIEE*, 34 (1915), 421–457.

———. "The Cottrell Process in Practice." *MCE*, 16 (Mar. 15, 1917), 336–340.

Braley, H. D. "Notes on Electrostatic Precipitation." *Trans. AES*, 35 (1919), 199–237.

Bush, H. J. "Electrostatic-Separation." *The Electrician*, 85 (Nov. 5, 1920), 533–535.

Butler, Nicholas Murray. "The University and Industry." *JIEC*, 7 (Dec. 1915), 1069–1071.

———. "Benjamin Bowden Lawrence, '78 Mines." *Columbia Alumni News*, 12 (Feb. 4, 1921), 265–266.

California Alumni Association. *Directory of Graduates of the University of California, 1864–1916*. Berkeley: University of California Press, 1916.

Chandler, Charles F. "Perkin Medal Presentation Address." *Chemical and Metallurgical Engineering*, 20 (Feb. 1, 1919), 102–104.

———. "Chemistry in the United States." *JIEC*, 13 (May 1921), 391–397.

Chauvenet, Regis. "Hydrometallurgy — Joys of Its Theory, Woes of Its Practice." *MCE*, 11 (Sept. 1913), 486–491.

Columbia University. *Columbia University Alumni Register: 1754–1931*. New York: Columbia University, 1932.

Cottrell, Frederick G. "Review of Physical Chemistry." *JACS*, 27 (May 1905), 615–636.

———. "The Liquid Air Plant of the Chemistry Department, University of California." *California Journal of Technology*, 6 (1905), 3–11.

———. "On Air Liquefiers." *Journal of Physical Chemistry*, 10 (Apr. 1906), 264–274.

———. "Recent Progress in Physical Chemistry." *JACS*, 30 (Feb. 1908), 288–302.

———. "Recent Progress in Physical Chemistry." *JACS*, 31 (Mar. 1909), 394–403.

———. "The Electrical Precipitation of Suspended Particles." *JIEC*, 3 (Aug. 1911), 542–550.

———. "Mineral Losses in Gases and Fumes." *JIEC*, 4 (Mar 1912), 182–185.

———. "The Research Corporation, An Experiment in Public Administration of Patent Rights." *JIEC*, 4 (Dec. 1912), 864–867. Also published in *Original Communications [to the] Eighth International Congress of Applied Chemistry, Washington and New York, September 4 to 13, 1912*. Concord, N.H.: Rumford Press, 1912–1913, Vol. 26, pp. 59–69.

———. "Electrical Fume-Precipitation." *Trans. AIME*, 43 (1912), 512–520 and 755–762.

———. "The Problem of Smelter Smoke." *Transactions of the Commonwealth Club of California*, 8 (1913), 487–492.

———. "Problems in Smoke, Fume, and Dust Abatement." *Annual Report of the Board of Regents of the Smithsonian Institution . . . for the Year Ending June 30, 1913*. Washington, D.C.: GPO, 1914, pp. 653–685.

———. "Electrical Precipitation: Historical Sketch." *Trans. AIEE*, 34 (1915), 387–396.

———. "Commercial Production of Helium." *Chemical and Metallurgical Engineering*, 20 (Feb. 1, 1919), 104–114.

———. "Medal Address: International Scientific Relations." *JIEC*, 12 (July 1920), 697–700.

———. "Patent Experiences of the Research Corporation." *Transactions of the American Institute of Chemical Engineers*, 28 (1932), 222–225.

———. "The Social Responsibility of the Engineer." *Science*, 85 (June 4, 1937), 529–33.

———. "The Social Responsibility of the Engineer-II." *Science*, 85 (June 11, 1937), 553–556.

"The Cottrell Dinner." *EMJ*, 99 (Jan. 23, 1915), 199–200.

"The Cottrell Fume-Condensing System at the Selby Smelter." *EMJ*, 86 (Aug. 1, 1908), 242.

"Cottrell Process for Condensing Smelter Fumes." *EMJ*, 86 (Aug. 22, 1908), 375–377.

"Dinner to Frederick G. Cottrell." *MCE*, 13 (Feb. 1915), 81–84.

Doremus, Charles A. "Charles Marchand." *JIEC*, 9 (Mar. 1917), 321.

Duncan, Robert Kennedy. "On Certain Problems Connected with the Present-Day Relation between Chemistry and Manufacture in America." *JIEC*, 3 (Mar. 1911), 177–186.

————. "Industrial Fellowships: Five Years of an Educational Industrial Experiment." *Journal of the Franklin Institute*, 175 (Jan. 1913), 43–57.

————. "Industrial Research." *Harper's Monthly Magazine*, 126 (Feb. 1913), 385–390.

————. "Industrial Fellowships of the Mellon Institute." *Science*, 39 (May 8, 1914), 672–678.

Egbert, H. D. "The Cottrell Precipitation Process and Its Application to Foundry Dust Problems." *Transactions of the American Foundrymen's Association*, 27 (1919), 266–283.

"Electric Smoke and Fume Precipitation before the American Institute of Electrical Engineers." *MCE*, 13 (Mar. 1915), 160.

"The Engineering Foundation." *Journal of the American Society of Mechanical Engineers*, 37 (Feb. 1915), III–X.

Eschholz, O. H. "Electrostatic Precipitation." *Transactions of the American Institute of Mining and Metallurgical Engineers*, 60 (1919), 243–279.

"First National Exposition of Chemical Industries." *MCE*, 13 (1 Oct. 1915), 690–697.

Fleming, John A. "Electrical (or Electrostatic) Machine." *Encyclopaedia Britannica*. 11th ed., Vol. 9 (1910), pp. 176–179.

Fulton, Charles H. *Metallurgical Smoke*. USBM Bull., No. 84. Washington, D.C.: GPO, 1915.

"Glimpses of New Pacific Coast Industries in the Making." *MCE*, 15 (Sept. 15 and Nov. 1, 1916), 285–288 and 511–513.

Gray, George W. "Science and Profits." *Harpers Monthly Magazine*, 172 (Apr. 1936), 539–549.

Hamerschlag, Arthur A. "Principles of the Research Corporation and Their Application to Industry." *Chemical Age*, 32 (Aug. 1924), 323–325.

Heaton, Lois. *A List of the Books, Bulletins, Journal Contributions, and Patents by Members of Mellon Institute of Industrial Research, 1911–1927*. Mellon Institute of Industrial Research, Bibliographic Series Bulletin, No. 2. (1927).

Hendrick, Ellwood. *Everyman's Chemistry: The Chemist's Point of View and His Recent Work Told for the Layman*. New York: Harper, 1917.

Hoffman, R. "Travels through the United States in Conjunction with the Eighth International Congress of Applied Chemistry at New York, by Members of the Congress." *JIEC*, 6 (Jan. 1914), 49–69.

Holland, Maurice. *Industrial Explorers*. New York: Harper and Brothers, 1928.

Holmes, Joseph A. "The New Purpose in State Development: The Safeguarding Its Own Future." *Science*, 32 (July 15, 1910), 65–72.

―――. "Carbon Wastes." *JIEC*, 4 (Mar. 1912), 160–164.

―――. "The National Phases of the Mining Industry." In *Original Communications [to the] Eighth International Congress of Applied Chemistry, Washington and New York, September 4 to 13, 1912*. Concord, N.H.: Rumford Press, 1912–1913, Vol. 26, pp. 733–751.

―――, Edward C. Franklin, and Ralph A. Gould. *Report of the Selby Smelter Commission*. USBM Bull., No. 98. Washington, D.C.: GPO, 1915.

Hooker, Elon H. "An Appreciation of Dr. Baekeland." *JIEC*, 8 (Feb. 1916), 183–184.

Horne, G. H. "Electrical Engineering Features of the Electrical Precipitation Process." *Trans. AIEE*, 41 (1922), 808–814.

Howard, W. H. "Electrical Fume Precipitation at Garfield." *Trans. AIME*, 49 (1915), 540–560.

Howe, Charles S. "The Function of the Engineer in the Conservation of the Natural Resources of the Country." *Science*, 28 (Oct. 23, 1908), 537–548.

Howe, H. E. "Dr. Cottrell, Recipient of the Washington Award." *Scientific Monthly*, 44 (Apr. 1937), 383–385.

Iles, Malvern W. "Methods for the Collection of Metallurgic Dust and Fume." [Columbia University] *School of Mines Quarterly*, 17 (Jan. 1896), 97–118.

"International Congress of Applied Chemistry." *JIEC*, 4 (Oct. 1912), 706–719.

Ionides, S. A. "The Dry Chlorination of Complex Ores." *Mining and Scientific Press*, 112 (May 27, 1916), 781–787.

Johnson, Ligon. "The History and Legal Phases of the Smoke Problem." *MCE*, 16 (Feb. 15, 1917), 199–204.

Knowles, Harry. "Blazing a Trail for the Industries: Contributions of the Mellon Institute . . . ." *Scientific American*, 115 (Sept. 2, 1916), 206 and 223–224.

Laist, Frederick. "Changes in Smelting Practice of Anaconda Copper Mining Co." *EMJ*, 102 (Oct. 7, 1916), 635–638.

Landolt, P. E. "Eliminating Waste and Nuisance in Smoke, Fume and Gas." *Chemical and Metallurgical Engineering*, 25 (Aug. 31, 1921), 428–432.

Lawrence, Benjamin B. "Engineering Professions." [Columbia University] *School of Mines Quarterly*, 31 (Apr. 1910), 203–207.

Lesley, Robert W. *History of the Portland Cement Industry in the United States*. 1924; rpt. New York: Arno Press, 1972.

Leuschner, A. O. "The Organization and Budget of the Graduate School and Its Relation to the Other Schools of the University." *Journal of Proceedings and Addresses . . . [of the Association of American Universities]*, 17 (1915), 40–57.

Lippmann, Walter. *Drift and Mastery: An Attempt to Diagnose the Current Unrest.* 1914; rpt. Englewood Cliffs, N.J.: Prentice-Hall, 1961.

Little, Arthur D. "The Chemist and the Community." *Science,* 25 (Apr. 26, 1907), 647–653.

———. "A Laboratory for Public Service." *Technology Review,* 11 (Jan. 1909), 16–24.

———. "Industrial Research in America: Presidential Address." *JIEC,* 5 (Oct. 1913), 793–801.

———. "Organization of Industrial Research." *Proceedings of the American Society for Testing Materials.* Vol. 18, Part 2 (1918), 22–31.

———. "Milton C. Whitaker." *Industrial and Engineering Chemistry,* 15 (Feb. 1923), 196–198.

———. "Chemical Engineering Research: Lifeblood of American Industry." In *Twenty-Five Years of Chemical Engineering Progress.* Ed. Sidney D. Kirkpatrick. New York: D. Van Nostrand, 1933, pp. 1–14.

Lodge, Oliver. "Dust-Free Spaces." *Nature,* 29 (Apr. 24, 1884), 610–613.

———. "Dust." *Nature,* 31 (Jan. 22, 1885), 265–269.

———. "The Electrical Deposition of Dust and Smoke, with Special Reference to the Collection of Metallic Fume, and to a Possible Purification of the Atmosphere." *JSCI,* 5 (Nov. 29, 1886), 572–576.

———. "Historical Note on Dust, Electrification, and Heat." *Nature,* 71 (Apr. 20, 1905), 582.

———. "Conference on Smoke Abatement: Presidential Address." *Journal of the Royal Sanitary Institute,* 27 (1907), 42–48.

———. "Public Service versus Private Expenditure." In *Socialism and Individualism.* Sidney Webb, Bernard Shaw, Sidney Ball, and Oliver Lodge. New York: John Lane, 1911, pp. 92–102.

———. "Foreword." To *Clouds and Smokes: The Properties of Disperse Systems in Gases and Their Practical Applications.* By William E. Gibbs. London: J. and A. Churchill, 1924, pp. viii–x.

———. *Electrical Precipitation: A Lecture Delivered before the Institute of Physics.* London: Oxford University Press, 1925.

———. *Advancing Science.* New York: Harcourt, Brace, 1932.

Low, George P. "The Great Carquinez Transmission Span." *Journal of Electricity, Power and Gas,* 11 (May 1901), 91–102.

———. "The World's Longest Electric Power Transmission." *Journal of Electricity, Power and Gas,* 11 (July 1901), 145–168.

Malm, John L. "Dry Chloridization of Ores." *MCE,* 12 (Feb. 1914), 128–129.

———. "The Malm Process." *EMJ,* 101 (May 13, 1916), 864.

Martin, Thomas Commerford. "The Longest Power-Transmission in the World." *American Monthly Review of Reviews,* 25 (Mar. 1902), 305–311.

————. "Mr. Carnegie's Noteworthy Endowment for Engineering." *Harpers Weekly*, 51 (Apr. 13, 1907). 546.

Massachusetts Institute of Technology. *Register of Former Students*. Cambridge, Mass.: MIT Press, 1930.

McClelland, Ellwood H. *Bibliography of Smoke and Smoke Prevention*. MI Smoke Investigation Bull., No. 2. (1913).

Meller, H. B. "Smoke Abatement, Its Effects and Its Limitations." *Mechanical Engineering*, 48 (Nov. 1926), 1275–1283.

Mellon Institute of Industrial Research. *Some Engineering Phases of Pittsburgh's Smoke Problem*. MI Smoke Investigation Bull., No. 8 (1914).

Meston, A. F. "Electrical Precipitation in the Chemical Industries." *Electric Journal*, 14 (June 1917), 248–252.

Moulton, Robert H. "Turning Smoke into Money: The Origin and Development of the Cottrell Electric Precipitation." *Scientific American*, 119 (July 20, 1918), 50 and 59–60.

Nesbit, A. F. "The Electrical Precipitation of Smoke, Dust, Etc." *Electrical Review*, 65 (Oct. 31, 1914), 877.

————. "The Theoretical and Experimental Consideration of Electrical Precipitation." *Trans. AIEE*, 34 (1915), 405–420.

"A New Application of Electricity." *Engineering*, 39 (June 5, 1885), 627–628.

Nicholson, Ralph. "Clearing House for Inventions." *American Industries*, 25 (Dec. 1924), 27–29.

O'Connor, John, Jr. "Four Points in the Indictment of the Smoke Nuisance." *Popular Science Monthly*, 87 (1915), 244–249.

O'Neill, Edmund. "History of the College of Chemistry." *California Engineer*, 2 (Aug. 1923), 3–4 and 10.

Original Communications [to the] Eighth International Congress of Applied Chemistry, Washington and New York, September 4 to 13, 1912. 29 Vols. Concord, N.H.: Rumford Press, 1912–1913.

Palmer, Archie MacInnes. "University Patent Policies." *Journal of the Patent Office Society*, 16 (Feb. 1934), 96–131.

Potter, A. A. "Research and Invention in Engineering Colleges." *Science*, 91 (Jan. 5, 1940), 1–7.

Pupin, Michael I. *From Immigrant to Inventor*. New York: Scribners, 1924.

————. "Machine Industry and Idealism." In *Toward Civilization*. Ed. Charles A. Beard. London: Longmans, Green, 1930, pp. 273–281.

Rathbun, Ross B. "Electrical Precipitation of Solids from Smelter Gases." *Trans. AIEE*, 41 (1922), 815–826.

"The Research Corporation." *Science*, 46 (Aug. 10, 1917), 131–132.

Research Corporation. New York: Research Corporation, 1917.

Research Corporation. New York: Research Corporation, 1923.

"Research Corporation and the Cottrell Process." *EMJ*, 97 (May 30, 1914), 1107–1109.

Research Corporation: Certificate of Incorporation, By-Laws, and Stockholders' Agreement. New York: Research Corporation, 1912.

Robertson, T. Brailsford. "The Cash Value of Scientific Research." *Scientific Monthly*, 1 (Nov. 1915), 140–147.

———. "The Strategies of Scientific Investigation." *Scientific Monthly*, 3 (Dec. 1916), 547–556.

———. "The Utilization of Patents for the Promotion of Research." *Science*, 46 (Oct. 19, 1917), 371–379.

Ross, W. H., J. N. Carothers, and A. R. Metz. "The Use of the Cottrell Precipitator in Recovering the Phosphoric Acid Evolved in the Volatilization Method of Treating Phosphate Rock." *JIEC*, 9 (Jan. 1917), 26–31.

Schmidt, Walter A. "The Control of Dust in Portland Cement Manufacture by the Cottrell Precipitation Process." In *Original Communications [to the] Eighth International Congress of Applied Chemistry, Washington and New York, September 4 to 13, 1912.* Concord, N.H.: Rumford Press, 1912–1913, Vol. 5, pp. 117–124.

———. "Cottrell Processes of Electrical Precipitation." *Transactions of the American Institute of Chemical Engineers*, 8 (1915), 35–63.

———. *Dust and Fume Collection by the Cottrell Process of Electrical Precipitation: Results Obtained at Smelter of International Smelting Company[,] Inspiration, Arizona[, and] Factory of Riverside Portland Cement Company[,] Riverside, California.* Paper presented at meeting of the American Institute of Mining and Metallurgical Engineers, Globe, Ariz., Sept. 21, 1915. Los Angeles, 1916.

———. "Recent Conclusions Pertaining to Electrical Precipitation." *Trans. AIEE*, 41 (1922), 802–807.

———. Electrical Precipitation in Retrospect. *Industrial and Engineering Chemistry*, 16 (Oct. 1924), 1038–1041.

———, and Evald Anderson. "Electrical Precipitation." *Electrical Engineering*, 57 (Aug. 1938), 332–338.

Scott, Lloyd N. *Naval Consulting Board of the United States.* Washington, D.C.: GPO, 1920.

Scott, Riley E. "Interesting Westerners: The Enemy of the Smoke Nuisance." *Sunset: The Pacific Monthly*, 33 (Nov. 1914), 976–978.

Slosson, Edwin E. *Great American Universities.* New York: Macmillan, 1910.

Smith, W. G., and A. A. Heimrod. "Application of the Cottrell Process to the Recovery of Fume from Silver Refining Operations." *Chemical and Metallurgical Engineering*, 21 (Sept. 15, 1919), 360–363.

Speed, Buckner. "An Appreciation of Dr. Cottrell." *JIEC*, 11 (Feb. 1919), 153–154.

Starrett, Agnes Lynch. *Through One Hundred and Fifty Years: The University of Pittsburgh.* Pittsburgh: University of Pittsburgh Press, 1937.

Steere, F. W. "An Electrical Process for Detarring Gas." *MCE*, 12 (Dec. 1914), 775–778.

Stockbridge, Frank Parker. "Harnessing Science to the Factory." *Popular Mechanics*, 21 (Apr. 1914), 474–481.

Strong, W. W. "The Electrical Precipitation of Suspended Matter in Gases." *Journal of the Franklin Institute*, 174 (Sept. 1912), 239–263.

———. "The Positive and Negative Corona and Electrical Precipitation." *Trans. AIEE*, 32 (1913), 1755–1765.

———. "Electrical Precipitation: Theory of the Removal of Suspended Matter from Fluids." *Trans. AIEE*, 34 (1915), 397–404.

———. "Some Theoretical Aspects of Electrical Fume Precipitation." *MCE*, 16 (June 1, 1917), 648–652.

———. *The New Science of the Fundamental Physics*. Mechanicsburg, Pa.: Scientific Instrument and Electrical Machine Co., 1918.

———. *The New Philosophy of Modern Science*. York, Pa.: Kyle Publishing Co., 1920.

Sultzer, N. W. "Recovery of Gold at the U.S. Assay Office, New York." *Chemical Age*, 33 (Jan. 1925), 5–8.

Swain, Robert E. "Atmospheric Pollution by Industrial Waste." *Industrial and Engineering Chemistry*, 15 (Mar. 1923), 296–301.

Tarbell, Arthur Wilson. *The Story of Carnegie Tech, Being a History of Carnegie Institute of Technology from 1900 to 1935*. Pittsburgh: Carnegie Institute of Technology, 1937.

Todd, Frank Morton. *The Story of the Exposition, Being the Official History of the International Celebration Held at San Francisco in 1915 . . . .* 5 Vols. New York: G. P. Putnam's Sons, 1921.

Van Gelder, Arthur Pine, and Hugo Schlatter. *History of the Explosives Industry in America*. 1927; rpt. New York: Arno Press, 1972.

Van Hise, Charles R. "Conservation." *JIEC*, 4 (Mar. 1912), 160.

Walcott, Charles D. "Relations of the National Government to Higher Education and Research." *Science*, 13 (June 28, 1901), 1001–1015.

———. "Research and the Smithsonian Institution." *The Independent*, 66 (Mar. 18, 1909), 585–586.

———. "Science and Service." *Science*, 61 (Jan. 2, 1925), 1–5.

Welch, Harry V. "Collection of Lead and Zinc Dusts and Fumes by the Cottrell Process." *Transactions of the American Institute of Mining and Metallurgical Engineers*, 121 (1936), 304–338.

Whitney, Willis R. "Willard Gibbs Medal Award: Presentation Address." *JIEC*, 12 (July 1920), 697.

Winne, H. A. "The Cottrell Process of Electrical Precipitation." *General Electric Review*, 24 (Nov. 1921), 910–921.

Witte, G. A. "Electrical Precipitation of Cement Mill Dust." *General Electric Review*, 25 (Feb. 1922), 125–128.

"The Work of the Research Corporation." *Engineering and Mining Journal-Press*, 115 (June 16, 1923), 1072–1073.

Wright, Hamilton. "Long-Distance High-Tension Transmission of Power in California." *Scientific American*, 88 (May 16, 1903), 373–374.

Selected Publications after 1940

Aldrich, Mark. "Preventing 'the Needless Peril of the Coal Mine': The Bureau of Mines and the Campaign against Coal Mine Explosions, 1910–1940." *Technology and Culture*, 36 (July 1995), 483–518.

Apple, Rima D. "Patenting University Research: Harry Steenbock and the Wisconsin Alumni Research Foundation." *Isis*, 80 (Sept. 1989), 374–394.

Baatz, Simon. *Knowledge, Culture, and Science in the Metropolis: The New York Academy of Sciences, 1817–1970*. New York: New York Academy of Sciences, 1990.

Bacon, W. Stevenson. "Research Corporation." In *Foundations*. Vol. 8, *Greenwood Encyclopedia of American Institutions*. Ed. Harold M. Keele and Joseph C. Kiger. Westport, Conn.: Greenwood Press, 1984, pp. 349–352.

Bailles, Kendall E., ed. *Environmental History: Critical Issues in Comparative Perspective*. Lanham, Md.: University Press of America, 1985.

Baldwin, Richard S. *The Fungus Fighters. Two Women Scientists and Their Discovery*. Ithaca: Cornell University Press, 1981.

Barker, Joseph Warren. *Research Corporation (1912–1952): Dedicated to Progress in Education and Science*. New York: The Newcomen Society in North America, 1952.

Birr, Kendall. *Pioneering in Industrial Research: The Story of the General Electric Research Laboratory*. Washington, D.C.: Public Affairs Press, 1957.

———. "Industrial Research Laboratories." In *The Sciences in the American Context: New Perspectives*. Ed. Nathan Reingold. Washington, D.C.: Smithsonian Institution Press, 1979, pp. 193–207.

Bledstein, Burton J. *The Culture of Professionalism: The Middle Class and the Development of Higher Education in America*. New York: Norton, 1976.

Bowden, Mary Ellen, and John Kenly Smith. *American Chemical Enterprise: A Perspective on 100 Years of Innovation to Commemorate the Centennial of the Society of Chemical Industry (American Section)*. Chemical Heritage Foundation Publication, No. 14. Philadelphia: Chemical Heritage Foundation, 1994.

Bremner, Robert H. *American Philanthropy*. 2nd ed. Chicago: University of Chicago Press, 1988.

Browne, Charles Albert, and Mary Elvira Weeks. *A History of the American Chemical Society: Seventy-Five Eventful Years*. Washington, D.C.: American Chemical Society, 1952.

Bruce, Robert V. *Bell: Alexander Graham Bell and the Conquest of Solitude*. Boston: Little, Brown, 1973.

Burnham, John C. "Essay." In *Progressivism*. Ed. John D. Buenker, John C. Burnham, and Robert M. Crunden. Rochester, Vt.: Schenkman Books, 1977, pp. 3–29.

Burns, Robert M. *A History of the Electrochemical Society, 1902–1976*. Princeton, N. J.: Electrochemical Society, 1977.

Bush, Vannevar. "Frederick Gardner Cottrell, 1877–1948." *Biog. Mem. NAS*, 28 (1952), 1–11.

Cameron, Frank T. *Cottrell: Samaritan of Science*. Garden City, N.Y.: Doubleday, 1952; rpt. Tucson, Ariz.: Research Corporation, 1975.

Carlson, W. Bernard. *Innovation as a Social Process: Elihu Thomson and the Rise of General Electric, 1870–1900*. Cambridge, England: Cambridge University Press, 1991.

CCH Trade Cases, 1946–1947. Chicago: Commerce Clearing House, 1948.

Chandler, Arthur D., Jr. *Strategy and Structure: Chapters in the History of the Industrial Enterprise*. Cambridge, Mass.: MIT Press, 1962.

———. *Scale and Scope: The Dynamics of Industrial Capitalism*. Cambridge, Mass.: Belknap Press of Harvard University Press, 1990.

Childs, Herbert. *An American Genius: The Life of Ernest Orlando Lawrence*. New York: E. P. Dutton, 1968.

Cochrane, Rexmond C. *Measures for Progress: A History of the National Bureau of Standards*. Washington, D.C.: National Bureau of Standards, U.S. Department of Commerce, 1966.

Cohen, Clive. "The Early History of Chemical Engineering: A Reassessment." *British Journal for the History of Science*, 29 (1996), 171–194.

Cowan, Ruth Schwartz. *A Social History of American Technology*. New York: Oxford University Press, 1997.

Dale, Ernest, and Charles Meloy. "Hamilton MacFarland Barksdale and the Du Pont Contributions to Systematic Management." *Business History Review*, 36 (Summer 1962), 127–152.

Daniels, George H. "The Pure-Science Ideal and Democratic Culture." *Science*, 156 (June 30, 1967), 1699–1705.

Dolby, R. G. A. "The Transmission of Two New Scientific Disciplines from Europe to North America in the Late Nineteenth Century." *Annals of Science*, 34 (May 1977), 287–310.

Duffy, John. *A History of Public Health in New York City, 1866–1966*. New York: Russell Sage Foundation, 1974.

Dupree, A. Hunter. *Science in the Federal Government: A History of Policies and Activities to 1940*. Cambridge, Mass.: Belknap Press of Harvard University Press, 1957.

Edwards, Junius. *The Immortal Woodshed: The Story of the Inventor Who Brought Aluminum to America*. New York: Dodd, Mead, 1955.

Etzkowitz, Henry, and Lois S. Peters. "Profiting from Knowledge: Organizational Innovations and the Evolution of Economic Norms." *Minerva*, 29 (Summer 1991), 133–166.

———. "Knowledge as Property: The Massachusetts Institute of Technology and the Debate over Academic Patent Policy." *Minerva*, 32 (Winter 1994), 381–421.

———, and Ashley J. Stevens. "Inching Toward Industrial Policy: The University's Role in Government Initiatives to Assist Small, Innovative Companies in the United States." In *Capitalizing Knowledge: New Intersections of Industry and Academia*. Ed. Henry Etzkowitz, Andrew Webster, and Peter Healey. Albany: State University of New York Press, 1998, pp. 215–238.

Faber, Eduard, ed. *Great Chemists*. New York: Interscience Publishers, 1961.

Finch, James Kip. *A History of the School of Engineering, Columbia University*. New York: Columbia University Press, 1954.

Forman, Paul, John L. Heilbron, and Spencer Weart. "Physics *circa* 1900: Personnel, Funding, and Productivity of the Academic Establishments." *Historical Studies in the Physical Sciences*, 5 (1975).

Fremont-Smith, Marion R. *Philanthropy and the Business Corporation*. New York: Russell Sage Foundation, 1972.

Galambos, Louis. "The Emerging Organizational Synthesis in Modern American History." *Business History Review*, 44 (Autumn 1970), 279–290.

———, with the assistance of Barbara Barrow Spence. *The Public Image of Big Business in America, 1880–1940: A Quantitative Study in Social Change*. Baltimore: The Johns Hopkins University Press, 1975.

———. "The American Economy and the Reorganization of the Sources of Knowledge." In *The Organization of Knowledge in Modern America, 1860–1920*. Ed. Alexandra Oleson and John Voss. Baltimore: The Johns Hopkins University Press, 1979, pp. 269–282.

———. "Technology, Political Economy, and Professionalization: Central Themes of the Organizational Synthesis." *Business History Review*, 57 (Winter 1983), 471–493.

Geiger, Roger L. *To Advance Knowledge: The Growth of American Research Universities, 1900–1940*. New York: Oxford University Press, 1986.

Goddard, Esther C., ed. *The Papers of Robert H. Goddard* .... 3 Vols. New York: McGraw-Hill, 1970.

Good, Gregory A., ed. *The Earth, the Heavens, and the Carnegie Institution of Washington*. Washington, D.C.: American Geophysical Union, 1994.

Gould, Stephen Jay. *Wonderful Life: The Burgess Shale and the Nature of History*. New York: Norton, 1989.

———. *Eight Little Piggies: Reflections in Natural History*. New York: Norton, 1993.

Graebner, William. *Coal-Mining Safety in the Progressive Period: The Political Economy of Reform*. Lexington: University of Kentucky Press, 1976.

Griffen, Clyde. "The Progressive Ethos." In *The Development of an American Culture.* Ed. Stanley Coben and Lorman Ratner. Englewood Cliffs, N.J.: Prentice-Hall, 1970, pp. 120–149.

Grinder, R. Dale. "The Battle for Clean Air: The Smoke Problem in Post–Civil War America." In *Pollution and Reform in American Cities, 1870–1930.* Ed. Martin V. Melosi. Austin: University of Texas Press, 1980, pp. 83–103.

Guédon, Jean-Claude. "From Unit Operations to Unit Processes: Ambiguities of Success and Failure in Chemical Engineering." In *Chemistry and Modern Society: Historical Essays in Honor of Aaron J. Ihde.* Ed. John Parascandola and James C. Whorton. Washington, D.C.: American Chemical Society, 1983, pp. 171–194.

Guston, David H., and Kenneth Keniston, eds. *The Fragile Contract: University Science and the Federal Government.* Cambridge, Mass.: MIT Press, 1994.

Haber, Samuel. *Efficiency and Uplift: Scientific Management in the Progressive Era, 1890–1920.* Chicago: University of Chicago Press, 1964.

Hall, Peter Dobkin. *Inventing the Nonprofit Sector and Other Essays on Philanthropy, Voluntarism, and Nonprofit Organizations.* Baltimore: The Johns Hopkins University Press, 1992.

Hammack, David C. *Power and Society: Greater New York at the Turn of the Century.* New York: Russell Sage Foundation, 1982.

Hannaway, Owen. "The German Model of Chemical Education in America: Ira Remsen at Johns Hopkins (1876–1913)." *Ambix,* 23 (Nov. 1976), 145–164.

Haynes, William, ed. *American Chemical Industry,* Vol. 6, *The Chemical Companies.* New York: D. Van Nostrand, 1949.

Hays, Samuel P. *Conservation and the Gospel of Efficiency: The Progressive Conservation Movement, 1890–1920.* Cambridge, Mass.: Harvard University Press, 1957.

Heilbron, J. L., and Robert W. Seidel. *Lawrence and his Laboratory: A History of the Lawrence Laboratory.* Vol. 1. Berkeley: University of California Press, 1990.

Heitmann, John A., and David J. Rhees. *Scaling Up: Science, Engineering, and the American Chemical Industry.* Center for History of Chemistry Publication, No. 2. Philadelphia: Center for History of Chemistry, 1984.

Hounshell, David A. "Edison and the Pure Science Ideal in 19th-Century America." *Science,* 207 (Feb. 8, 1980), 612–617.

———, and John Kenly Smith, Jr. *Science and Corporate Strategy: Du Pont R&D, 1902–1980.* Cambridge, England: Cambridge University Press, 1988.

Hughes, Thomas P. *Elmer Sperry: Inventor and Engineer.* Baltimore: The Johns Hopkins University Press, 1971.

———. "Frederick Gardner Cottrell." *DAB,* Supp. 4 (1974), pp. 183–185.

———. "The Development Phase of Technological Change: Introduction." *Technology and Culture,* 17 (July 1976), 423–431.

———. "Inventors: The Problems They Choose, the Ideas They Have, and the Inventions They Make." In *Technological Innovation: A Critical Review of Current Knowl-*

edge. Ed. Patrick Kelly and Melvin Kranzberg. San Francisco: San Francisco Press, 1978, pp. 166–182.

―――. "The Electrification of America: The System Builders." *Technology and Culture*, 20 (Jan. 1979), 124–161.

―――. *Networks of Power: Electrification in Western Society, 1880–1930*. Baltimore: The Johns Hopkins University Press, 1983.

―――. "The Evolution of Large Technological Systems." In *The Social Construction of Technological Systems: New Directions in the Sociology and History of Technology*. Ed. Wiebe E. Bijker, Thomas P. Hughes, and Trevor J. Pinch. Cambridge, Mass.: MIT Press, 1987, pp. 51–82.

―――. "The Era of Independent Inventors." In *Science in Reflection*. Vol.110, *Boston Studies in the Philosophy of Science*. Ed. Edna Ullmann-Margalit. Dordrecht, Holland: Kluwer Academic Publishers, 1988, pp. 151–168.

―――. *American Genesis: A Century of Invention and Technological Enthusiasm, 1870–1970*. New York: Viking, 1989.

Hunt, Bruce J. *The Maxwellians*. Ithaca: Cornell University Press, 1991.

Jewkes, John, David Sawers, and Richard Stillerman. *The Sources of Invention*. London: Macmillan, 1958.

Jolly, William L. *From Retorts to Lasers: The Story of Chemistry at Berkeley*. Berkeley: College of Chemistry, University of California, 1987.

Josephson, Matthew. *Edison*. New York: McGraw-Hill, 1959.

Kahn, E. J., Jr. *The Problem Solvers: A History of Arthur D. Little, Inc.* Boston: Little, Brown, 1986.

Kargon, Robert H., ed. *The Maturing of American Science: A Portrait of Science in Public Life Drawn from the Presidential Addresses of the American Association for the Advancement of Science 1920–1970*. Washington, D.C.: American Association for the Advancement of Science, 1974.

―――. *The Rise of Robert Millikan: Portrait of a Life in American Science*. Ithaca: Cornell University Press, 1982.

―――, and Elizabeth Hodes. "Karl Compton, Isaiah Bowman, and the Politics of Science in the Great Depression." *Isis*, 76 (Sept. 1985), 300–318.

―――, Stuart W. Leslie, and Erica Schoenberger. "Far Beyond Big Science: Science Regions and the Organization of Research and Development." In *Big Science: The Growth of Large-Scale Research*. Ed. Peter Galison and Bruce Hevly. Stanford: Stanford University Press, 1992, pp. 334–354.

―――, and Scott G. Knowles. "Knowledge for Use: Science, Higher Learning, and America's New Industrial Heartland, 1880–1915." *Annals of Science*, 59 (Jan. 2002), 1–20.

Karl, Barry D., and Stanley N. Katz. "The American Private Philanthropic Foundation and the Public Sphere, 1890–1930." *Minerva*, 19 (Summer 1981), 236–270.

Kennedy, Eugene. "The Tragedy at Tower No. 2." *NYT Magazine*, 3 Dec. 1978, 54–57f.

Kevles, Daniel J. "George Ellery Hale, the First World War, and the Advancement of Science in America." *Isis*, 59 (Winter 1968), 427–437.

———. *The Physicists: The History of a Scientific Community in Modern America*. New York: Knopf, 1978.

Kohler, Robert E. *From Medical Chemistry to Biochemistry: The Making of a Biomedical Discipline*. Cambridge, England: Cambridge University Press, 1982.

———. "Science, Foundations, and American Universities in the 1920s." *Osiris*, 2nd Ser., Vol. 3 (1987), 135–164.

———. *Partners in Science: Foundations and Natural Scientists, 1900–1945*. Chicago: University of Chicago Press, 1991.

Kohlstedt, Sally Gregory. "Institutional History." *Osiris*, 2nd Ser., Vol. 1 (1985), 17–36.

Koskoff, David E. *The Mellons: The Chronicle of America's Richest Family*. New York: Thomas Y. Crowell, 1978.

Lamborn, John E., and Charles S. Peterson. "The Substance of the Land: Agriculture v. Industry in the Smelter Cases of 1904 and 1906." *Utah Historical Quarterly*, 53 (Fall 1985), 308–325.

Lamoreaux, Naomi R., and Kenneth L. Sokoloff. "Inventors, Firms, and the Market for Technology in the Late Nineteenth and Early Twentieth Centuries," In *Learning by Doing in Markets, Firms, and Countries*. Ed. Naomi R. Lamoreaux, Daniel M. G. Raff, and Peter Temin. Chicago: University of Chicago Press, 1999, pp. 19–60.

Layton, Edwin T., Jr. "Veblen and the Engineers." *American Quarterly*, 14 (Spring 1962), 64–72.

———. "Mirror-Image Twins: The Communities of Science and Technology in 19th-Century America." *Technology and Culture*, 12 (Oct. 1971), 562–580.

———. *The Revolt of the Engineers: Social Responsibility and the American Engineering Profession*. Cleveland: Case Western Reserve University Press, 1971.

LeCain, Timothy. "The Limits of 'Eco-Efficiency': Arsenic Pollution and the Cottrell Electrical Precipitator in the U.S. Copper Smelting Industry." *Environmental History*, 5 (July 2000), 336–351.

Lécuyer, Christophe. "MIT, Progressive Reform, and 'Industrial Service,' 1890–1920." *Historical Studies in the Physical and Biological Sciences*, 26 (1995), 35–88.

Lehman, Milton. *This High Man: The Life of Robert H. Goddard*. New York: Farrar, Straus, 1963.

Manchester, Harlan F. *New Trailblazers of Technology*. New York: Scribners, 1976.

Matkin, Gary W. *Technology Transfer and the University*. New York: National University Continuing Education Association; American Council on Education; Macmillan, 1990.

McKusick, Vincent Lee. "A Study of Patent Policies in Educational Institutions, Giving Specific Attention to the Massachusetts Institute of Technology." *Journal of the*

Franklin Institute, 245 (Mar. and Apr. 1948), 193–225 and 271–300.

Melosi, Martin V. "Environmental Reform in the Industrial Cities: The Civic Response to Pollution in the Progressive Era." In *Environmental History: Critical Issues in Comparative Perspective*. Ed. Kendall E. Bailles. Lanham, Md.: University Press of America, 1985, pp. 494–515.

Mernitz, Kenneth S. "Governmental Research and the Corporate State: The Rittman Refining Process." *Technology and Culture*, 31 (Jan. 1990), 83–113.

Metz, Lance E., and Ivan M. Viest. *The First 75 Years: A History of the Engineering Foundation*. New York: Engineering Foundation, 1991.

Miles, Wyndham D., ed. *American Chemists and Chemical Engineers*. Washington, D.C.: American Chemical Society, 1976.

Miller, Howard S. *Dollars for Research: Science and Its Patrons in Nineteenth-Century America*. Seattle: University of Washington Press, 1970.

Moore, A. D. "Electrostatics." *Scientific American*, 224 (Mar. 1972), 47–58.

Mowery, David C., and Nathan Rosenberg. "The U.S. National Innovation System." In *National Innovation Systems: A Comparative Analysis*. Ed. Richard R. Nelson. New York: Oxford University Press, 1993, pp. 29–75.

———, and Bhaven N. Sampat. "Patenting and Licensing University Inventions: Lessons from the History of the Research Corporation." *Industrial and Corporate Change*, 10 (June 1, 2001), 317–355.

———, and Bhaven N. Sampat. "University Patents and Patent Policy Debates in the USA, 1925–1980." *Industrial and Corporate Change*, 10 (Aug. 1, 2001), 781–814.

Noble, David F. *America By Design: Science, Technology, and the Rise of Corporate Capitalism*. New York: Knopf, 1977.

Nye, David E. *American Technological Sublime*. Cambridge, Mass.: MIT Press, 1994.

Ochs, Kathleen H. "The Rise of American Mining Engineers: A Case Study of the Colorado School of Mines." *Technology and Culture*, 33 (Apr. 1992), 278–301.

Ochser, Paul H. *Sons of Science: The Story of the Smithsonian Institution and Its Leaders*. New York: Henry Schuman, 1949.

Oleson, Alexandra, and John Voss, eds. *The Organization of Knowledge in Modern America, 1860–1920*. Baltimore: The Johns Hopkins University Press, 1979.

Olson, Sherry H. *The Depletion Myth: A History of Railroad Use of Timber*. Cambridge, Mass.: Harvard University Press, 1971.

Orlans, Harold. *The Nonprofit Research Institute: Its Origin, Operation, Problems, and Prospects*. New York: McGraw-Hill, 1972.

Owens, Larry. "MIT and the Federal 'Angel': Academic R&D and Federal-Private Cooperation before World War II." *Isis*, 81 (June 1990), 188–213.

Penick, James, Jr. "The Progressives and the Environment: Three Themes from the First Conservation Movement." In *The Progressive Era*. Ed. Lewis L. Gould. Syracuse, N.Y.: Syracuse University Press, 1974, pp. 115–131.

Plotkin, Howard. "Edward C. Pickering and the Endowment of Scientific Research in America, 1877–1918." *Isis*, 69 (Mar. 1978), 44–57.

Porter, Glen. *The Rise of Big Business, 1860–1910*. Arlington Heights, Ill.: Harlan Davidson, 1973.

Powers, Jack W., and David G. Black. "Research as a Vital Element in the Undergraduate College." *Journal of Chemical Education*, 54 (Sept. 1977), 565.

Pursell, Carroll. "Conservation, Environmentalism, and the Engineers: The Progressive Era and the Recent Past." In *Environmental History: Critical Issues in Comparative Perspective*. Ed. Kendall E. Bailles. Lanham, Md.: University Press of America, 1985, pp. 176–192.

Quinn, M. -L. "Early Smelter Sites: A Neglected Chapter in the History and Geography of Acid Rain in the United States." *Atmospheric Environment*, 23 (1989), 1281–1292.

―――. "Industry and Environment in the Appalachian Copper Basin, 1890–1930." *Technology and Culture*, 34 (July 1993), 575–612.

Reich, Leonard S. *The Making of American Industrial Research: Science and Business at GE and Bell, 1876–1926*. Cambridge, England: Cambridge University Press, 1985.

Reingold, Nathan. "American Indifference to Basic Research: A Reappraisal." In *Nineteenth-Century American Science: A Reappraisal*. Ed. George H. Daniels. Evanston, Ill.: Northwestern University Press, 1977, pp. 38–62.

―――. "National Science Policy in a Private Foundation: The Carnegie Institution of Washington." In *The Organization of Knowledge in Modern America, 1860–1920*. Ed. Alexandra Oleson and John Voss. Baltimore: The Johns Hopkins University Press, 1979, pp. 313–341.

―――, ed. *The Sciences in the American Context: New Perspectives*. Washington, D.C.: Smithsonian Institution Press, 1979.

Research Corporation. *A 75th Anniversary Report*. Research Corporation's Annual Report for 1987.

"The Research Corporation's Five-Year Program of Postwar Collegiate Research." *School and Society*, 62 (Oct. 20, 1945), 246.

Reynolds, Terry S. *75 Years of Progress: A History of the American Institute of Chemical Engineers, 1908–1983*. New York: American Institute of Chemical Engineers, 1983.

Rodgers, Daniel T. "In Search of Progressivism." *Reviews in American History*, 10 (Dec. 1982), 113–132.

Rome, Adam W. "Coming to Terms with Pollution: The Language of Environmental Reform, 1865–1915." *Environmental History*, 1 (July 1996), 6–28.

Rosenberg, Robert. "American Physics and the Origins of Electrical Engineering." *Physics Today*, 36 (Oct. 1983), 48–54.

Ross, Steven S. *Construction Disasters: Design Failures, Causes, and Prevention*. New York: McGraw-Hill, 1984.

Rydell, Robert W. *All the World's a Fair: Visions of Empire at American International Expositions, 1876–1916.* Chicago: University of Chicago Press, 1984.

Schauer, Charles H. "How Firm a Foundation?" *Physics Today,* 3 (Oct. 1950), 6–11.

———. "Support for Research." *Sky and Telescope,* 14 (Mar. 1955), 190.

———. "Research Corporation—Experiment in Administration of Patent Rights for the Public Good." *Research Management,* 5 (July 1962), 229–235.

Science, Invention, and Society: The Story of a Unique American Institution. Research Corporation, 1972.

Segrè, Emilio. *From X-Rays to Quarks: Modern Physicists and Their Discoveries.* San Francisco: W. H. Freeman, 1980.

Servos, John W. "The Industrial Relations of Science: Chemical Engineering at MIT, 1900–1939." *Isis,* 71 (Dec. 1980), 530–549.

———. *Physical Chemistry from Ostwald to Pauling: The Making of a Science in America.* Princeton: Princeton University Press, 1990.

———. "Changing Partners: The Mellon Institute, Private Industry, and the Federal Patron." *Technology and Culture,* 35 (Apr. 1994), 221–257.

Sheridan, John. H. "It Wasn't a Mirage that Fooled Him." *Industry Week,* 197 (June 12, 1978), 88–90 and 95–96.

Skolnik, Herman, and Kenneth M. Reese, eds. *A Century of Chemistry: The Role of Chemists and the American Chemical Society.* Washington, D.C.: American Chemical Society, 1976.

Smith, Duane A. *Mining America: The Industry and the Environment, 1800–1980.* Lawrence: University Press of Kansas, 1987.

Smith, Michael L. *Pacific Visions: California Scientists and the Environment, 1850–1915.* New Haven: Yale University Press, 1987.

Sparkes, Boyden. "Latter-Day Ben Franklin." *Saturday Review,* 35 (May 3, 1952), 18–19 and 46.

Spence, Clark C. *Mining Engineers and the American West: The Lace-Boot Brigade, 1849–1933.* New Haven: Yale University Press, 1970.

Stadtman, Verne A., ed. *The Centennial Record of the University of California.* Berkeley: University of California Press, 1967.

———. *The University of California, 1868–1968.* New York: McGraw-Hill, 1970.

Starr, Kevin. *Americans and the California Dream: 1850–1915.* New York: Oxford University Press, 1973.

Steed, James A. "Smithsonian Institution." In *Research Institutions and Learned Societies.* Vol. 5, *Greenwood Encyclopedia of American Institutions.* Ed. Joseph C. Kiger. Westport, Conn.: Greenwood Press, 1982, pp. 439–443.

Stradling, David, and Peter Thorsheim. "The Smoke of Great Cities: British and American Efforts to Control Air Pollution, 1860–1914." *Environmental History,* 4 (Jan. 1999), 6–31.

————. *Smokestacks and Progressives: Environmentalists, Engineers, and Air Quality in America*. Baltimore: The Johns Hopkins University Press, 1999.

Stranges, Anthony N., and Richard C. Jones. "Frederick Gardner Cottrell." *ANB*, 5 (1999), pp. 569–570.

Summerscales, William. *Affirmation and Dissent: Columbia's Response to the Crisis of World War I*. New York: Teachers College Press, Columbia University, 1970.

Swain, Robert E. "Smoke and Fume Investigations: A Historical Review." *Industrial and Engineering Chemistry*, 41 (Nov. 1949), 2384–2388.

Tarr, Joel A. *The Search for the Ultimate Sink: Urban Pollution in Historical Perspective*. Akron, Ohio: University of Akron Press, 1996.

Thomas, Robert E. *Salt & Water, Power & People: A Short History of Hooker Electrochemical Company*. Niagara Falls, N.Y.: 1955.

Townes, Charles H. *How the Laser Happened: Adventures of a Scientist*. New York: Oxford University Press, 1999.

Trescott, Martha Moore. *The Rise of the American Electrochemicals Industry, 1880–1910: Studies in the American Technological Environment*. Westport, Conn.: Greenwood Press, 1981.

————. "Unit Operations in the Chemical Industry: An American Innovation in Modern Chemical Engineering." In *A Century of Chemical Engineering*. Ed. William F. Furter. New York: Plenum Press, 1982, pp. 1–18.

Vaughan, Floyd L. *The United States Patent System: Legal and Economic Conflicts in American Patent History*. Norman: University of Oklahoma Press, 1956.

Veysey, Laurence R. *The Emergence of the American University*. Chicago: University of Chicago Press, 1965.

"W. H. McBryde, 59th ASME President, 1876–1959." *Mechanical Engineering*, 81 (May 1959), 140–141.

Wachhorst, Wyn. *Thomas Alva Edison: An American Myth*. Cambridge, Mass.: MIT Press, 1981.

Wall, Joseph Frazier. *Andrew Carnegie*. New York: Oxford University Press, 1970.

Weart, Spencer R. "The Rise of 'Prostituted' Physics." *Nature*, 262 (July 1, 1976), 13–17.

Weidlein, Edward R. "A Thumbnail History of Mellon Institute." In *Science and Human Progress: Addresses at the Celebration of the Fiftieth Anniversary of Mellon Institute*. Ed. Harold P. Klug. Pittsburgh: Mellon Institute of Industrial Research, 1964, pp. 19–25.

Weiner, Charles. "Science in the Marketplace: Historical Precedents and Problems." In *From Genetic Experimentation to Biotechnology – The Critical Transition*. Ed. William J. Whelan and Sandra Black. New York: Wiley, 1982, pp. 123–131.

————. "Universities, Professors, and Patents: A Continuing Controversy." *Technology Review*, 89 (Feb./Mar. 1986), 32–43.

———. "Patenting and Academic Research: Historical Case Studies." *Science, Technology, and Human Values,* 12 (Winter 1987), 50–62.

White, Harry J. *Industrial Electrostatic Precipitation.* Reading, Mass.: Addison-Wesley, 1963.

———. "Centenary of Frederick Gardner Cottrell." *Journal of Electrostatics,* 4 (1977/1978), 1–34.

———. "The Art and the Science of Electrostatic Precipitation." *Journal of the Air Pollution Control Association,* 34 (Nov. 1984), 1163–1167.

Wiebe, Robert H. *The Search For Order: 1877–1920.* New York: Hill and Wang, 1967.

Williams, James C. *Energy and the Making of Modern California.* Akron, Ohio: University of Akron Press, 1997.

Williams, Robert R. *Williams-Waterman Fund for the Combat of Dietary Diseases: A History of the Period 1935 through 1955.* New York: Research Corporation, 1956.

Wirth, John D. "The Trail Smelter Dispute: Canadians and Americans Confront Transboundary Pollution, 1927–41." *Environmental History,* 1 (Apr. 1996), 34–51.

Wise, George. "A New Role for Professional Scientists in Industry: Industrial Research at General Electric, 1900–1916." *Technology and Culture,* 21 (July 1980), 408–429.

———. "Ionists in Industry: Physical Chemistry at General Electric, 1900–1915." *Isis,* 74 (Mar. 1983), 6–21.

———. *Willis R. Whitney, General Electric, and the Origins of U.S. Industrial Research.* New York: Columbia University Press, 1985.

Wolfe, Margaret Ripley. *Lucius Polk Brown and Progressive Food and Drug Control: Tennessee and New York City, 1908–1920.* Lawrence: Regents Press of Kansas, 1978.

Yochelson, Ellis W. "Charles Doolittle Walcott: 1850–1927." *Biog. Mem. NAS,* 39 (1967), 471–540.

———. "Walcott in Albany, New York: James Hall's 'Special Assistant.'" *Earth Sciences History,* 6 (1987), 86–94.

———. "Andrew Carnegie and Charles Doolittle Walcott: The Origin and Early Years of the Carnegie Institution." In *The Earth, the Heavens, and the Carnegie Institution of Washington.* Ed. Gregory A. Good. Washington, D.C.: American Geophysical Union, 1994, pp. 1–19.

———. *Charles Doolittle Walcott: Paleontologist.* Kent, Ohio: Kent State University Press, 1998.

———. *Smithsonian Institution Secretary, Charles Doolittle Walcott.* Kent, Ohio: Kent State University Press, 2001.

ABOUT THE AUTHOR

Thomas D. Cornell has been a member of the Department of History and the Department of Science, Technology, and Society in the College of Liberal Arts at the Rochester Institute of Technology since 1982. He received his baccalaureate from Rhodes College in 1974, his master's degree from the Georgia Institute of Technology in 1977, and his Ph.D. in the history of science from the Johns Hopkins University in 1986.